May 13, 1997

Presented this date to

██████████████████

Chief, U.S. Forest Service

from the

Forest Farmers -

D1224972

and Farm Foresters of the

Del - Mar - Va

██████████████████

, retired Maryland & Delaware

forester

██████████████████ TREE FARMER

KENT CO. MARYLAND, WESTMORELAND

CO. VIRGINIA

██████████████ - It's been

a pleasure to work

with you today! 5/13/97

AMERICAN HOLLY

Adopted 1939 as the

STATE TREE OF DELAWARE

DELAWARE TREES

*A Guide to the Identification of the
Native Tree Species*

by

WILLIAM S. TABER, B. F.

State Forester

THIRD EDITION

DELAWARE DEPARTMENT
OF AGRICULTURE FOREST SERVICE
DOVER

1995

PRINTED BY
ASSOCIATES INTERNATIONAL, INC.
WILMINGTON, DELAWARE

PREFACE TO THE THIRD EDITION

This reprinting of *The Delaware Tree Book* was made possible through the generosity of the 1994 Delaware General Assembly and the people of Delaware. It is dedicated to the memory and legacy of William S. Taber, who not only authored and illustrated this book, but helped establish a forestry program in Delaware. William "Bill" Taber devoted most of his adult life to the advancement of forestry in the First State. He was hired as Delaware's first State Forester in 1927 and continued working for the Forest Service of the Delaware Department of Agriculture for over 40 years. Under Taber's four decades of leadership, hundreds of acres of forest land were purchased to create the Redden/Ellendale and Blackbird State Forests. Taber personally planted thousands of tree seedlings on acres of barren land that now make up major portions of Redden State Forest near Georgetown. Throughout his career, Taber's actions always reflected his philosophy—manage the land so it will be a resource for the future. This ideology was also exhibited in his constant efforts to promote forestry education. He combined his forestry education from Mt. Alto College in Pennsylvania with his love of the outdoors to lecture classes at various Delaware colleges. He realized education was the key to understanding. It was this love of education and his natural artistic talent that resulted in writing *The Delaware Tree Book* in 1936. This beautifully-illustrated book was published in 1939 and reprinted again in 1960. With the exception of this preface, two updated tree lists, and typographical corrections, this reprinting is an exact duplication of the original 1939 book. It is a small tribute to the man who always had big dreams for forestry in Delaware. Many of those dreams were fulfilled during his lifetime. He was known and recognized as a leader in forestry both in Delaware and in the Nation. He was chosen as Delaware Conservationist of the Year and the National Forester of the Year during his career. He would never dream, however, that one day a state forest would carry his name. In 1993, the Delaware Department of Agriculture Forest Service officially named a forest, located in the southwest corner of Kent County, the William S. Taber State Forest. Taber died in 1981, but his legacy will continue on through this state forest. It will also endure through this book that is once again being presented to the people of the State of Delaware. It is hoped a new generation will discover and enjoy the natural wonder of Delaware's trees through this book.

—The Delaware Department of Agriculture
March 1995

The State Forestry Commission at its first meeting in 1927 adopted a policy for the operation of the State Forestry Department. That policy is the foundation upon which forestry in the State is being built and the program adopted at that same meeting has been the guide for the progress thus far made. One of the provisions of that program called for the publication of information on the identification, range and distribution of forest trees native to the State. The manuscript, plates and cuts for such a publication have been prepared from time to time as funds would permit, but until the present time sufficient funds have not been available to so much as print a portion of the text. This matter of funds has not only dictated that the publication be printed a section at a time, but has also limited the amount of subject matter that could be included in the bulletin. It, therefore, assumes the form of a guide or handbook rather than the text book common to many state publications of similar nature. If, when presented in this form, it serves to acquaint the layman or the schoolchild with the trees he sees in his daily travels, it will have served its purpose well. And if perchance it leads such individuals to a desire to delve deeper into the intricacies of dendrology, the numerous complete text and reference books to be found in our public libraries are at their disposal.

Trees are by far the most conspicuous members of the plant kingdom. They surpass all other organic beings in height, size and age. But what constitutes a tree is not easily defined for the reason that a given species may assume tree form under certain conditions of climate, soil and other factors, and only shrub form under other conditions. For this reason authorities differ in their respective classifications but in the interest of clarification so far as this text is concerned, a tree is a woody plant which, over a period of years, in natural habit has a central upright axis attaining a height of 10 or more feet.

Approximately 600 different species of trees are native to the United States. Of these about 115 species, with their varieties, are native to Delaware.

The order and nomenclature used in this publication are essentially those given in the "Manual of Trees of North America" by Charles Sprague Sargent, published by Houghton Mifflin Company, New York City. The common name appearing in large print heading the description of each species is, in most cases, the one given in the "Check List of Forest Trees of the United States" by George B. Sudworth, U. S. Dept. of Agriculture, Mis. Cir. No. 92. In conformity with Sudworth's rule and in the interest of preventing confusion to the layman, the first letter of formerly capitalized technical species and variety names has been decapitalized. Also in keeping with recent trends, the capitalizing of the first letter in common names has been dropped.

Since trees of wide distribution, particularly those of commercial importance, may be known by a common name other than the one given herein, an effort has been made to include many of the local names, special notation being made of the lumber trade name by a (c) inserted following this name.

The halftone illustrations are from photographs made by the author or from those purchased from Romeyn B. Hough Company, and now a part of the photograph files of the State Forestry Department. The line etchings were made from pen and ink drawings by the author from specimens collected in Delaware.

The writer claims little originality for the descriptive matter or its arrangement in the text. Many authors and botanical observers have written and published much on the subject and free reference use has been made of that which was available.

Special acknowledgment and credit is made to Romeyn B. Hough Company, publishers of the "Handbook of the Trees of the United States and Canada," for permission to use halftone reproductions of the tree parts photographs from their collection.

To the many authors, the members of the State Forestry Commission, co-workers in the State Forestry Department, and others who have contributed information or aided in any way in the preparation, printing and distribution of this bulletin, I express my sincere and grateful appreciation.

WILLIAM S. TABER

Dover
1939

DELAWARE'S LARGEST NATIVE LIVING TREES

(Of record in the files of the Delaware Forest Service 1995)

Species	Circumference (4½ feet above ground)	Location
White oak	21 Feet	Chambers Rock Road New Castle County
Yellow poplar	22 Feet, 5 inches	County Route 68 Southeast Dover
Basswood	12 Feet, 6 inches	Fort Delaware State Park Delaware City
American sycamore	24 Feet, 5 inches	County Route 32 West of Greenwood
Willow oak	11 Feet, 9 inches	County Road 15 West of Dover
American beech	18 Feet, 3 inches	Buena Vista Conference Center New Castle County
American elm	16 Feet, 3 inches	The Green Dover
White ash	13 Feet, 5 inches	Hagley Museum Wilmington
Loblolly pine	10 Feet, 6 inches	County Roads 280 & 285 Lewes
Osage orange	2 Feet	Hagley Museum Wilmington
Baldcypress	24 Feet, 7 inches	James Branch Nature Preserve—East of Laurel **Delaware's largest tree**
American holly	8 Feet, 1 inch	302 Clinton Street Delaware City

NOTE: Today, Delaware's largest trees are determined by a combination of measurements of circumference, height of tree, and crown spread.

PART I

*Normal Bark Characteristics of
Tree Trunks*

FIG. 2. TRUNK OF OPEN GROWN BALD CYPRESS
ON UPLAND SITE, MILLSBORO

FIG. 3. CHARACTERISTIC BARK PATTERN
OF LARGE SASSAFRAS TREE

FIG. 4. YELLOW POPLAR

FIG 5. BITTERNUT HICKORY

FIG. 6. EASTERN WHITE PINE

FIG. 7. LOBLOLLY PINE

FIG. 8. SHORTLEAF PINE

FIG. 9. PITCH PINE

FIG. 10. VIRGINIA PINE

FIG. 11. HEMLOCK

FIG. 12. EASTERN RED CEDAR

FIG. 13. SOUTHERN
WHITE CEDAR

FIG. 14. BLACK WALNUT

FIG. 15. BUTTERNUT

FIG. 16. SMALL FRUITED
        HICKORY

FIG. 17. PALE LEAF
        HICKORY

FIG. 18. PIGNUT HICKORY

FIG. 19. SHAGBARK
HICKORY

FIG. 20. HOP HORNBEAM

FIG. 21. SERVICEBERRY

FIG. 22. WILD BLACK
CHERRY

FIG. 23. RIVER BIRCH

FIG. 24. PAWPAW

FIG. 25. SEASIDE ALDER

FIG. 26 SOUTHERN
RED OAK

FIG. 27. BLACK OAK

FIG. 28. WATER OAK

FIG. 29 NORTHERN
RED OAK

FIG. 30. PIN OAK

FIG. 31. WILLOW OAK

FIG. 32. POST OAK

FIG. 33. SWAMP WHITE OAK

FIG. 34. CHESTNUT OAK

FIG. 35. BASKET OAK

FIG. 36. BLACK GUM

FIG. 37. RED GUM

FIG. 38. WITCH HAZEL   FIG. 39. HOLLY

PART II

MANUAL OF DELAWARE

TREES

Descriptions of Genera
and Species

Class I. GYMNOSPERMAE
  Family I. PINACEAE
    Genus I. PINUS (LINNAEUS)

THE PINES

Resinous evergreen trees or rarely shrubs with deeply furrowed usually thick and often layered scaly reddish or brown bark. **Buds,** scaly, generally more or less resinous, the large terminal one in a cluster of smaller ones, the bud scales becoming bracts on the spring shoot. Branches, more or less in whorls about the main trunk, being more pronounced in the soft pines. **Leaves,** needle shaped, of two kinds—primary and secondary; the primary ones usually occurring singly on one year seedlings, new growth, or on new shoots from adventitious buds; the secondary in clusters of 2 to 5 or rarely singly in the axils of scale-like primary leaves, surrounded at the base with a sheath of fibrous material which, except in the soft pines, usually persists for the life of the cluster. **Flowers** are monoecious (unisexual); staminate (male) flowers in clusters at the base of new shoots of the year, catkin like, usually yellow or a shade of orange, when ripe releasing large quantities of sulfur yellow pollen; the pistillate (female) flowers near the tips or attached laterally, singly or in whorls on the new shoots, light green, yellow or often crimson tipped, consisting of numerous spirally arranged bracts and scales. Pollen, wind disseminated, fertilization taking place some months after pollenation. **Fruit,** a woody cone, maturing at the end of the second or rarely the third season, conical of varying lateral shapes, made up of closely appressed woody scales, the exposed surfaces (apophysis) of which are more or less thickened and are terminated by the previous years exposed area (umbo), appearing as either a protuberance or depression. Often the umbo is surmounted by a

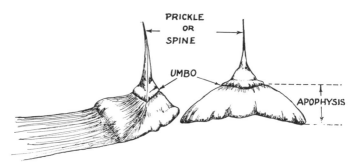

spine of varying form. The **seed** is generally obovoid, equipped with a wing or rarely wingless, and encased in an outer hard, usually thin, bony coat ranging in color from gray to brown-black, or mottled and occasionally ribbed, held enclosed between the cone scales until the separation of the latter at, or after maturity releases them when they may be carried long distances in the wind. The **heartwood** of all *pinus* species is generally darker than the sapwood in color; and annual rings usually marked by dense darker bands of summer wood which contain most of the resin.   This is particularly characteristic of the species of the hard pine group.

Pinus is represented by about 66 recognized species distributed over the northern hemisphere from the Arctic Circle to Central America, northern Africa, the Philippine Islands and Sumatra.

Two distinct groups of species are recognized; i.e., soft pines and hard pines.   Only one species of the first group is native to Delaware, i.e., eastern white pine *P. strobus,* L.   All other native pine species are in the latter group.

Exotic species formerly used but not now recommended for general reforestation purposes are the Scotch or Scots pine, *P. sylvestris,* L., American red pine, *P. resinosa,* Ait., Japanese red pine, *P. densiflora,* Sieb. & Zucc., Japanese black pine, *P. thunbergii* Parl., and Austrian pine, *P. nigra,* Arnold.

There is probably no other single genus of the Gymnosperms which has contributed more to civilization than *Pinus.*   In usefulness to mankind, in extent of distribution and in the economic importance of lumber or timber products it surpases the best of the coniferous world.

Acknowledging that other groups such as the firs, spruces, cedars and junipers may surpass the pines in attractiveness when used as ornamentals, the pines, nevertheless serve a wealth of purpose in decorative landscape work.   In this respect their attractiveness may be exceeded by their usefulness and adaptability to adverse and extreme conditions of soil fertility and moisture.   In their youth their beauty might be considered as competitive with other conifers and in old age there are few conifers more picturesque.   The time when they are most likely to present an unattractive picture is during the intermediate stage of development.

EASTERN WHITE PINE

1. A needle cluster, x ½.
2. Tip of needle, enlarged.
3. Section of needle cluster showing location of resin ducts and fibro-vascular bundles, enlarged.
4. Section of needle showing resin ducts (a and b), greatly enlarged.
5. Thrifty bud with leaves cut away, natural size.
6. Open and closed cone, x ½.
7. Branchlet showing female flower (top) and previous season cone (bottom), x ½.
8. Branchlet showing female flower cluster, x ½.
9. Lower side of cone scale showing winged seeds, x ½.
10. Seed, enlarged.

EASTERN WHITE PINE
Pinus strobus, Linnaeus

The eastern white pine, also known as cork pine, Weymouth pine, Canadian white pine (c) and northern white pine (c), in Delaware rarely exceeds 85′ in height and 2′ in diameter. Trees 200′ tall and 6′ in diameter have been recorded for Pennsylvania and New England. In dense stands it develops a tall straight stem, free of limbs, terminating in a small narrow crown. Young trees in the open develop a broad pyramidal form; old trees an irregular head composed of spreading or ascending branches with picturesque foliage masses. Lateral branches (usually 5) extend from the main stem in horizontal or slightly ascending whorls, the space between branch whorls normally representing a year's height growth. Reaches commercial maturity in 80 to 100 years but may rarely attain an age of 250 to 300 years.

LEAVES—In clusters of five surrounded by a narrow basal sheath early deciduous; slender, flexible, blue green, 2½″ to 5″ long; triangular in cross section, having one fibro-vascular bundle, two or occasionally three resin ducts peripheral, 3 to 5 rows of stomata on the two ventral surfaces, and leaf margins finely serrate. Cluster usually deciduous by the end of the second season.

BARK—On young twigs, at first often slightly hairy—later lustrous, smooth, gray green to brownish green. On old trees, 1″ to 2″ or more thick, dark gray, divided by shallow fissures into long broad connecting ridges, which flake with difficulty. See Fig. 6.

BUDS—Of the terminal cluster, ovate-oblong, acuminate, ¼″ to ½″ long, covered with long pointed overlapping scales which are slightly fringed on the margins. Lateral buds smaller ovoid acuminate.

FLOWERS—Appear in May; the male as ½″ long yellow catkins clustered at the base of new growth; the female, terminal on the new growth, about 1/3″ long, light carmine when first observed, later purplish and stalked.

FRUIT—A long stalked, drooping, slender cone 5″ to 10″ long, usually curved, maturing at end of second season and deciduous within 6 months; cone scales thin, unarmed, their tips and apophyses usually covered with pitch exudations. Seed ¼″ long, dark brown, black mottled, wings about 1″ long, widest near the middle and attached primarily to the ventral surface of the seed.

WOOD—Non-porous, resinous, soft, straight grained, easily worked; heartwood cream or reddish-cream; sapwood cream white. Not strong or durable in contact with the soil, dry weight—25 lbs. per cu. ft. Used for construction, doors, sash, weatherboarding, pattern making, interior finish, matches, cabinet making, ship masts, woodenware and novelties. Known commercially as Northern white pine.

RANGE AND DISTRIBUTION—Occurs from Newfoundland to Manitoba, south along the Mountains of Kentucky and Tennessee to Georgia, westward to Iowa. In Delaware originally occurred scattered in all counties. There remains only one known natural stand situated west of Harrington, in Kent County. Scattered trees in woodlands and natural stand as established from the seed of ornamentally planted trees may be occasionally seen in the State.

HABITAT—Prefers a fertile, moist and well drained site but will grow quite well on light soils or dry locations when once established.

NOTES—White pine at one time was the most important timber tree in North America. It has lost that high place largely because of lack of supply and subsequent substitute woods coupled with the inferiority of second growth products when the users were accustomed to the light, clear, straight-grained product from virgin stands. It is to be recommended for reforestation planting in any part of the State on soils and sites not waterlogged or sterile. As an ornamental, the species ranks among the best, being much in demand for all kinds of aesthetic uses.

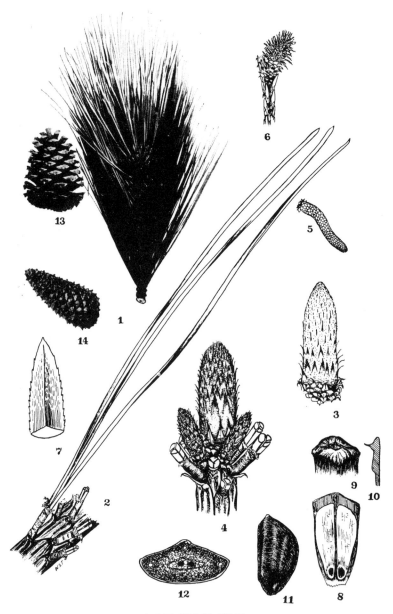

LOBLOLLY PINE

1. Branchlet with one season cones and needles, x ¼.
2. Needle cluster, x about 2/3.
3. Resinous bud, x 2.
4. Non-resinous bud, leaves cut away, x 2.
5. Single male flower, x ½.
6. Single female flower, natural size.
7. Tip of needle, enlarged.
8. Lower side of cone scale showing winged seed, x ¾.
9. Tip of cone scale showing spine, x ¾.
10. Tip of cone scale in cross section, x ¾.
11. Seed, greatly enlarged.
12. Section of leaf showing 3 resin ducts and 2 fibro-vascular bundles, greatly enlarged.
13. Opened cone, x ¼.
14. Unopened cone, x ¼.

LOBLOLLY PINE
Pinus taeda, Linnaeus

The loblolly pine, also known as longshat pine, oldfield pine, bull pine, cornstalk pine, foxtail pine, longleaf pine and North Carolina pine (c), is a tree usually 60' to 80' tall and 1' to 2' in diameter but may occasionally reach a height of 125' and a diameter of 5'. Young trees in the open have spreading branches forming a rounded pyramidal head. Old trees and trees in close stands have a tall, clean, straight trunk terminating in a short-branched, compact, rounded head. Reaches commercial maturity in 40 years or less but may attain an age of 100 to 150 years.

LEAVES—In clusters of 3; 6" to 9" long, slender, stiff, slightly twisted, bright green, marked by 10 to 12 rows of large stomata on each of the 3 faces, leaf edges finely serrate and tip ending in an acute horny point; in cross section, resin ducts 3, large, situated in the angles of the leaf surfaces within parenchyma, fibro-vascular bundles 2. The 1" sheath persists for life of the cluster which is 3 to 4 years.

BARK—On new growth, light green, soon turning yellow-brown and becoming darker and prominently roughened by elevated leaf bundle bases the following year. On old trees ¾" to 1½" thick, bright red-brown and divided by shallow fissures into wide, flat scaly ridges. See Fig. 7.

BUDS—Oblong, ¼" to ½" long, may be either resinous or non-resinous. When non-resinous, light brown, composed of numerous serrate margined, sharp pointed, closely appressed scales, free at the tips.

FLOWERS—Appear in April and May; male, in crowded clusters at base of new growth, catkin-like, yellow ½" to 1½" long; female, solitary or in clusters lateral below the tips of new growth, short stalked, yellow.

FRUIT—A cone, maturing in 2 years, 3" to 6" long, cylindrical, ovoid or oblong, very short stalked, light red-brown; apophysis thickened with a very prominent transverse ridge and umbo ending in a short, stout prickle which usually curves outward. Cones opening from October to January and are usually deciduous during the following year. Seed are rhombic in shape about ½" long, with a thin, nearly black, often corrugated and wide margined seed coat. The 1" long and ¼" wide wing which encircles the seed on its produced margin is broadest above the middle.

WOOD—Non-porous, resinous, not strong, coarse grained, not durable in contact with the soil; heartwood yellowish brown; sapwood lighter brown often white and comprising the larger portion of the tree. Both heartwood and sapwood are marked by dense, darker bands of summer wood. Manufactured into lumber, railroad ties, piling, mine props, box shooks, staves, basket veneer, paper pulp and charcoal. Weighs 38 lbs. per cubic foot. The lumber is known commercially as North Carolina pine.

RANGE AND DISTRIBUTION—From southern New Jersey south along the Coastal Plain below altitudes of 500 feet to Florida, westward to San Antonio, Texas, southern Arkansas and Oklahoma. In Delaware, found principally in lower Kent and Sussex Counties, the most northern natural outpost known to the author being on the banks of the Delaware-Chesapeake Canal at Summit Bridge, New Castle County.

HABITAT—Further south in its range, this tree prefers moist or often swampy situations but in Delaware seems equally well adapted to moist and dry sites reaching its greatest height, however, on the heavier soils.

NOTES—This pine is commercially the most important pine in the State, being the tree from which is derived most of the manufactured pine lumber. As a reforestation tree, it surpasses all other species; first, because it is a rapid grower capable of attaining sawlog size in 35 to 40 years; second, because it is adapted to a wide range of soil and moisture conditions; third, because it recovers rapidly from the effects of transplanting; and fourth, because of the many uses which it serves, the financial returns are greater. That it may be safely planted in any part of the State south of the Delaware-Chesapeake Canal is an established fact and the Department is at present conducting experimental plantings in various parts of New Castle County in order to ascertain if it is hardy much further north of its natural distribution. So far these experiments have proven that seedlings grown from seed collected in Delaware are hardy anywhere in the State regardless of exposure or elevation.

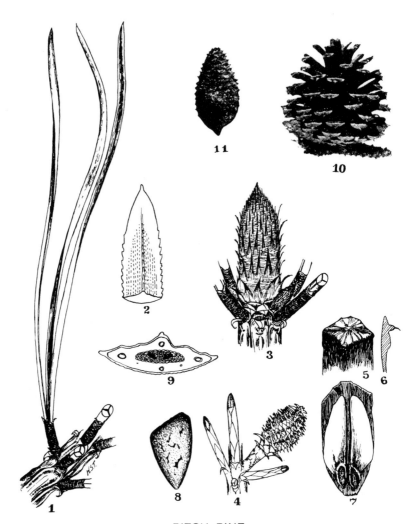

PITCH PINE

1. Needle cluster, natural size.
2. Tip of needle, enlarged.
3. Terminal bud cluster, with leaves cut away, x 2.
4. Female flower and emerging leaf cluster, natural size.
5. Tip of cone scale, natural size.
6. Cross section of tip of cone scale, natural size.
7. Bottom view of cone scale showing 2 winged seeds, natural size.
8. Seed, greatly enlarged.
9. Cross section of leaf, greatly enlarged.
10. Open cone, x ½.
11. Unopened cone, x ½.

PITCH PINE
Pinus rigida, Miller

The pitch pine, also known as hard pine, black pine, sap pine, longshat pine and Virginia pine (c), is a tree rarely over 80' tall or with a trunk diameter exceeding 3'; usually 40' to 65' tall and 1' to 1½' in diameter with a crown of irregular, broad pyramidal shape; in old age becoming rounded and very straggly so that it presents a somewhat grotesque appearance. This appearance is emphasized by the irregular, often heavy, contorted and gnarled branches and persistent cones. Trees 10' to 12' tall are not unlike other hard pines but in the pole state they begin to take on the rugged appearance characteristic of the species. Reaches commercial maturity in 50 years but may rarely attain an age of 100 years.

LEAVES—In bundles of 3, dark green, stout, rigid, spreading, slightly curved and twisted, ending in a horny point; 2½" to 5½" long; margins finely toothed; marked by many rows of stomata on the three faces; resin ducts 3, large, situated in the parenchyma at the apex of leaf faces with 2 to 4 smaller ducts scattered in parenchyma; fibro-vascular bundles 2; basal sheath ¼" to ½" long persisting for the life of the cluster which is normally 2 years.

BARK—On new branches bright green, becoming yellow-brown by the end of the year, second year darker and prominently roughened by elevated leaf bundle bases and partly persistent bracts. On young trunks, red brown, thin and broken into scales; on old trunk, becoming 1" to 1½" thick, darker and broken into deep, irregular, much broken but flat topped ridges which exfoliate in irregular thick scales. See Fig. 9.

BUDS—Brown, cylindrical or ovate, sharp pointed, ¼" to ¾" long, usually somewhat resinous; bud scales pressed together but usually free at the tips.

FLOWERS—Appear in May. Male, numerous, short, catkin-like, clustered at the base of new growth, yellow at first, changing to orange and producing large quantities of yellow pollen. Female, lateral on new growth singly or in whorls of two or more, at first yellow green, later green tinged with carmine especially the tip, composed of spirally arranged bracts and ovules; similar in appearance to mature cone.

FRUIT—A cone maturing in two seasons; ovoid, acute at the apex, nearly sessile, 1½" to 3" long, yellow brown at maturity, often in clusters about the branch; apophysis little elevated, umbo triangular ending in a recurved, stout, sharp prickle. Cones persist for many years.

SEED—Triangular in shape, full and rounded or slightly fluted, about 3/16" long, light steel gray, slightly mottled with black; wing broadest below the middle.

WOOD—Non-porous, resinous, light, brittle, coarse grained, slightly durable in contact with the soil; heartwood reddish; sapwood usually much thicker than heartwood and light yellow or white being very susceptible to blue stain in seasoning. Used and sold as other southern pine timber for lumber, railroad ties, mine props, piling, charcoal and fuel. Weighs 32 pounds per cubic foot.

RANGE AND DISTRIBUTION—Maine to Ontario south to Georgia, Tennessee and westward to Ohio. In Delaware, present in all counties but principally in Sussex County in mixture with other pine species.

HABITAT—Seems to prefer no particular soil and is indifferent to moisture content, being found in swamps and on dry uplands, thriving well on either site. May be found as single trees or forming pure stands.

NOTES—The pitch pine cannot be said to be commercially important as a timber producer but its adaptability to a wide range of soils coupled with its extremely fire resistant properties make it a species suited to special reforestation projects where quality timber production is not the primary purpose. A distinguishing characteristic of this species, especially in burned areas, is the presence of leaf clusters and sprouts along the trunk of the tree in such masses as to often cover a large portion of the trunk. In Delaware it is not uncommon to see full grown trees that have regenerated from stump shoots after a fire or logging operation.

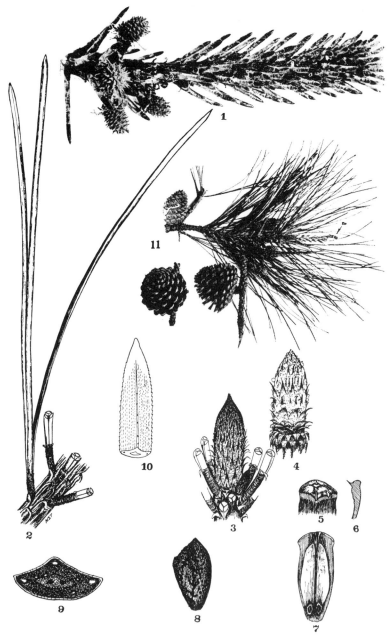

POND PINE

1. Branchlet showing female flowers and new growth, x ½.
2. Needle cluster, natural size.
3. Non-resinous terminal bud with leaves cut away, natural size.
4. Resinous bud, natural size.
5. Tip of cone scale, natural size.
6. Tip of cone scale in section, natural size.
7. Bottom view of cone scale with seed, natural size.
8. Seed, greatly enlarged.
9. Cross section of needle showing large and small resin ducts and 2 fibro-vascular bundles, greatly enlarged.
10. Tip of needle, greatly enlarged.
11. Branchlet showing mature unopened cone, immature cones, and female flower (a) x ¼.
12. Two opened cones, x ¼.

POND PINE
Pinus rigida serotina, (Michaux) Loudon

The pond pine, also known as swamp pine, longshat pine, bull pine, black bark pine, and North Carolina pine (c), is a tree usually 40' to 50' tall, and 1' to 2' in diameter. Sometimes 80' tall and 4' in diameter, with stout, often contorted branches more or less pendulous at the extremities, forming an open, broad head. In general appearance resembling somewhat the form of pitch pine but with foliage characteristics similar to loblolly pine.

LEAVES—In bundles of three, green, 5½" to 8" long, stiffer than loblolly pine and not as stiff as pitch pine spreading from branches more or less radially; the three faces marked by numerous rows of stomata, tips of needles ending in a sharp, horny point; resin ducts 3, large, situated in parenchyma at the apex of the faces viewed in cross section and with two or four smaller ducts scattered in parenchyma; fibro-vascular bundles 2; basal sheath ½" to ¾" long, usually quite loose at the top, persist for the life of the bundle which is 3 to 4 years.

BARK—Similar to pitch pine.

BUDS—Brown, cylindrical, oblong ovate, sharp pointed, ¼" to 1" or occasionally 1½" long, often resinous with bud scales long, serrate, pointed, often free and curved at the tips.

FLOWERS—Appear in May. Male, numerous, clustered at the base of the new growth, catkin-like, dark orange in color about 1¼" long. Female, subglobose, in whorls or pairs on stout stems, lateral on the new growth. Base color of flower lavender or light carmine with tips of bracts pale yellowish green. Bud scales forming a broad rosette shaped fringe about the base of the flower.

FRUIT—A cone maturing in two years; ovoid, or subglobose; rounded at the apex, short stalked, usually pointing slightly backward from the shoot; 2" to 2½" long, tan or light yellow-brown in color; apophysis glossy, usually thicker than pitch pine ending in a poorly defined and small umbo with short, thin, often deciduous slightly curved prickle; cones often remain closed for one or two years after maturity and are so persistent as to occasionally become partly overgrown by accretion of the limb. Seed triangular in shape, full and rounded, often fluted or ridged centrally, nearly ¼" long, coat roughened, very dark gray, usually mottled with black; wing ¾" long and nearly ¼" wide, broadest below the middle.

WOOD—Non-porous, very resinous, heavy, soft, coarse grained, dark orange in color with thick cream colored sapwood. Used for the same purposes as pitch pine.

RANGE AND DISTRIBUTION—Southern New Jersey and southeastern Virginia southward on the Coastal Plain to northern Florida and central Alabama. In Delaware found usually in Sussex County most abundant along the water courses emptying into the Atlantic Ocean; rare in Kent County.

HABITAT—Although in the South this tree habits the low wet flat places and peat swamps, in Delaware it may be found also on the dry, sandy locations mixed with other native hard pines.

NOTES—Other than as a rather attractive ornamental, the pond pine has little importance in the State. In describing this species many botanists refer to it as a distinct species and give it the name *Pinus serotina.* However, the author, after an examination of specimens found in Delaware, feels that for the purpose of Delaware tree students, the difference between this tree and pitch pine does not warrant its classification as a distinct species, hence the variety name is adhered to. The distinguishing differences between this tree and pitch pine are manifested in the longer needles, shorter, flatter cones and very shiny usually weak prickled tips of the cone scales and the somewhat longer buds.

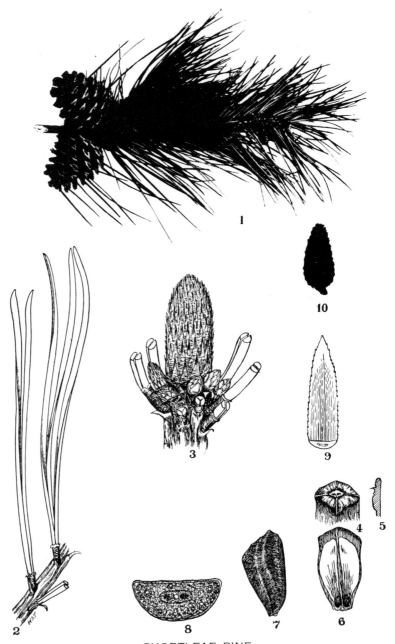

SHORTLEAF PINE

1. A branchlet with needles, one year cone and opened cones, x ½.
2. Needle clusters, natural size.
3. Bud cluster, enlarged.
4. Tip of cone scale, x 2.
5. Cross section of tip of cone scale, x 2.
6. Lower side of cone scale with 2 winged seed, x 2.
7. Seed, greatly enlarged.
8. Cross section of leaf, greatly enlarged.
9. Tip of needle, enlarged.
10. Unopened cone, x 1/3.

SHORTLEAF PINE
Pinus echinata, Miller

The shortleaf pine, also known as shortshat pine, slick bark pine, yellow pine, rosemary pine, southern yellow pine (c) and Arkansas soft pine (c) is a tree usually attaining a height of 80' to 90' and a diameter of 2' to 3' but may attain a height of 120' and a diameter of 4'. Young trees develop a narrow pyramidal crown which in old age is round, rather thin and short. The trunk of the tree is usually tall, clear of limbs for the greater portion of its length and tapers but slightly from base to the beginning of crown where the abrupt change in taper is usually quite noticeable. Reaches commercial maturity in 100 years or less but may rarely attain an age of 300 years.

LEAVES—Usually in clusters of two and often three or occasionally four, slender, flexible, usually straight but may be slightly twisted; dark blue-green, 2″ to 4½″ long surrounded by a persistent sheath about ¼″ long. Resin ducts within parenchyma 2 or 3, large, near leaf faces and often 3 to 4 smaller ones scattered in parenchyma; 2 fibro-vascular bundles; numerous rows of stomata on each surface; margins evenly and finely toothed; apex with a short, horny point. Bundles persist 2 to 5 years.

BARK—On young branches, at first light green or purplish and usually covered with a glaucous bloom later becoming dark red-brown. On young trees dark brown, fissured and flaky. On old trees rich red-brown, ¾″ to 1″ thick and fissured into large flat topped ridges broken so as to form large irregularly rectangular plates which will readily peel off in thin irregularly shaped scales, often revealing very small spherical pitch pockets. See Fig. 8.

BUDS—Ovoid, round pointed, ¼″ to ½″ long, covered with numerous sharp pointed closely appressed brown scales. Often resinous and knobby near apex.

FLOWERS—Appear in May. Male, clustered near the base of new growth, about ¾″ long, yellowish purple. Female sometimes solitary, but usually in pairs on whorls of 3 to 4 on stout stems near the tip of the new growth; pale rose colored.

FRUIT—A cone maturing in 2 years and persisting for a number of years after opening; sessile or short stalked, oblong ovoid 1½″ to 2″ long; apophysis slightly thickened, having a sharp transverse ridge and often less prominent ridge at right angles to it extending from the depressed umbo toward the base of the scale. Umbo projected into a small, weak, often deciduous prickle. Seed, triangular in shape, 3/16″ long, dark gray, fluted, their wings broadest near the middle ½″ long, ⅛″ wide.

WOOD—Non-porous, resinous, hard, strong, slightly durable, heartwood orange or yellowish brown, sapwood cream yellow. Weighs 38 lbs. per cubic foot. The wood is used extensively for all kinds of construction and furnishes the most desirable lumber of the yellow pine group for all round general purposes. Preferred use is for flooring.

RANGE AND DISTRIBUTION—From Long Island to Florida west to Tennessee, Texas, Arkansas, Missouri and Illinois. In Delaware rarely occurring in pure stands. Found in Sussex and the lower part of Kent Counties usually mixed with other hard pines of the region.

HABITAT—Prefers well drained, gravelly soils of clay, sand or loam, devoid of lime. Reaches its largest development west of the Mississippi River where growth conditions are most favorable.

NOTES—Of the Southern pines only the longleaf pine, *Pinus palustris,* exceeds this species in commercial importance and in fact very often lumber from this species is sold as longleaf pine. Because of its rapid growth, freedom from serious natural enemies and adaptability to planting worn-out and eroded soils, its use for reforestation anywhere in the State is recommended.

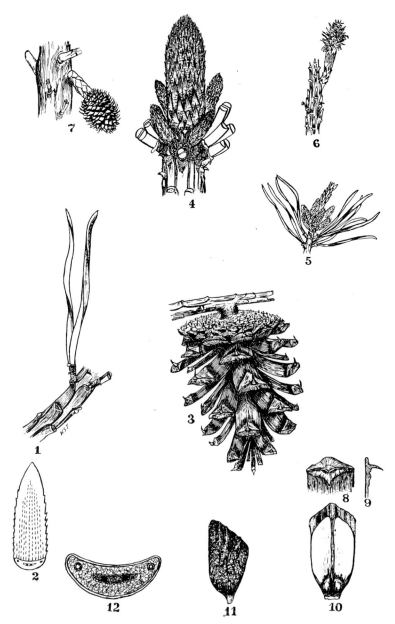

VIRGINIA PINE

1. Needle cluster, natural size.
2. Tip of needle, enlarged.
3. Opened cone, natural size.
4. Bud cluster with needles cut away, x 2.
5. Branch with male flowers, x ½.
6. Female flower, x ½.
7. One year cone, about natural size.
8-9. Cone scale tip and section, x 2 to natural size.
10. Lower side of cone scale with seed, x 2 to natural size.
11. Seed, greatly enlarged.
12. Cross section of leaf, greatly enlarged.

VIRGINIA PINE
Pinus virginiana, Miller

Virginia pine, also known as scrub pine, Jersey pine, shortshat pine, spruce pine, spruce, and shortleaved pine, is a tree which usually attains a height of 40' to 50' and a diameter of less than 12" but may reach a height of 100' and a diameter of 3'. Young trees in the open are broadly pyramidal in shape with limbs extending nearly horizontal and clothing the tree to the base. Old trees in thick stands are often crooked and their trunks marred by numerous persistent dead branches; crown, thin, small and more or less flat topped. Reaches commercial maturity in 60 years or less but may rarely attain an age of 150 years.

LEAVES—In clusters of two, stout, twisted, curved, acute pointed, blue green, 1½" to 3" long with short sheath persisting for the life of the cluster which is 3 to 4 years. Resin ducts 2 within parenchyma, 2 fibro-vascular bundles and leaf edges finely serrate.

BARK—On the young slender twigs at first light green, soon becoming light purple and covered with a glaucous bloom, later light gray-brown. On old trees ¼" to ½" thick, dark reddish brown, broken by shallow fissures into small flat plate-like scales which are closely appressed. Compared with the bark of other native pines the bark of this species is quite smooth and thinner than any of the others. See Fig. 10.

BUDS—Oblong, ⅛" to ½" long, covered with numerous overlapping, sharp pointed, dark brown scales.

FLOWERS—Appear early in May. Males in crowded clusters, at the base of the new growth, orange-brown, oblong, about ½" long; female appear lateral near the middle of the season's growth on stalks about ¾" to 1½", long, singly or in whorls, pale green in color the scale tips and tip of flower usually light carmine.

FRUIT—A cone maturing the second season 1½" to 2½" long, conical when closed, ovoid in shape when open, dark brown, persisting on the branches for 3 to 4 or more years; apophysis slightly elevated marked by a prominent transverse ridge, and poorly defined umbo ending in a stout based slender persistent prickle. Seed rather angular, thick, about 3/16" long, ⅛" wide, with thin, fluted, yellowish brown shell, mottled with black, the wing more or less parallel sided, broadest through the middle, ¾" long, 3/16" wide.

WOOD—Non-porous, resinous; heartwood light, soft, not strong, coarse grained, durable in contact with the soil, light orange in color; sapwood thick, nearly white. Used for construction timbers, lumber, railroad ties, pulpwood, piling, mine props and fuel. Weighs 33.9 pounds per cubic foot.

DISTRIBUTION AND RANGE—From New Jersey and Pennsylvania south to Georgia and Alabama, west to Ohio, Indiana, Mississippi and Arkansas. In Delaware found throughout the State in pure stand or mixed with other species.

HABITAT—Prefers any but the wet or poorly drained soils.

NOTES—As a timber tree the Virginia pine has many superiors but it serves its purpose as a land reclaimer and soil builder on sites too poor to support other tree growth. It plays an important part in supplying the market with certain low grade materials for which there is a demand. As a reforestation tree it has little to recommend it. Its thin bark, brittle wood and shallow root system makes it quite subject to injury from fire, wet snow, ice and strong winds.

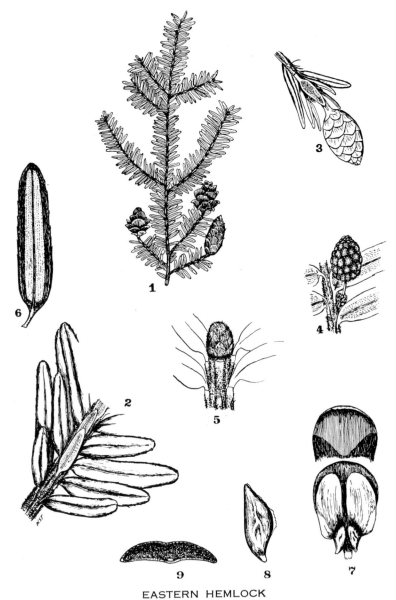

EASTERN HEMLOCK

1. Spray showing open and unopened cones, x ½.
2. Section of branchlet, enlarged.
3. Female flower, enlarged.
4. Male flower, enlarged.
5. Bud enlarged.
6. Under surface of leaf showing stomatic bands and leaf margin serrations, enlarged.
7. Lower side of cone scale showing winged seed; top, side of scale, x 2.
8. Seed with wing removed, enlarged.
9. Cross section of leaf showing resin duct, enlarged.

EASTERN HEMLOCK
Tsuga canadensis, (Linnaeus) Carriere

This tree, also known as Canadian hemlock, hemlock spruce, and white hemlock (c), usually attains a height of 60' to 70' and trunk diameter of 1'–2' but may attain a height of 100' and a diameter of 4'. Trees in the open develop a wide pyramidal form with branches often sweeping the ground. In close stands the long, slender, horizontal or slightly drooping branches form a pyramidal crown, the length of which is determined by the amount of shade endured, the lower branches dying only when subjected to dense shade. Reaches commercial maturity in 100 years or less but usually is 250 years to 600 or more years old.

LEAVES—Spirally arranged about the twig but appear to be arranged in two ranks (with a row of miniature leaves scattered on the top of the twig), the upper rank shorter than the lower; ¼″ to ½″ long, tapering slightly from the base to the blunt or rounded apex, glossy, dark green and obscurely grooved above; pale green and dull beneath and marked by 2 white bands of stomata on each side of the midrib, each band being made up of 5 to 6 rows of stomata; leaf margin near the tip minutely long serrate; leaf cross section shows a single resin duct located beneath the single fibro-vascular bundle. Leaves persist 3 to 4 years.

BARK—On new growth at first hairy, light yellow-green soon becoming yellowish-brown and glabrous the following year. On old trees, gray ½″ to 1″ thick and broken by deep fissures into long connected, rounded ridges, made up of small closely appressed scales. The inner bark, purplish red; used for tanning leather. See Fig. 11.

BUDS—Rather inconspicuous, obtuse, light brown 1/16″ long usually slightly hairy.

FLOWERS—Appear in May, male and female usually on the same branch but on separate branchlets; male, small, irregularly ovate, appearing on a short stalk on branchlets of the previous year, auxiliary to leaves or between the leaf projections. Female less than ½″ long, cone-like, pale green, terminal on the new growth with a stalk about ¼″ long.

FRUIT—A short-stalked, ovoid cone about ¾″ long maturing in one year. Cone scales broad, rounded, thin and enclosing the seed whose wings are about 3/16″ long above the seed and broadest near the base which extend beyond the edge of the scale. The seeds are about ⅛″ long, rhombic in outline and contain 2 or 3 large oil vesicles.

WOOD—Non-porous, non-resinous, light, hard, not strong, coarse grained, difficult to work, not durable and splinters when broken; heartwood light reddish-brown; sapwood thin and slightly darker. Weighs 26 lbs. per cubic foot. Used for interior construction such as framework and sheathing lath. The long fiber and absence of resin make it suitable for paper pulp.

RANGE AND DISTRIBUTION—From Nova Scotia to eastern Minnesota southward in the moist locations along the Allegheny Mountains to northern Georgia and Alabama, westward to Indiana and Wisconsin. In Delaware native only in New Castle County and now quite rare naturally. Much planted throughout the State as an ornamental.

HABITAT—Prefers the moist locations such as deep stream valleys and cool northern slopes of mountains. It is essentially a shade loving species.

NOTES—Hemlock was important two decades or more ago when its bark provided the major tannin material for leather. At that time vast forests of the species were lumbered primarily for the bark and the choicest logs, the rest being left in the woods to rot or become food for forest fires. Because the species is slow of growth, exacting in its requirements of soil moisture and temperature and affords products which other less exacting species will provide on similar sites in less time, it is not advocated for reforestation purposes. As an ornamental, few if any conifers surpass it in youthful beauty.

The hemlock used as a poison by the Ancients was not *Tsuga* as is sometimes supposed, but a poisonous herb having the scientific name of *Conium maculatum.*

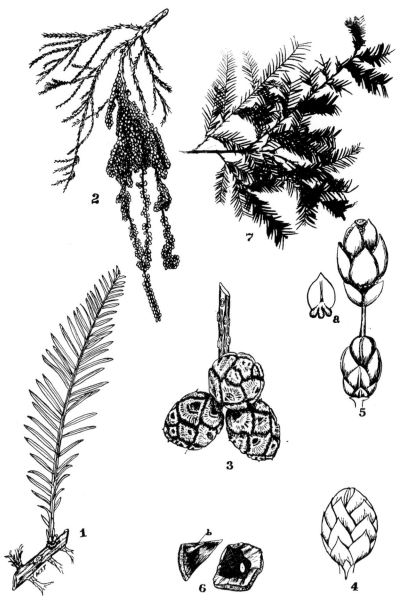

BALD CYPRESS

1. Deciduous branchlet, natural size.
2. Branchlet showing scale leaves and male flower cluster.
3. A fruit cluster, x ½.
4. Female flower, greatly enlarged.
5. Male flower and single flower scale showing pollen sacks (a), greatly enlarged.
6. Two seeds; one sectioned to show bony coat and tip of cotyledon; (b) indicates resin sack; natural size.
7. Spray showing foliage types, x ½.

BALD CYPRESS
Taxodium distichum, (Linnaeus) Rich.

GENUS DESCRIPTION—Taxodium, when translated means: "resembling the yew (tree),'' which probably refers to the shape of the leaves since in most other respects, there is little resemblance betwen *Taxus* and *Taxodium.* Although in prehistoric ages this genus had representatives widely distributed over the Northern Hemisphere, it now has but four living species. Three of these, *T. distichum* L., *T. ascendens* Brong., and *T. mucronatum* Ten., are native to North America; the other *Taxodium heterophyllum* Brong., is native to China.

The bald cypress, also known as southern cypress, swamp cypress, Gulf cypress (c) and tidewater red cypress (c) is a deciduous tree usually 70' to 90' tall and 2' to 3' in diameter but may attain a height of 120' and a diameter of 10'. Of pyramidal form when young but in old age developing a wide, often flat-topped or irregular crown. When situated on well drained soil, the trunk usually tapers from the base to the tip but when growing in swamps inundated for extended periods, the base is wide buttressed and usually hollow. In this latter environment, irregularly conical, spongy wooded protuberances often 4' tall and 6" or more in diameter develop from the lateral roots. These are known as "knees" and since they rarely develop on trees situated on well drained soils, their apparent purpose is to provide the tree with a means of absorbing air into the roots. May reach commercial maturity in 80 years or less but trees 1000 years old have been recorded.

LEAVES—Of two kinds, scale-like and linear; the scale-like ones spirally arranged on the persistent branches, short, light green in spring, yellow-green in summer with grayish stomata on the under surface, linear leaves, ½" to ¾" long, short pointed, arranged in 2 vertical ranks on spreading branchlets, bright yellow-green, turning red-brown in autumn and falling with the branchlet.

BARK—On new branches, light glaucous green, turning light brown and roughened by the round scars of deciduous branchlets; on old trees, light cinnamon brown, fibrous or slightly flaky, broken by narrow, more or less continuous fissures and narrow flat-topped ridges. See Fig. 2.

BUDS—Ovoid or globular, small, covered with overlapping, sharp pointed, reddish brown scales; the flower buds about ⅛" long, silver-gray during the winter and purple in spring.

FLOWERS—Male and female on the same tree, the male ones terminal, in drooping tassel-like clusters 4" to 5" long, the flower short stalked consisting of numerous scale-like stamens having pollen sacks basally attached; the female flowers inconspicuous, lateral on the previous season's growth, solitary, in pairs or in groups and consisting of numerous overlapping bracts and scales.

FRUIT—A knobby ball about 1" in diameter; short stalked, reddish or purplish brown at maturity and maturing in one season when it usually drops from the tree as a ball breaking into angular pieces as it strikes the ground. The cotyledon is enclosed in a thick, woody, angular shaped covering that originally formed a part of the ball. On the external faces of the seed coat near the base will be found large orange-red gland sacks filled with fragrant liquid resin.

WOOD—Non-porous, resinous, easily worked; heartwood light brown to dark brown or occasionally nearly black, very durable; sapwood light brown to white. Used for cooperage, interior or exterior construction, ship building, shingles, railroad ties, posts or anywhere that a durable and serviceable wood is required. Weighs 28.31 pounds per cubic foot and according to color is marketed as red cypress, southern cypress, white cypress, etc.

RANGE AND DISTRIBUTION—From Delaware southward to the Florida Keys, westward to Texas, Oklahoma and Illinois. In Delaware it is no longer abundant being found naturally only along some streams and in a few swamps and ponds in Sussex County or the southern part of Kent County.

HABITAT—Prefers swamps and wet peaty bottomlands where the roots are covered with water for a period during the year.

NOTES—The bald cypress is one of the few conifers in the world that sheds all its needle-like leaves in the fall of the year. The soft green foliage, straight stem and ascending branches which form the conical shaped crown make it one of the most attractive ornamentals, worthy of much wider use than it now enjoys. As a reforestation tree, it promises rapid growth on all but the driest soils. *T. ascendens* or pond cypress is rare in this State.

SOUTHERN WHITE CEDAR

1. Branch, x ½.
2. Fruit or opened cone, natural size.
3. Portion of branch showing leaf arrangement and glandular dots, greatly enlarged.
4. Female flower, greatly enlarged.
5. Male flower, greatly enlarged.
6. Winged seed, greatly enlarged.

SOUTHERN WHITE CEDAR
Chamaecyparis thyoides, (Linnaeus) B. S. P.

GENUS DESCRIPTION—The genus *Chamaecyparis* is credited with but six distinct species of which 3 are native to North America and 3 native to Japan and Formosa. Only one species, *Chamaecyparis thyoides* is native to eastern United States but many garden forms of both the native and exotic species are to be found planted in this country.

Southern white cedar (c), also known as Atlantic white cedar, swamp cedar, boat cedar and post cedar, is a tree which in Delaware usually attains a height of 60' to 70' and a diameter of 12" to 18" but further south in its range often reaches a height of 80' and a diameter of 4'. The trunk is usually straight, clean of limbs for a good portion of its length and tapers gradually from the base to a narrow conical crown composed of slender horizontal branches ending in tufts of foliage. Reaches commercial maturity in 150 years or less but may attain an age of 500 or more years.

LEAVES—Of two kinds—awl-shaped and scale-like; the awl-shaped ones occurring only on young seedlings and vigorous shoots; the scale-like ones small, ovate pointed, closely appressed and overlapping in such a manner as to give the branchlet a four-angled appearaoce. They are dark blue-green in color and often have a glandular depression or dot on the back. Upon dying at the end of the second season, they persist as a branch covering for many years.

BARK—On old trees, gray-brown or dark gray in color, thin, broken by shallow fissures into long, flat-topped connecting ridges, which exfoliate in long fibrous strips. See Fig. 13.

BUDS—Inconspicuous.

FLOWERS—Minute; male and female on the same tree but on separate branchlets appear late in March or April; the male ones longer than the female and made up of numerous shield-shaped scales; the female subglobose in form and consisting of fewer scales (6) having minute bottle shaped ovules at the base.

FRUIT—A small (¼") globose, stalked cone, at maturity and before opening bluish purple covered with glaucous bloom and marked by rough contours and numerous prominences or knobs above. Maturing in one season and opening in autumn liberating the ⅛" long, broad winged, red-brown seed.

WOOD—Non-porous, light, soft, brittle, close grained, mildly fragrant; heartwood light brown tinged with red; sapwood lighter; easily worked and very durable. Weight 20.7 pounds per cubic foot. Used for posts, poles, piling, boat building, cooperage, shingles, wooden ware and lumber.

RANGE AND DISTRIBUTION—From New Hampshire and Maine south along the coast to Florida and Mississippi. In Delaware found only along the water courses, ponds and swamps, principally in Sussex and lower Kent Counties.

HABITAT—Prefers swamps and wet locations where it grows in pure stands but is occasionally found on drier sites mixed with other tree species.

NOTES—Many decades ago, Delaware boasted of vast areas of cedar and cypress swamps where the trees stood so thick that semi-darkness prevailed beneath the canopy of their matted crowns and sphagnum moss grew luxuriantly over their roots. For untold centuries the moss, leaves and other vegetation died and partially rotted, forming a heavy layer of peat over the soil. The agricultural possibilities of these peat swamps did not long go unrecognized by tillers of the soil and as rapidly as drainage and clearing could be done, they were converted to agricultural use. The inexcusable part of this conversion process was that fire, started on the clearing areas, was permitted to spread to the uncleared areas with the result that most of the cedar forests and the high peat on which they grew have been destroyed. These fire-scarred areas, although divested of much of the fertility, can be again brought back to production by proper forest protection. Perhaps not alone to white cedar, because the natural condition has been so altered that the species will no longer thrive, but where conditions have not been greatly altered, no other species would thrive better and hence reforestation is warranted.

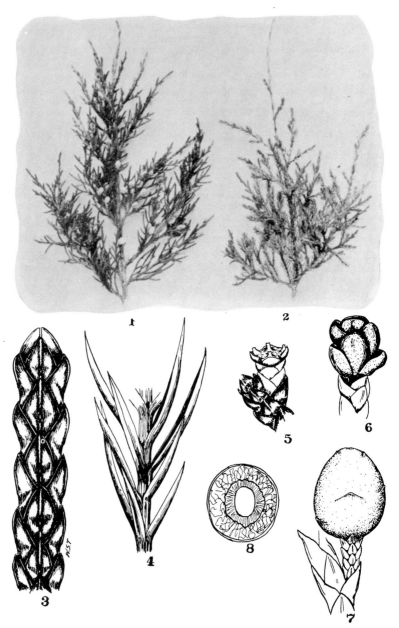

EASTERN RED CEDAR

1. Branchlet with scale-like leaves and fruit, x ½.
2. Branchlet with awl-shaped leaves, x ½.
3. Branchlet showing shape and arrangement of scale-like leaves, greatly enlarged.
4. Showing shape and arrangement of awl-shaped leaves, greatly enlarged.
5. Female flower, greatly enlarged.
6. Male flower, greatly enlarged.
7. Fruit, greatly enlarged.
8. Cross section of fruit showing flesh and seed coat, greatly enlarged

EASTERN RED CEDAR
Juniperus virginiana, Linnaeus

GENUS DESCRIPTION—There is perhaps no other genus having members more widely scattered over the Northern hemisphere than that of *Juniperus* which is the ancient Latin name of the genus. It has representatives in most every location from the Arctic Circle to Mexico in the Western Hemisphere and to the mountains of Tropical Africa, China and Japan in the Eastern Hemisphere. Authorities credit it with 40 species and as many more varieties. Only one species, *Juniperus virginiana,* is native to Delaware.

The eastern red cedar (c), also known as juniper, red juniper, and post cedar, is generally a small tree 30' to 45' tall and 1' to 2' in diameter but may occasionally attain a height of 100' and a diameter of 4'. Two general forms are recognized; one with a narrow, compact, pyramidal head made up of short ascending branches; the other broadly pyramidal and ofttimes quite round top- ped with spreading horizontal or slightly drooping branches. Reaches commer- cial maturity in 80 years or less but may attain an age of 200 or more years.

LEAVES—Are of two kinds, awl-shaped and scale-like; the scale-like ones being characteristic of older trees. They are usually opposite, acute or obtuse having a glandular depression on the back, smooth, dark blue-green, about 1/16" long, ridged, closely imbricated and appressed to the branchlet in such a manner as to give it an angular appearance. The awl-shaped kind, which usually appear opposite on young trees or vigorous shoots, are about ½" long, "U" shaped in cross section, slightly curved and tapering to a sharp point. Both kinds of leaves begin to die and turn brown after the second or third season; the scale-like ones persisting 2 to 3 years after browning.

BARK—On young branches after the leaves have fallen, reddish or grayish brown; on the trunk thin, light gray-brown, separating in long shreds or adhering closely to the tree. See Fig. 12.

BUDS—Inconspicuous.

FLOWERS—Appear in May. Male and female on separate trees but may rarely be found on the same tree. The male ones minute, terminal on the new growth, consisting of 10–12 stamens with rounded connectives appearing like a minute opened spineless cone. The pistillate, very small, at first yellow- ish, soon turning bluish with a glaucous bloom.

FRUIT—An oblong or subglobose, bluish or purplish berry about ¼" in diameter, normally covered with a glaucous bloom. Flesh of the fruit thin and enclosing 1, 2 or rarely 4 bony shelled seeds. Some species of birds feed on the fruit and there are many among the human race who do not dislike the sweetish resinous flavor of the pulpy seed coat.

WOOD—Non-porous and non-resinous, light, soft, close grained, brittle, straight grained pieces easily worked; heartwood distinctly red, very durable in contact with the soil; sapwood thin, cream white or white. Weighs 31 pounds per cubic foot. Used for fence posts, sills of buildings, linings of closets and chests, lead pencils and furniture. The fragrant odor of the wood is often re- garded as a clothes moth repellant but it has been definitely proved that chests or closets lined with the wood does not render them moth proof.

RANGE AND DISTRIBUTION—From Nova Scotia to Ontario and North Dakota, south to Florida and Texas rarely ascending to elevations of more than 2,000 feet. In Delaware the species is found abundantly through- out the State.

HABITAT—Not particular as to soil or moisture but prefers the heavier soils and drier sites and although preferring full sunlight as do most of the junipers, it may often be found growing in dense stands of other species.

NOTES—The red cedar produces one of the most durable of our native woods and deserves cultivation in situations where it does not interfere with more valuable species or is not in close proximity to apple orchards for it is one of the alternate host plants of the cedar rusts *Gymnosporangium juniperi* and G. *globosum* which causes a leaf rust of apples. Contrary to general opinion, the growth of red cedar in the open is not slow. This is particularly true during the first 12 to 15 years of its life. Oils and decoctions manufac- tured from the fruit, leaves and wood are used in perfume, medicine, and gin.

Class II. ANGIOSPERMAE
  Division II. DICOTYLEDONES
    Family: SALICACEAE
      Genus: POPULUS (Linnaeus)

THE POPLARS

The genus *populus* belongs to the same family as the willows and resembles the latter in many respects, particularly as to flower, fruit and seed. Common names such as poplar and popple, aspen and asp or cottonwood and cotton tree, applied to this genus obviously have originated from names applied to members of the genus and refer to a distinguishing feature thereof. The name "poplar" may be confusing in that it is applied to the well-known yellow poplar or tulip tree which is unrelated and belongs to the magnolia family.

The poplars are, for the most part, fast-growing medium-sized and short-lived trees.

Leaves of most species are deltoid or heart-shaped, glandular lobed or dentate on the margins with long often laterally flattened petioles sometimes having at the junction with the blade 2 conspicuous nectar glands. The compressed leaf petiole of some representatives of the genus permits the slightest movement of air to cause them to flutter, tremble or "quake" and one species in which this characteristic is most pronounced has earned both common and scientific names descriptive thereof, viz., trembling aspen, *P. tremuloides*. The **bark** on young trunks and limbs is usually light in color but on old trunks usually very dark and furrowed. The often resinous winter **buds** are made up of two opposite bottom scales and numerous imbricated scales increasing in size toward the tip. Male and female **flowers** appear before the leaves and on separate trees as worm-like catkins from buds of the previous season. The **fruit,** which ripens before the leaves are fully grown, consists of numerous oblong conical shaped capsules on a raceme of varying length. The capsules, upon ripening and splitting open, liberate large quantities of light, long white hair or "cotton" covered seeds. This cotton is an objectionable feature of the female trees and gives rise to the common name cottonwood. The **wood** of the American species is largely manufactured into paper pulp but some species furnish lumber used for interior finish, wooden packages, woodenware and novelties. This genus has perhaps the widest **distribution** of any other in the world and like the willows, they sport and hybridize freely. Representatives are found from the Arctic Circle to Mexico and from coast to coast on the North American Continent and throughout Europe, Asia and northern Africa in the Eastern Hemisphere (Sarg.). Despite the bewilderment in the botanical classification of the genus, about 34 species are recognized of which some 15 are native to North America and 2 to Delaware. Of the introduced species, white poplar, *P. alba,* L., and the Lombardy poplar, *P. nigra italica,* DuRoi., are common in the State. All Lombardy poplars are staminate trees and are reputed to have a common origin in a single sport which was found on the plains of Lombardy (France) early in the 17th century. Species indigenous to the United States but not to Delaware are occasionally found in the State either as ornamentals or as escapes from cultivation. Most common of these are the balm of gilead *P. candicans,* Ait., balsam poplar *P. balsamifera,* L., and American aspen *P. tremuloides,* Michaux. The fragrant balsam contained in the buds of the balm of gilead is occasionally used in medicines, perfumes, etc.

The rapid growth made by species of *populus,* their hardiness, ease of planting and propagation by cuttings, has led to their use for wind breaks and ornamentals. However, the many undesirable features of most species, particularly the extensive fibrous root system which often clogs sewers and drain pipes in the quest for water, voids their use in the vicinity of such sanitary improvements. They are accordingly not recommended for ornamental planting in Delaware.

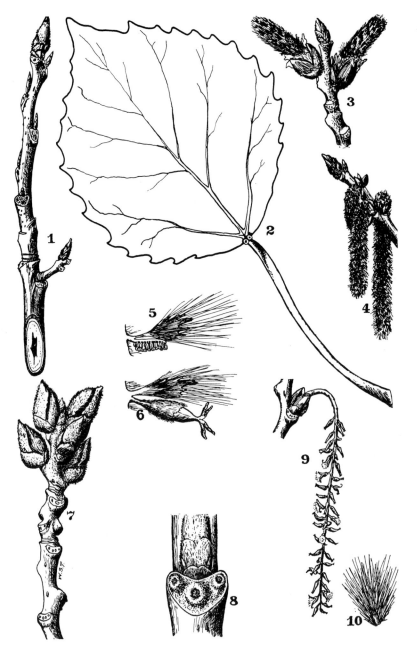

LARGE-TOOTH ASPEN

1. Winter twig, natural size.
2. Leaf showing nectariferous glands, natural size.
3. Portion of twig with female flowers, natural size.
4. Portion of twig with male flowers, natural size.
5. Male flower, enlarged.
6. Female flower, enlarged.
7. Winter twig with flower buds, natural size.
8. Section of winter twig enlarged to show normal leaf scar.
9. Fruiting catkin with ripening capsules x ½.
10. Seed, greatly enlarged.

LARGE-TOOTH ASPEN
Populus grandidentata, Michaux

The large-tooth aspen also known as large-toothed aspen, poplar (c), white poplar, popple, large aspen and asp, is a tree which in Delaware usually attains a height of 30' to 40' and a diameter of 1' to 1½', but may occasionally attain a height of 70' and a diameter of 2'. Trunk, normally straight, slender, tapering and clear of limbs for the greater portion of its length, ending in narrow, usually round topped crown. Reaches commercial maturity in 40 years or less but seldom exceeds 80 years of age.

LEAVES—Alternate, simple broadly ovate, with short tipped apex; upper margins coarsely toothed and basal margin entire or nearly so; 2" to 3½" long, 2" to 2½" wide, dark green above, paler beneath; petiole, or leaf stem 1½" to 2½" long, laterally flattened and at its junction with the leaf surface often equipped with two nectariferous glands.

BARK—At the base of old trees ¾" to 1" thick; dark gray to black, irregularly fissured and ridges flat topped; on younger trunks, light gray-green, smooth and broken by shallow irregular fissures; on the stout but brittle twigs at first hoary tomentose, later becoming smooth and dark orange in color, marked by conspicuous lenticels and roughened by the large leaf bases exhibiting a 3 bundled leaf scar.

BUDS—Leaf buds conical pointed, flower buds ovate, blunt pointed; covered with 6–7 light chestnut brown scales, which are coated with a dull, granular, white pubescence.

FLOWERS—Appear in April. Male and female flowers on different trees as pubescent drooping catkins; the male ones 1½" to 2½" long; the female becoming 4" to 5" long and bearing flowers equipped with short spreading stigmas.

FRUIT—An ament, 4" to 5" long, maturing before the leaves are fully grown and bearing scattered, light green 2 valved capsules, which upon splitting open, release minute dark brown seed equipped with an abundance of long white hair.

WOOD—Diffuse-porous, the pores rarely visible without a lens; medullary rays very fine and indistinct; texture fine and silky, lustre high; light brown to white in color; neither strong nor durable; weighs 25 lbs. per cubic foot. Manufactured into paper pulp, interior finish lumber, wooden packages, woodenware and novelties.

RANGE AND DISTRIBUTION—From Nova Scotia to Ontario and Minnesota southward to North Carolina. In Delaware common throughout the State.

HABITAT—Prefers the rich moist soil of the flood plain of streams, but may be found on drier sites especially following forest fire. Occurs in small pure stand or mixed with other species.

NOTES—This tree may be distinguished from other *Populus* species by the coarsely toothed leaf margins (which gives rise to the scientific name, *grandidentata*), the non-resinous buds and non-ridged red-brown twigs. Commercially it is of minor importance and aesthetically is not recommended in this State where other species will thrive.

SWAMP COTTONWOOD

1. Summer branchlet, with leaves and mature fruit x ½.
2. Winter twig, natural size.
3. Portion of winter twig, enlarged to show leaf scar and bud.
4. Raceme of female flowers, natural size.
5. Twig of developing male flowers, natural size.
6. Female flower, enlarged.
7. Male flower, enlarged.
8. A seed, enlarged.

SWAMP COTTONWOOD
Populus heterophylla, Linnaeus

The swamp cottonwood, also known as downy poplar, black cottonwood, black poplar (c), swamp poplar and river cottonwood, is a tree 40' to 50' tall and 1½' to 2' in diameter, but may occasionally reach a height of 100' and a diameter of 3', with short, rather heavy, contorted branches forming a round topped head.

LEAVES—Alternate, 4" to 7" long and 3" to 6" wide, heart shaped, broad pointed, rounded or truncate at the base; margin coarsely or finely serrate with incurved glandular teeth; when first unfolding thickly covered with matted white hairs, later becoming smooth and deep dark green above, paler and smooth beneath; furnished with a stout, pale yellow midrib and slender, round, downy or smooth, leaf stalk 2" to 3" long.

BARK—On old trunks ¾" to 1" thick, light brown tinged with red, broken by long fissures into narrow plates which are normally loose at both ends; on young trunks and branches similar to old trunks but fissures shallower and ridges broad and flat topped. The stout twigs are thickly tomentose covered at first, later becoming yellowish brown, growing dark brown and smooth the second year, marked by scattered pale lenticels and roughened by the large raised leaf bases.

BUDS—Alternate, slightly resinous and shiny, broadly ovate, reddish brown, pubescence present on most of the 5–7 scales and more on the inner scales at the tip; leaf buds about ¼" long; flower buds longer and larger.

FLOWERS—In April-May, male and female on separate trees; the male catkins 1" long and at first stout and erect on the shoot, later drooping and 2" to 3" long, densely flowered, female catkins raceme-like, 1" to 2" long, small, slender, few flowered and becoming more or less erect and 3" to 6" long before maturing.

FRUIT—An ament ripening before the leaves are half grown, consisting of small, pear shaped, green, thick walled, 3 to 4 valved capsules which become red-brown when ripe and upon splitting release the small, hair-covered, red-brown seeds.

WOOD—Diffuse-porous, pores indistinct; heartwood grayish brown, sapwood lighter, weighs 25.4 lbs. per cubic foot. It is neither a strong nor durable wood. The darker lumber, under the commercial name of black poplar, is used for interior finsh.

RANGE AND DISTRIBUTION—From Connecticut southward near the coast to southern Georgia and western Florida to eastern Texas, Arkansas, southern Missouri, southern Illinois and Indiana. In Delaware observed by the author in only Kent and Sussex Counties where it is comparatively rare.

HABITAT—Throughout its range this tree prefers low wet swamps, stream borders and edges of ponds. In Delaware it has been observed only in such location.

NOTES—This tree may be distinguished from all other populus species by its large leaves and rounded leaf stalks, rugged, light red-brown trunk bark and orange colored pith of the twigs. Commercially it is of little importance because of its rare and local occurrence. In this State the wood is marketed with the wood of other poplars.

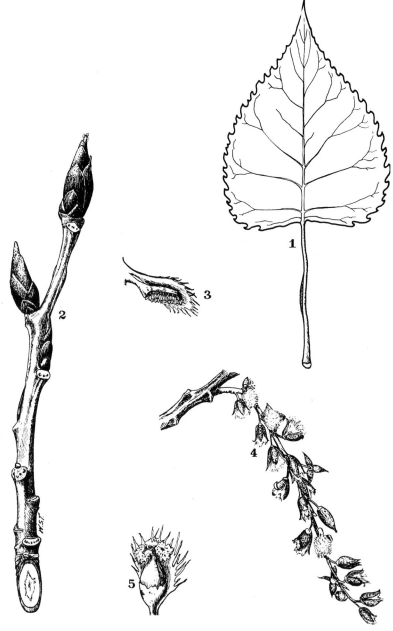

EASTERN COTTONWOOD

1. Leaf x ½.
2. Winter twig, natural size.
3. Male flower, enlarged.
4. Fruiting branchlet, natural size.
5. Female flower, enlarged.

EASTERN COTTONWOOD
Populus deltoides, Marsh.

AUTHOR'S NOTE: Although this species is indigenous to eastern United States it is not believed to occur naturally in Delaware. It is included herein on the assumption that there may be places in the State where it has escaped cultivation and become established as a forest tree.

The eastern cottonwood, also known as Carolina poplar, necklace poplar and cotton tree, is the largest and most stately representative of the genus *populus*. It usually attains a height of 50' to 75' and a diameter of 2' to 3' but may attain a height of more than 100' and a diameter of 6' to 8'. The trunk, in forest stands, is usually clean of limb for the greater portion of its length, tapers uniformly to the small symmetrical pyramidal crown composed of small ascending branches above and heavier nearly horizontal branches below.

LEAVES—Alternate, simple, broadly triangular, coarsely serrate with incurved glandular teeth and long pointed tip; thick and firm; smooth, shiny and bright green above; slightly paler beneath; 3" to 5" long and broad; leaf stalks 2" to 3" long, smooth, laterally flattened, yellow or often tinged with red which extends part way up the central leaf vein.

BARK—On old trees 1½" to 2" thick, ashy gray, deeply and more or less continuously and parallel fissured into broad round topped ridges composed of closely appressed scales. On branches and young trunks thin, greenish-yellow and smooth. On the stout angled or ridged twigs normally yellow tinged with green, shiny and marked by scattered elongated lenticles.

BUDS—Alternate, large, ½" long, ovoid acute, the terminal bud usually angled and the lateral ones much flattened, divergent and curved; covered by 6–7 light chestnut brow scales which are very resinous on the inside and smooth and varnished on the outside.

FLOWERS—March or April. Male and female on separate trees, short stalked, glabrous; male aments 3" to 4" long, drooping, densely flowered; the female ones sparsely flowered, smaller at first but lengthening toward maturity to 8" to 10".

FRUIT—Maturing in May on a drooping ament 8" to 12" long, consisting of a dark green, thin walled, 3 or 4 valved capsule which upon splitting releases the small light brown cottony (coma) covered seed.

WOOD—Diffuse-porous, pores in spring wood visible without a lens; medullary rays indistinct; soft, tough, rather coarse and woolly in texture; lustre dull; warps badly in seasoning; heartwood dark brown; sapwood wide, white. Weight 23 lbs. per cubic foot. Used for paper pulp, wooden packages and novelties.

RANGE AND DISTRIBUTION—From southern Canada southward through the Atlantic States generally west of the Allegheny Mountains to Florida and Texas to the Rocky Mountains on the west and Vermont and western New York, on the east. Although occasionally planted in Delaware as an ornamental it has not been observed by the author as occurring in forest stands and accordingly not considered native.

HABITAT—Prefers the rich moist soils of bottomlands and stream banks where it occurs in open stands, but may occasionally occupy uplands and drier sites in the western limits of its range.

NOTES—There appears to be some confusion among botanists on the nomenclature and identification of this species due to varying botanical characteristics present in specimens in different parts of its range. Numerous hybrids and varieties are listed by authors of more complete botanical and dendrological works. The tree may be distinguished from other members of the genus *Populus* by its larger resinous buds and yellowish twigs which are strongly angled by the prominent ridges extending downward from the large 3 lobed leaf scars. Because it is difficult to manufacture lumber from this tree without curling or warping in seasoning, its value for this product is questionable. It is, however, one of the best trees for the production of pulp wood and because of its extremely rapid growth is recommended as a reforestation tree to be grown and harvested for such use. Propagation is usually by cuttings.

Aside from its rapid growth, attractive form and the pleasant balsam odor emitted from the leaves, it has little to recommend it as an ornamental. It should never be planted as a street tree or ornamental in built-up section because of its excessive root development which often lifts pavements and clogs drains and sewers.

The name *deltoides* is derived from the Greek letter "delta" and refers to the characteristic shape of the leaves.

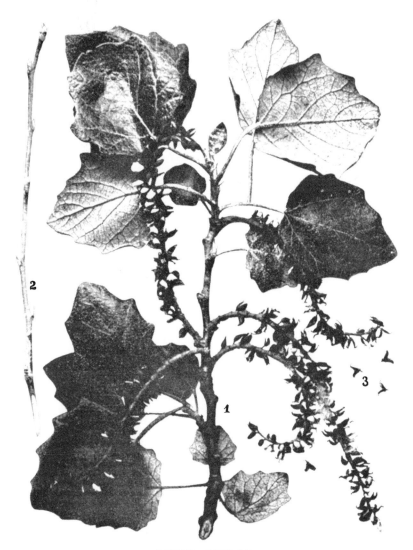

WHITE POPLAR

1. Summer branchlet with leaves and fruit raceme, x ½.
2. Winter twig, x ½.
3. Opened seed capsules, x 2/3.

WHITE POPLAR
Populus alba, Linnaeus

The white poplar, also known as silver-leaf poplar, abele and white bark poplar, is not a native species. Having been early introduced from Europe into this Country as an ornamental, it has now become naturalized in many localities and is quite often found in Delaware woodlands. It is a tree often attaining 100′ in height and a diameter of 3′ to 4′. The large short trunk, broad spreading limbs and open round topped crown, make it a distinctive feature of any landscape where it grows.

LEAVES—Alternate, variable, usually 2″ to 4″ long and nearly as broad, broadly egg-shaped, irregularly toothed or lobed; usually white velvety tomentose when they unfold, later becoming shiny dark green above but retaining the silvery white velvet beneath or often becoming nearly smooth and light green; leaf stem shorter than or about the same length as the blade, slender, laterally flattened and velvety. The movement of the leaves in the slightest breeze and the contrast of color between their upper and lower surfaces largely accounts for its common names.

BARK—On old trunks dark gray and broken by more or less continuous fissures and rounded ridges becoming less broken and light greenish gray on the upper trunk and limbs. Twigs greenish, covered with white pubescence and whitish bloom.

BUDS—Alternate, about ¼″ long, ovoid, acute pointed, non-resinous, covered with white down.

FLOWERS—April and May before the leaves; male and female on separate trees; the male catkins 2″ to 4″ long, slender, drooping; the female ones 1″ to 2″, more slender than the male ones composed of capsule like flowers with spreading stigmas.

FRUIT—A drooping ament maturing in May–June, 2″ to 4″ long, composed of narrow pear shaped capsules which upon ripening split in half, releasing small light brown, white hair tufted seeds.

WOOD—Diffuse-porous, heartwood reddish yellow; sapwood white; light, soft, tough and recently much in demand for furniture veneer so sliced that a rippled satiny sheen is obtained.

RANGE AND DISTRIBUTION—Introduced from Europe and Asia and now naturalized in Delaware.

HABITAT—Prefers moist, fertile soils but thrives on poorer and drier sites.

NOTES—This tree, like other members of the genus, is a hardy rapid grower which in a measure may account for its popularity with early settlers. Its great size, buttressed base, and habit of sending up numerous suckers unusual distances from the parent tree, condemn it for city or lawn use. However, it appears to be one tree that is hardy and root firm enough to thrive in exposed locations adjacent to the Atlantic Ocean and Delaware Bay in Delaware. The hardiness of the species is attested by the fact that in a survey of the damage done to trees by a tropical storm that visited Delaware a few years ago, no large tree of this species was observed to be uprooted or seriously damaged.

Family: SALICACEAE
  Genus: SALIX (LINNAEUS)

THE WILLOWS

The origin of the scientific name *Salix* is attributed to two Celtic words *Sal* meaning "near" and *Lis* meaning "water," appropriately denoting the habitat of most members of the genus.* The genus belongs to the same family as *populus* and by some botanical authorities is given priority over the latter genus in the order of classification.

Representative of Salix are small trees and shrubs of broad irregular growth and comparatively short life. When they attain or approximate tree size the trunk is usually crooked, inclined and vested with contorted limbs for the greater portion of its length and forming a wide spreading usually round topped crown. Branchlets, round, long, slender, flexible and tough, but often breaking readily at the joints. The **leaves** are alternate, simple, usually long and narrow but of other shapes such as long egg shaped, rounded, sickle-shaped, etc., equipped with short leaf stems which are sometimes glandular at the junction with the leaf blade. That the willows are close relatives of the conifers is attested by the fact that in this region they are among the last trees to shed their leaves in late autumn and the first to blossom and leaf in the new year. The elevate leaf scars are usually U-shaped or crescent shaped and show 3 small, equally spaced, bundle scars. Stipule scars present, often prominent on thrifty twigs but usually minute. Bark on trunks usually rough and deeply furrowed to form flat topped, thick scaled ridges; contains tannic acid and used in tanning leather and yields salicin, a bitter substance used in medicines. (Sarg.) **Buds**, alternate, covered by a single scale, terminal bud absent. The male and female **flowers** occur on separate trees before or during the unfolding of the leaves, catkin like and of varying length and color. The **fruit** is similar to populus and consists of an ament bearing the one celled capsules which at maturity split into 2 recurving valves releasing the minute chestnut brown, long hair covered seeds. The **wood** of the willows is diffuse-porous with pores visible without a lens; light, soft, non-durable, weak but fairly tough and except for the long thin shoots used in basket weaving, etc., is of minor commercial importance. Formerly the wood of some species was much in demand for the manufacture of charcoal used in the production of black powder.

About 170 species are credited to this genus of which about 70 are native to North America, 24 of which attain tree size and habit. (Sarg.) Since the willows seem to sport and hybridize to their own content and the despair of botanists and dendrologists, a true determination of the number of native Delaware species has not been

---

* After J. S. Illick in "Tree Habits" published by American Nature Association, Washington, D. C.

attempted. However, it may be safely assumed that at least 10 species can be catalogued. Of the exotic species much planted in this country the white willow *S. alba,* L., weeping willow *S. babylonica,* L., and crack willow *S. fragilis,* L., are most often seen and now quite naturalized in many localities.

The form and grace of the willows in early life, particularly the weeping types, affords them considerable popularity for aesthetic purposes. Although they prefer the wet soils adjacent to streams, ponds and fresh water swamps, they will thrive when planted on drier sites. Propagation is usually by cuttings taken and planted in June to August, but with proper care it is not difficult to cause them to root at any time of year. This particular characteristic of the willows permits its ready establishment on banks and soils subject to washing. The subsequent rapid root and stem development soon fixes the soil and permits the introduction of more permanent tree species.

Because of the extensive and fibrous nature of the root development, the brittleness of the twigs of some species which leaves the ground strewn with the refuse, and the fact that the willows generally are host to a number of diseases and insect pests, their use as shade and street trees in towns and cities is to be discouraged.

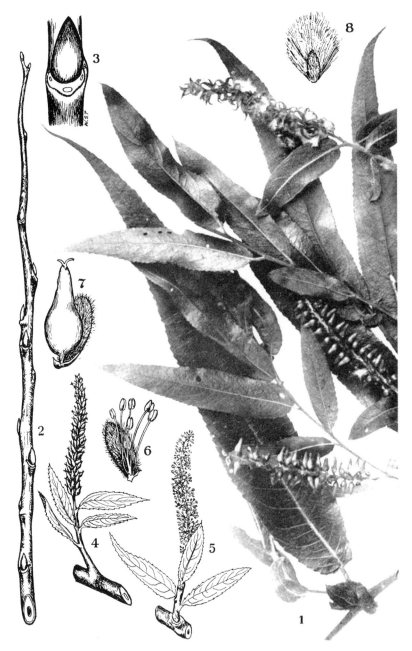

BLACK WILLOW

1. Summer branchlet showing opened and unopened fruit, natural size.
2. Winter twig, natural size.
3. Portion of twig showing winter bud and leaf scar, enlarged.
4. Branchlet with female ament, x ½.
5. Branchlet with male ament, x ½.
6. Male flower, enlarged.
7. Female flower, enlarged.
8. A seed, enlarged.

BLACK WILLOW
Salix nigra, Marshall

The black willow or swamp willow, is a tree which in Delaware usually attains a height of 30' to 50' and a diameter of 1' to 1½' but may rarely attain a height of 80' and a diameter of 3'. Trunks usually in clusters, crooked and inclined, clothed with numerous upright spreading branches to form a broad irregular open round topped head. It is the largest of the native willows—the variety *altissima,* Sarg., occurring in the lower Mississippi Valley, sometimes reaching a height of 120'. A comparatively short lived tree.

LEAVES—Alternate, simple, long, narrow, sharp pointed and often curved like a sickle; base rounded or tapering; margins finely toothed; thin and rather lustrous, bright light green above, pale yellow-green below, 3" to 6" long, ¼" to ¾" wide; short slender leaf stems are often pubescent and usually fitted at the base with a pair of round, leaf-like appendages called stipules which appears to encircle the branchlet.

BARK—On old trunks 1" to 1¼" thick, light to dark brown and deeply furrowed into broad flat ridges made up of thick plates and connected by narrower transverse ridges. On young trunks greenish mottled by light brown patches; on the slender brittle twigs, smooth, reddish brown to orange.

BUDS—Alternate, about ⅛" long, covered by a single sharp pointed reddish brown scale.

FLOWERS—Male and female on different trees, the "pussies" or catkins pushing from the bud very early (March and April) before the leaves appear, drooping and terminal on the pubescent branchlets, 1" to 3" long; individual male flower with 3 to 5 or more yellow anthered stamens attached to a small hairy, yellow, elliptical scale; the individual female flower pear shaped on a short stalk attached to a scale which drops before the capsule matures.

FRUIT—An ament bearing ⅛" long, reddish brown, smooth, stalked capsules which upon maturity in June split in half liberating hair tufted seeds. As in other willows, the seed has the inherent ability to germinate in a few hours but rarely retains this power for periods longer than 3 days.

WOOD—Diffuse-porous, pores abundant and readily visible to the unaided eye; medullary rays indistinct; heartwood reddish brown, coarse texture, dull lustre, soft, weak, not durable; weighs about 28 lbs. per cu. ft. In the Mississippi Valley sawed into lumber and used in the manufacture of wooden packages, toys, charcoal, etc. Lumber does not warp, check or split in seasoning.

RANGE AND DISTRIBUTION—New Brunswick to Florida westward to Arizona and northward from New Mexico to North Dakota and Ontario. In Delaware common throughout the State.

HABITAT—Prefers the wet situations adjacent to fresh water and is not tolerant of shade.

NOTES—The black willow has the widest range of any of our native species and because it is the willow most likely to be found as a woodland tree is not too difficult to identify. Commercially it is of minor importance and aesthetically has little to recommend it largely because of the brittleness of the branchlets which often litter the ground after an ordinary storm. Its greatest merit lies in the ease with which it may be propagated from cuttings and as a result is often used to clothe embankments and soils subject to rapid water or wind erosion.

GLAUCOUS WILLOW

1. Leaf, natural size.
2. Female flower, enlarged.
3. Male flower, enlarged.
4. Male catkin, slightly enlarged.
5. Female catkin, slightly enlarged.
6. Winter twig, slightly enlarged.
7. Fruiting twig, x 2/3.

GLAUCOUS WILLOW
Salix discolor, Muhlenberg

The glamorous willow, commonly called pussy willow, is a shrub or small tree usually 6' to 15' tall with a diameter of 3" to 6" but may occasionally attain a height of 25' and a diameter of 10". In the forest is generally a shrub but as an ornamental on lawns is usually a tree with a short trunk bearing many upright stout, arching branches, and curving branchlets forming a compact, round topped head.

LEAVES—Alternate, simple, narrow oblong, 2" to 5" long and ½" to 1½" wide, usually broadest above the middle and tapering gradually or abruptly to the apex and to the often unsymmetrical base; margins wavy, finely toothed or rarely entire; at first pubescent but later thick and firm, bright green above and white bloom covered (glaucous) below. Leaf stem ½" to 1" long, slender. Stipules small, semi-circular and finely toothed on the margin, usually early deciduous.

BARK—On old trunks thin red-brown and at the base broken by irregular plates; on young trunks and branches light blue-green to red-brown, smooth and marked by scattered enlarged lenticel spots. Twigs pubescent at first, later smooth bright yellow to dark orange in color and marked by scattered yellow lenticels and much roughened by the raised leaf bases.

BUDS—Alternate ¼" to ½" long, closely appressed and somewhat flattened on the twig side; pointed and covered by a single shiny reddish purple scale having lateral wing-like ridges. Flower buds much larger than leaf buds and occasionally appear to be stalked.

FLOWERS—In late February and March, before the leaves, male and female on different trees in erect, soft, silky white, densely flowered catkins; the male flowers at blooming appearing bright yellow from the numerous anthers.

FRUIT—An ament 2" to 2½" long, bearing narrow conical, stalked, hairy, light brown capsules.

WOOD—Light brown streaked with red, otherwise similar in character to wood of other willows.

RANGE AND DISTRIBUTION—Nova Scotia to Manitoba southward to Illinois and Delaware. Believed to be truly native only in northern New Castle County but much planted as an ornamental and occasionally cultivated in "holts" for the twigs sold in floral markets.

HABITAT—Prefers the moist soils of stream banks, ponds and fresh water swamps but will thrive when planted in drier locations.

NOTES—The wood of this willow has no commercial importance, but as a tree or shrub for ornamental use it appears to be one member of the genera that may be recommended for city use in that it has fewer of the features so objectionable to the willows and many desirable ones. Its attractive and abundantly produced, sweet scented, silky flowers appear early in the new year and are among the first sought by honey bees and early butterflies. Propagation is usually by cuttings of ripened wood planted in the spring. Male trees are more desirable for ornamentation.

CRACK WILLOW

1. Winter twig, natural size.
2. Male ament, natural size.
3. Female ament, natural size.
4. Winter twig showing bud, leaf scar and lenticels, enlarged.
5. Leaf, natural size.
6. Fruiting branchlet, natural size, ripened seed capsule, enlarged.
7. Female flower, enlarged.
8. Male flower, enlarged.

CRACK WILLOW
Salix fragilis, Linnaeus

AUTHOR'S NOTE: This tree is a native of Europe and Asia where it is valued for the production of timber. Having been early introduced into this Country it has now become extensively naturalized in many localities.

The crack willow, also known as brittle willow and gray willow, is a tree of rapid growth, attaining a height of 60′ to 70′ and a diameter of 3′ to 4′. Trunk normally short and straight, clothed with stout ascending branches and slender basally brittle branchlets forming a wide spreading round topped crown.

LEAVES—Alternate, simple, 3″ to 6″ long, ¾″ to 1″ wide, widest near the middle tapering rather evenly to the sharp pointed apex and to the wedge shaped base; margins coarsely glandular notched; at maturity smooth and dark green above; smooth and paler beneath; leaf stem ¼″ to ¾″ long, fairly stout and furnished with 2 glands near its junction with the leaf blade; stipules early deciduous.

BARK—On old trunks 1″ to 1½″ thick, gray, deeply fissured into narrow and irregular rough scaly ridges; on young trunks and branches gray and smooth. Twigs at first pubescent, later becoming smooth and yellow-green or reddish and often marked by 3 ridges extending downward from the enlarged leaf shoulders.

BUDS—Alternate, about ¼″ long, appressed and flattened on the twig side, covered by a single smooth bright red-brown scale marked by a prominent lateral ridge extending from the base to the tip.

FLOWERS—April–May, with the leaves; male and female on separate trees but male trees rare; born in slender pubescent catkins 1″ to 3″ long; individual male flower usually with 2 stamens on a sparsely pubescent scale; individual female flower long pear-shaped, short stalked on a sparsely pubescent scale.

FRUIT—May–June, an ament bearing short stalked, long conical, green capsules which upon splitting release many low vitality seeds equipped with long silky white hairs.

WOOD—Similar to other willows but tough and in Europe reputed to be more durable than other willow wood. Formerly much used for the production of charcoal used in manufacturing black powder.

RANGE AND DISTRIBUTION—Native of Europe and Asia. Originally much planted in the State for production of gunpowder charcoal and now escaped cultivation. Many pollarded trees are to be seen along streams in New Castle County.

HABITAT—Prefers the rich moist soils of stream banks but will grow on drier sites.

NOTES—The crack willow derives its common name from the extreme brittleness of the branchlets at their base which in a strong wind are broken off in such great numbers that the ground beneath the tree is strewn with them. It is easily distinguished from other willows by the large leaves and yellow-green twigs. Its extremely rapid growth and ease of propagation from cuttings make it useful in erosion control and for the production of shoots used in basket weaving. It is not recommended for ornamental or commercial planting.

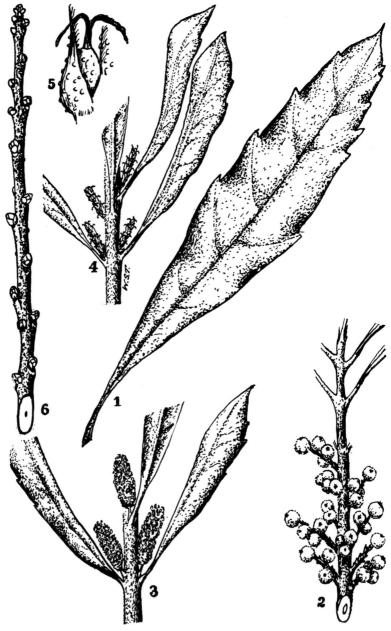

WAX MYRTLE

1. Leaf, natural size.
2. Fruiting branchlet, natural size.
3. Branchlet of male flowers, natural size.
4. Branchlet of female flowers, natural size
5. Female flower, enlarged.
6. Winter twig, natural size.

WAX MYRTLE

Myrica cerifera, Linnaeus

GENUS DESCRIPTION—The sweet gale family has only the genus *Myrica* L., which is credited by Sargent with "30 or 40 species of small trees and shrubs, widely distributed through the temperate and warmer parts" of the world. Of the 4 species native to the United States only 3 attain tree size and but one of which is native to Delaware. The shrubby species native to the State are bayberry, *M. carolinensis*, Miller, and sweet fern, *M. asplenifolia*, L. The bark of some species is occasionally used in tanning and contains an astringent used in medicines and dyes. Wax obtained from the fruit and essence from the leaves are used in the manufacture of candles and other incense materials.

The wax myrtle, also known as bayberry, waxberry, and candleberry, is a shrub or small tree usually 10' to 20' tall and 2" to 3" in diameter, but may rarely attain a height of 40' and a diameter of 8" to 10". Trunks usually in clusters, crooked and inclined, clothed with a few irregularly forked branches and slender branchlets forming a narrow rather open round topped crown.

LEAVES—Alternate, 1½" to 5" long, ½" to 1" wide, usually widest above the middle tapering to a rounded abruptly pointed apex and long tapering base with leaf following down the short petiole to near its junction with the branchlet; margins often entire to above the middle or entire throughout and sparsely indent toothed toward the acute apex, the tip of the tooth often ending in a small very weak prickle; yellow-green, rather thick, resinous dotted and shiny above, golden resinous gland dotted and often pubescent on the midrib below; fragrant when crushed; leaves deciduous in this climate in early winter.

BARK—Similar on old and young trunks, thin smooth and light gray; on the slender branchlets at first coated with a red-brown fuzz, later nearly smooth grayish brown marked by small circular pale lenticels and deciduous resin glands.

BUDS—Alternate, ovate or globular, composed of numerous imbricated red-brown scales.

FLOWERS—March–April with the leaves, male and female on different plants; the male catkins oblong, ½" to ¾" long, the female ones smaller and more cylindric, both golden colored.

FRUIT—A short spike, bearing clusters of ⅛" diameter, globular, pale blue, granular wax coated, bony nuts; maturing in September and October and persisting through the winter and often until the middle of the following year.

WOOD—Diffuse-porous, soft and brittle, dark brown with thin yellowish sapwood. Occasionally used in turnery and small woodenware.

RANGE AND DISTRIBUTION—Along the coast from Cape May, N. J. to Florida westward to eastern Texas and northward in the Mississippi Valley to northern Mississippi. Abundant in the Coastal Plain region of Delaware.

HABITAT—Prefers moist sandy soils but not particular.

NOTES—This species often occurs in company with the shrubby members of the genus and because of its similarity to *M. carolinensis* may be misidentified. The latter species differs from *M. cerifera* in being of shrubby growth and having broader, thinner, less tough and often entire margined green leaves and larger fruit. The wood is of no commercial value, but in some parts of its range the fruit is gathered and the waxy covering extracted and manufactured into candles which burn with a blue flame. In recent years well fruited leafless branchlets have found ready sale in the floral markets, and the female plant of the shrubby species is enjoying increased use in ornamental plantings.

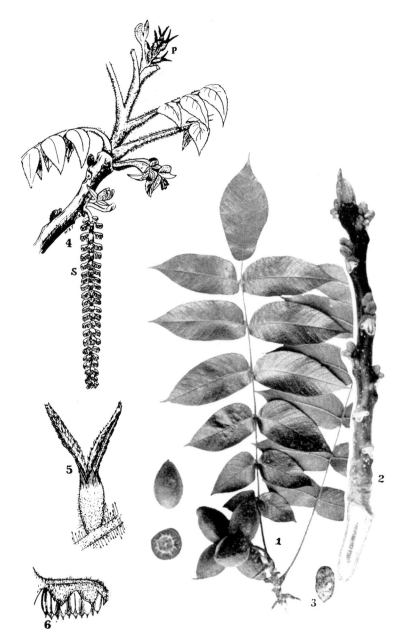

BUTTERNUT

1. Branchlet, with leaves and fruit, x 1/6.
2. Winter twig, natural size. Note chambered pith.
3. Fruit with hull removed, x 1/6.
4. Spring branchlet showing male flower (s) and female flowers (P), x ½.
5. Female flower, enlarged.
6. Male flower, enlarged.

BUTTERNUT
Juglans cinerea, Linnaeus

GENUS DESCRIPTION—The genus *Juglans* comprises about 15 species found in the temperate zones of which 6 are native to North America and 2 to Delaware. Of the exotic species the Persian or English walnut is probably the most popularly known, particularly on the Pacific coast where it is cultivated for the edible nuts important in our food and confection markets. Of lesser cultivation in this Country is the Japanese walnut, *J. sieboldiana* Maxm. and its variety *cordiformis* or heart nut.

The butternut also known as white walnut (c) and oil nut is a tree usually 30' to 50' tall and 1' to 2' in diameter, but may rarely attain a height of 100' and a diameter of 2' to 3½'. In forest stands the trunk is clean and straight for about half its length, but being rather intolerant of shade it often occupies open sites where it develops a short trunk with stout spreading and forked limbs and branches forming a rather open orchard-like tree. Subject to several serious insect and disease enemies and consequently short lived.

LEAVES—Alternate, compound, 15" to 30" long with 11 to 17 leaflets on the stout, pubescent petiole; leaflets 3" to 5" long, 1½" to 2" wide; margins finely toothed except on the unevenly rounded base, sessile or short stalked, pubescent and sticky when they first unfold, later thin yellow-green and wrinkled above, paler and pubescent beneath.

BARK—On old trunks ¾" to 1" thick, ashy gray or light brown, marked by shallow fissures and connecting flat topped ridges; on young trunks and branches, ashy gray and smooth; on the stout twigs at first rusty pubescent orange-brown or green, later becoming smooth and gray. The pith of twigs is chambered and dark brown. See Fig. 15.

BUDS—Alternate, the terminal one ½" long or longer and ¼" wide; blunt pointed laterally lobed and covered with short dense down. Lateral flower buds smaller, pineapple-like and slightly flattened, densely downy below a similarly appearing leaf bud, both superposed above the large 3 lobed leaf scar which has a fringe of hairs above its upper margin and is marked with a horseshoe shaped bundle scar in each lobe.

FLOWERS—May, with the developing leaves, male and female on the same tree; the male ones in many flowered light green catkins 3" to 5" long from axillary buds of the previous year; the female ones in 6–8 flowered spikes on the new growth.

FRUIT—October, singly or in clusters of 3 to 5, about 2½" long and 1" in diameter, oblong and often slightly 4 angled, light green and covered with rusty stick pubescence; the thick, non-dehiscent husk covers a hard, bony, deeply sculptured, 4 ribbed nut, the seed kernel of which is sweet, oily and edible.

WOOD—Diffuse-porous, pores vary in size so as to occasionally appear ring-porous; rays fine and inconspicuous; heartwood light brown, soft, not strong, coarse grained, durable. Weighs about 25 lbs. per cu. ft. Used for cabinet work and interior finish.

RANGE AND DISTRIBUTION—New Brunswick to Delaware southward along the Appalachian Mountains to Alabama, westward to Arkansas and northward to Minnesota. In Delaware occurs naturally in New Castle County and planted elsewhere.

HABITAT—Prefers the rich moist soils of stream banks where it may occur singly or in open pure stands.

NOTES—In summer the butternut may be distinguished from other walnuts by the number of leaflets (11–17) and in winter by the dark brown chambered pith of the twigs, ashy white bark, mustache-like fringe above the leaf scar and sharp edged sculpturing of the long nut. A sweet syrup is sometimes made from the sap, the bark contains mild cathartic properties and during earlier times and in some parts of the country, the green husks of the nuts were used in dying fabrics a yellow color. Butternut meats are rather extensively used in baking and other food in regions where trees are plentiful. The green immature fruit is occasionally pickled.

Ornamentally the tree has little to recommend it, but as a nut producer is probably worthy of more extensive cultivation than it now enjoys.

BLACK WALNUT

1. Leaf, x ¼.
2. Branchlet with fruit, x ¼.
3. Section of fruit, x ¼.
4. Winter twig, natural size. Note chambered pith.
5. Fruits with hull removed, x ¼.
6. Female flower, enlarged.
7. Male flower, enlarged.
8. Male catkin, enlarged.

BLACK WALNUT
Juglans nigra, Linnaeus

The black walnut (c) is a tree 60' to 80' tall with a diameter of 2' to 3', but may occasionally attain a height of 150' and a diameter of 6' or more. In the forest the trunk is usually straight and clean of limbs for the greater portion of its length, ending in a narrow round topped medium foliaged head, composed of stout branches and branchlets. Open grown trees reach commercial maturity in 75 years or less but often attain an age of more than 300 years.

LEAVES—Alternate, compound, with 15 to 23 leaflets on a finely pubescent leafstem, the terminal leaflet usually absent. Leaflet 3" to 3½" long and half as wide; margins finely toothed except on the unevenly rounded base, thin, smooth and light or yellow-green above, soft pubescent especially on the midrib and veins or smooth and lighter beneath; strongly aromatic when crushed.

BARK—On old trunks dark brown to black, 1" to 3" thick, longitudinally divided by deep fissures and rounded ridges; on young trunks and branches light brown and scaly; on the stout twigs at first orange-brown and rusty pubescent, becoming darker and smooth except for the pale lenticels and large raised, heart shaped or 3 lobed, light brown, leaf scars. Pith chambered and pale brown. See Fig. 14.

BUDS—Terminal bud normally less than ½" long, ovate, blunt pointed, and covered with thick grayish down; lateral buds alternate, often one above the other in the "V" of the leaf scar.

FLOWERS—May, when leaves are about half grown, male and female on the same tree; the male ones in 3" to 5" long drooping light green catkins from buds of the previous year; the female flowers on a common stem of the new growth.

FRUIT—October, singly or in clusters of 2–3, globular 1" to 3" in diameter consisting of a thick pulpy nondehiscent hull surrounding a single, hard, grooved shell containing a sweet, slightly oily, edible kernel, which in recent years has become popular in confections and bakery foods.

WOOD—Diffuse-porous with ring-porous tendency; tyloses present; rays scarcely visible; heartwood chocolate brown and having a mild characteristic odor, soft to hard, strong but splits easily, easily worked and finishes well but crystals in wood structure quickly dulls tools, very durable in contact with the soil; weight about 38 lbs. per cu. ft. Used for gun stocks, furniture, interior finish, boat trim, woodenware, etc.

RANGE AND DISTRIBUTION—Massachusetts to Nebraska south to Texas and Florida. Common throughout the State.

HABITAT—Prefers deep rich moist soil and is not tolerant of shade.

NOTES—This tree may be distinguished in summer from other walnuts by the larger number of leaflets, the round fruit, and distinctive trunk bark. In winter, the as-broad-as-long but slightly flattened terminal bud and chambered light brown pith of twigs, are characteristic. Commercially, black walnut is one of our most valuable native trees and deserves much more planting on farms than it now enjoys. It is not recommended for planting in pure extensive stands and attains its best growth when planted as a pasture or fence line tree. Neither is it recommended as a street tree but is a satisfactory lawn tree if planted where it has ample room. Coniferous trees should not be planted within its normal root spread. Propagation is by seed planted with the husk on, in late fall.

Genus: CARYA (NUTTALL)

THE HICKORIES

The genus name *Carya* as applied to the hickories is in dispute by some botanists who apply the genus name *Hicoria*, but the long established usage of the former establishes its priority under the International Code and is accordingly used in this publication. According to Illick in "Tree Habits" the word "hickory" is believed to be the result of English contraction of the Indian name of the tree "Powcohiscora" as first spelled by John Smith of the Virginia colony. All representatives of the genus are important timber trees native only to North America. They have alternate, compound and odd pinnate **leaves** which upon falling expose large elevated leaf scars displaying a varying arrangement of bundle scars. The male and female **flowers** are borne on the same tree, the male ones usually as 3 stemmed drooping aments united near the base into a single stem and produced either from buds of the previous year's growth or from the terminal bud at the base of the new growth. The **fruit** matures in one season and consists of a more or less thick bony-shelled nut covered by a usually dehiscent woody husk and containing a sweet edible or bitter kernel. The **wood** of the hickories is ring-porous, hard, tough, and elastic. Used largely for tool handles, wheel spokes, bent wood furniture, sporting goods articles, etc. The wood is not durable in contact with the soil but when seasoned is an exceptionally good fuel wood. Tests made by the U. S. Forest Products Laboratory show practically no difference in the qualities of heartwood and sapwood.

Of the 10 to 15 species native to North America, 7 are found in Delaware. Fossil remains prove that the hickories at one time existed in Greenland and northern Europe but were totally destroyed in those countries during the ice age. Even today the northern limits of the range of hickory species is comparatively little farther north than the southern limits of the prehistoric ice cap.

The hickories are tap rooted trees and as a rule require rich moist soil. Because of this root characteristic they are not easily transplanted even as one year old seedlings. Hence, propagation, except for the cultivated varieties, which are usually patch budded or cleft grafted below ground with mediocre success, is by seed planted in the fall where the tree is wanted. Propagation from a natural tree may be more easily done by turning up and staking a side root which when it puts out shoots, is severed from the parent and later transplanted.

Horticulturally as well as ornamentally speaking, the species *C. pecan* with its numerous varieties is probably the most important member of the genus, but the varieties cultivated in the southern states for the production of the large, thin shelled nuts common in our winter markets, seem to be too tender for the climate and shorter growing season of Delaware. In evaluating the food importance of the genus, the fact that certain members of it supply the main winter food of some game animals should not be overlooked.

The wood of the hickories is important commercially as a special use wood, but in regions where it is not locally manufactured into such articles, the market is limited to low grade lumber and fuel.

BITTERNUT HICKORY

1. Branchlet with fruit and leaf-upper surface (left) and leaf showing lower surface (right), x ½.
2. Fruit and nuts with husk removed; in cross section and with shell removed, x ½.
3. Winter twigs, natural size.

BITTERNUT HICKORY
Carya cordiformis, K. Koch

[*Hicoria cordiformis*, (Wangenheim) Britton]
[*Hicoria minima*, (Marsh) Britton]

The bitternut hickory, also known as tight bark hickory, swamp hickory and bitter hickory, is a tree which usually attains a height of 50' to 75' and a diameter of 1' to 2' but may reach a height of 100' and a diameter of 2½' to 3'. Trunk long, clean, straight with stout spreading branches and slender, often semi-pendulous branchlets, forming a broad, usually rounded head.

LEAVES—Alternate, 6" to 10" long, compound, with 7 to 11 sessile leaflets on a slender hairy petiole. Leaflets 4" to 6" long and ¾" to 1¼" wide, lance shaped or ovate long pointed, finely toothed on the margins, thin, firm and dark yellow-green above, paler and pubescent, especially on the midrib, beneath.

BARK—On old trunks ½" to ¾" thick, light gray, roughened by shallow fissures and narrow ridges; on young trunks and branches, smooth and hard; on twigs at first bright green and thickly covered with rusty hairs, turning reddish brown and shiny by the following spring and marked by oblong pale lenticels and light colored, elevated, irregularly heart-shaped leaf scars showing numerous bundle scars in various arrangements. Pith brown and angular. See Fig. 5.

BUDS—Alternate, the terminal one ¼" to ¾" long, compressed and blunt pointed, covered by 2 pairs of bright yellow glandular dotted scales; the lateral buds often superposed, the axillary one small and blunt pointed, the upper one larger and often stalked and angled.

FLOWERS—Appear in May when leaves are about half grown; male and female on the same tree; the male ones on 3" to 4" long, 3 branched, pubescent aments; the female ones in 2 flowered spikes on the new growth, ½" long, slightly 4 angled and covered with yellow scurfy hairs.

FRUIT—October, spherical to obovate, often slightly compressed, ¾" to 1½" long. The thin, yellowish glandular dotted husk is 4 ridged from the tip to about the middle and when ripe usually splits for the extent of, and along these ridges or wings, exposing a smooth, thin shelled, light reddish to white nut about 1" in diameter, containing a shiny, red-brown skinned, bitter kernel.

WOOD—Ring-porous, pores in summer wood large, rather evenly distributed, but not in lines; rays inconspicuous but abundant; heavy, very hard, strong, tough and elastic, usually straight grained, not durable in contact with the soil. Heartwood dark brown; sapwood lighter. Weighs about 47 pounds per cubic foot. Not as strong, hard or tough as wood of other hickories, but used for the same purposes generally, i.e., tool handles, wagon spokes, fuel, etc.

RANGE AND DISTRIBUTION—Southern Maine to northern Minnesota and Nebraska, south to eastern Texas and Florida. In Delaware common throughout the State.

HABITAT—Prefers low wet but fertile locations adjacent to streams and swamps but may often be found on drier locations where the soil is fairly fertile. Intolerant of shade.

NOTES—This hickory may be distinguished from other native hickories in winter by the yellow buds having scales arranged in pairs that do not overlap one another and in summer by the narrow lance-shaped leaflets which are pubescent on the under surface. It is one of the most rapid growing and straightest of the hickories.

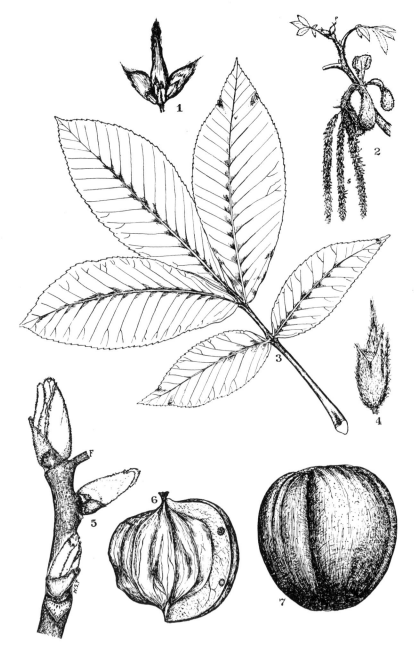

SHAGBARK HICKORY

1. A single staminate (male) flower, enlarged.
2. Branchlet with staminate (S) and pistillate (P) flowers, x ½.
3. Leaf, x ½.
4. A single pistillate (female) flower, enlarged.
5. Portion of thrifty winter twig, natural size.
6. Nut with portion of husk attached, natural size.
7. Fruit, natural size.

SHAGBARK HICKORY

Carya ovata, (Mill.) K. Koch

[*Hicoria ovata,* (Miller) Britton]

The shagbark hickory, also known as shellbark hickory and common shagbark hickory, is a tree usually attaining a height of 50′ to 75′ and a diameter of 2′ but may occasionally reach a height of 120′ and a diameter of 3′ to 4′. Trunk normally straight and, in forest stands, free of branches for the greater portion of its length. Branches stout and ascending but usually pendulous at the extremities, forming an irregular round-topped crown. Reaches commercial maturity in 75 years or less but trees 300 years old are occasionally found.

LEAVES—Alternate, 8″ to 14″ long, compound, composed of 5 or rarely 7 leaflets on a stout large based smooth or sometimes finely pubescent petiole. The leaflets vary in size—the terminal one on a short stalk, obovate, 5″ to 7″ long, 2″ to 3″ wide, slightly larger than the adjacent sessile or short stalked upper leaflets and two to three times larger than the lower pair which are normally widest below the middle; finely toothed and often finely hairy on the margins; dark yellow-green and smooth above; pale and usually smooth and shiny beneath. Leaflets turn bright yellow in autumn and often drop from the petiole before it falls from the twig.

BARK—On old trunks, ¾″ to 1″ thick, gray and broken into long thick hard ragged plates which are loose and sprung outward at one or both ends giving the tree the characteristic shaggy appearance indicated by its common names (Fig. 19); on young trunks and branches, smooth and light gray; on the stout twigs at first often slightly downy, later smooth glossy dark reddish brown and marked by numerous longitudinally elongated pale lenticels. Leaf scars elevated, light colored, broadly heart-shaped and marked by numerous bundle scars. Pith, star-shaped.

BUDS—Alternate, the terminal one broadly ovoid, ½″ to ¾″ long, blunt pointed; the 3 to 4 outer scales broadly triangular, sharp pointed, dark brown, usually hairy especially along the margin and deciduous before the unfolding of the leaves; the inner scales densely downy on the outside, smooth within, yellow-green or buff, elongating in spring to 2½″ to 3½″ and persisting until the staminate (male) flowers fall from the tree.

FLOWERS—In May or June when the leaves are nearly full grown, male and female on the same tree; the male ones at the base of the new growth, as 3 clustered and many flowered aments 4″ to 5″ long; the female ones in 2 to 5 flowered spikes on the new growth, nearly ½″ long, rusty wooly.

FRUIT—October; globular, 1″ to 2½″ in diameter, usually depressed at the apex and 4 lobed. The ⅛″ to ½″ thick woody husk, at maturity, is brown and splits in 4 pieces freely to the base. Nut ¾″ to 1¼″ long and broad, oblong, compressed, prominently or obscurely 4 ridged, with or without a basal point and usually thin shell enclosing a light brown, sweet, edible kernel.

WOOD—Ring-porous, pores in summer wood large, rather evenly distributed but not in lines; heavy, very hard and strong, tough, close grained, very stiff and exceedingly high in shock resistance, but not durable in contact with the soil; heartwood light brown or reddish; sapwood white. Weighs about 52 pounds per cubic foot. Used for agricultural implements, tool handles, wagon spokes, sporting goods, bent wood furniture and fuel. Wood with less than 20 annual rings per radial inch is usually specified for handle stock.

RANGE AND DISTRIBUTION—Southern Maine to Minnesota, southward to Texas and northern Georgia, generally west of the Atlantic Coastal Plain. In Delaware believed native only in New Castle and Kent Counties; rare in the latter and not abundant in the former except for the extreme northern portion where it is quite common.

HABITAT—Requires rich, deep moderately moist soils and plenty of light.

NOTES—The shagbark hickory is one of the most valuable of the hickories. Its wood is excellent for special uses and the nut meats, apart from those of pecan, are about the only ones of the genus that are marketed. Reproduction is by seed planted in the fall of the year on the site where the tree is wanted but one is to be reminded that the sweet kernel is much sought after by squirrels and rodents as winter food. Planting should, therefore, be confined to locations where the seed can be protected.

Although not observed by the author as native to Delaware, it may be that the big brother of the shagbark hickory—the big shagbark hickory—*C. laciniosa* Loudon, is also native. It may be identified by the larger leaves having 5 to 9, but usually 7 leaflets which are dark green and lustrous above and pale yellow-green or bronze-brown and pubescent beneath. The nuts of the big shagbark hickory are light reddish brown, 1¼″ to 2¼″ long and 1½″ to 1¾″ wide—being darker in color and 2 to 3 times larger than those of the common shagbark. The shells of nuts of the big shagbark, in dry storage, will usually pin crack sufficiently that the operation of cracking and removing the meat is made easier. A number of horticultural varieties, developed for their nut qualities, are now available from commercial nut tree nurseries. These and the native species make attractive lawn and shade trees worthy of greater use for such purposes than they now enjoy.

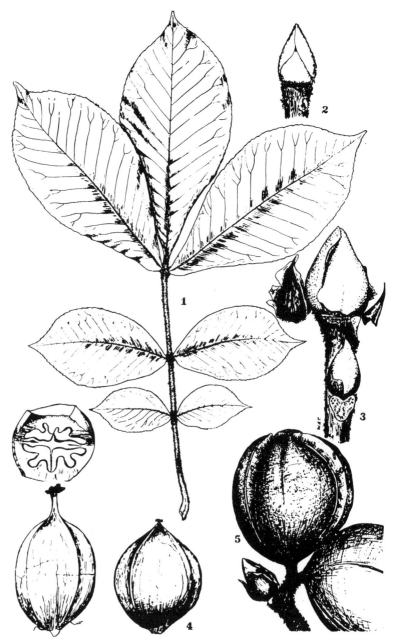

MOCKERNUT HICKORY

1. Leaf, x ½.
2. Terminal bud in late winter, natural size.
3. Portion of twig in late fall, showing casting of outer scales, natural size.
4. Nuts, natural size.
5. Fruiting branchlet at maturity, slightly reduced.

MOCKERNUT HICKORY
Carya alba, K. Koch

[*Hicoria alba*, (Linnaeus) Britton]
[*Carya tomentosa*, Nuttall]

The mockernut hickory, also known as big bud hickory, white hickory (c) and white heart hickory, is a tree usually 50' to 75' tall and 1½' to 2' in diameter but may rarely attain a height of 100' and a diameter of 3'. In dense forest stands the trunk is straight with little taper and clean of limbs for about one-half its length. Of variable form and branching.

LEAVES—Alternate, 8" to 12" long, compound, composed of 7 or 9 sessile or short stalked leaflets on a hairy large based petiole. Leaflets broadly lance-shaped or obovate, very finely toothed on the margins, dark yellow-green above, paler or light orange colored and often downy beneath, the upper leaflets 5" to 8" long and 2½" to 4½" wide, being 2 to 3 times larger than those of the lowest pair; fragrant, especially when crushed.

BARK—On old trunks, ½" to ¾" thick, gray, close, roughened by shallow interrupted fissures and obscure ridges of closely appressed scales; on young trunks smooth, usually dark gray; on the stout twigs during the first season pubescent reddish brown, later gray and marked by pale longitudinally elongated lenticels and roughened by the large, irregular shaped leaf scars.

BUDS—Alternate, the terminal one usually very large, ½" to ¾" long and covered by 2 outer dark red-brown hairy scales which fall off by late fall exposing the silky yellowish gray of buff colored inner scales.

FLOWERS—In May, when leaves are more than half developed; the male ones on 4" to 5" long, slender, 3 clustered catkins on a common stem; the female ones in 2 to 5 flowered pale hairy spikes on the new growth.

FRUIT—October, globular, ovoid or ellipsoidal, 1½" to 2" long, with a smooth ¼" to ⅜" thick husk splitting nearly to the base, light green to red-brown when ripe. Nut ellipsoidal or globular, usually slightly compressed and prominently or obscurely 4 ridged but ridges more prominent near the apex, light reddish brown with a very thick, hard shell, in storage often turning darker and cracking transversely and in fine cracks elsewhere. Kernel small, glossy light brown and sweet.

WOOD—Similar to other hickories in appearance and in mechanical properties differs little from that of the shagbark hickory. Heartwood dark brown; sapwood thick, white and accounting for the common name "white hickory" and the specific name *alba*. Used for the same purposes as the wood of other hickories.

RANGE AND DISTRIBUTION—Massachusetts to Michigan and eastern Kansas, southward to eastern Texas and northern Florida, being one of the predominating hickory species throughout its range. Common throughout the State.

HABITAT—This species seems to thrive equally well on dry or moist soils, but prefers the more fertile bottomlands.

NOTES—The mockernut hickory most closely resembles the shellbark hickories but is distinguished from them by the close fitting bark which does not "shag," and by the densely clustered hairs on the leaves and new twigs. The winter buds are uniformly larger than those of other hickories. The common name "mockernut" aptly describes the fruit in that in size and appearance it "mocks" the shellbark fruit but, when the thick bony shelled nut is finally cracked, the reward of edible meat, if any, is small and difficult to extract. From the standpoint of human consumption, the nut meat is not worth the trouble of getting it but where the shellbark is not found the nuts of this tree form an important part of the winter food of forest rodents. For this reason alone, its preservation in Delaware woodlands is warranted.

PIGNUT HICKORY

1. Portion of thrifty winter twig, natural size.
1-a. Portion of lateral winter twig, natural size.
2. Leaf, x ½.
3. Branchlet with staminate flower cluster (S) and pistillate flowers (P), x ½.
4. Fruit in cross section, natural size.
5. Fruit at maturity, natural size.
6. A single pistillate (female) flower, enlarged
7. A single staminate (male) flower, enlarged

PIGNUT HICKORY
Carya glabra, Sweet

[*Hicoria glabra,* (Miller) Sweet]
[*Carya porcina,* Nuttall]

The pignut hickory, or brown hickory, is a medium size tree usually 50' to 60' tall with a diameter of 2' to 3' but may occasionally attain a height of 90' and a diameter of 4'. In forest stands the trunk is normally straight and clean for more than half its height and terminates in a narrow head composed of small spreading branches above and drooping ones below. Attains commercial maturity in 80 years or less but may rarely attain an age of 350 years.

LEAVES—Alternate, 8" to 12" long, compound, with 5 or rarely 7 lance-shaped or broadly lance-shaped leaflets on a slender smooth petiole. Leaflets finely and sharply toothed on the margins, the terminal leaflet 3" to 6" long and 2" to 3" wide with short petiole, being slightly larger than the adjacent pair of short stalked leaflets and 2 to 3 times larger than the lower pair of sessile leaflets; thick, glossy, and dark green above; paler and smooth or occasionally pubescent on the midrib beneath.

BARK—On old trunks dark gray, ½" to ¾" thick, close, roughened by shallow narrow fissures and flat topped interlacing ridges (Fig. 18); on young trunks smooth, gray; on the slender twigs at first yellowish green and smooth, later reddish brown and marked by numerous pale, longitudinally elongated lenticels and flat or slightly elevated leaf scars of varying shapes.

BUDS—Alternate, oval, blunt pointed, smooth red-brown to gray. The terminal bud ¼" to ½" long—larger than the lateral ones. Outer bud scales often deciduous during the winter, exposing the chamois skin-like inner scales.

FLOWERS—In May, when the leaves are about half developed—the male ones in 3" to 5" long, 3 branched drooping aments; the female ones in 2 to 5 flowered spikes on the new growth.

FRUIT—October, variable in shape and size, usually pear-shaped, 1" to 1½" long, with a thin husk often equipped with wing-like ridges extending down from the apex, upon ripening turn red-brown and remain closed or open part way or sometimes to the base by one or two sutures. Nut, pinkish white or gray brown, oblong to oval, without ridges and with thick hard shell containing a kernel which is sometimes sweet but usually bitter, or occasionally at first sweet and then bitter.

WOOD—Similar to other hickories in appearance but in physical properties, superior to that produced by other members of the genus.

RANGE AND DISTRIBUTION—Southern Vermont to Ontario and Iowa, southward to eastern Texas and Florida. Common throughout the State.

HABITAT—Prefers hillsides and dry locations and is rarely found in wet places. Like the hickories in general, this species is intolerant of shade.

NOTES—In summer the pignut hickory may be identified by the smooth leaves and twigs (hence *glabra* as the specific name). In winter, its small oval buds covered by smooth or glandular outer scales, which upon falling expose the pale velvety inner ones, distinguish it from the bitternut hickory bud which is yellow and rough. The nut of this species is characteristic and differs from that of the bitternut in being thick shelled.

SMALL FRUITED HICKORY

1. Branchlet with fruit, x ½.
2. Winter twig, natural size.

SMALL FRUITED HICKORY
Carya microcarpa, Darling

[*Carya ovalis,* var. *obcordata,* Sargent]
[*Hicoria microcarpa,* Britton]

The small fruited hickory, also known as small shagbark hickory, false shagbark hickory, and small pignut hickory, is a tree usually 60' to 75' tall and 1' to 2' in diameter but may occasionally attain a height of 100' and a diameter of 2' to 3'. Trunk and branching similar to the pignut hickory, *C. glabra.*

LEAVES—Alternate, compound, 8" to 12" long, with 5 or 7 leaflets on a slender petiole which is at first scurfy pubescent but soon smooth. The terminal leaflet of this species (variety of Sargent) is 5" to 6½" long and 2" to 2½" wide, widest at or above the middle, broad pointed and tapers to a short petiole at the base; adjacent pair of upper leaflets similar in size but usually with a more acute apex and broader base, being about twice the size of the lower pair; margins finely but sharply toothed; thick, firm, smooth and dark yellow-green above, lighter beneath; fragrant when crushed.

BARK—On old trunks gray, hard and roughly divided into irregular shaggy ridges (Fig. 16); on young trunks and branches, smooth, gray; on the slender twigs at first green and pubescent, later smooth and red-brown.

BUDS—Alternate, the terminal one ovate, blunt pointed, often ½" long and much larger than the lateral, covered by 6–8 scales, the outer ones smooth, shiny and red-brown.

FLOWERS—May and June after the leaves; the male ones as 3" to 7" long slender 3 branched catkins; the female ones in 2–5 flowered spikes, each ¼" long, yellow.

FRUIT—September, globular, less than 1" in diameter, with a thin husk which splits tardily to or nearly to the base; nut obscurely 4 ridged, compressed, broadest above the middle, with thin shell and deliciously flavored kernel.

WOOD—Similar to that of the shagbark hickory and used for the same purposes.

RANGE AND DISTRIBUTION—Southern New England to Iowa, southward to Arkansas and eastward to Tennessee, western North Carolina and northern Virginia. Generally common within its range and in New Castle County but comparatively rare elsewhere in Delaware.

HABITAT—Prefers well drained slopes and uplands where it occurs in company with other hickories, oaks, sassafras, etc.

NOTES—The name "small fruited hickory" is quite descriptive of this species, and when also recognized by its other common name—"false shagbark"—is easily distinguished from other hickories. The real confusion surrounding this tree appears to be in its botanical classification by different botanists and authors. When classified under *Hicoria* it assumes species importance, but under the *Carya* name, it may become a variety of *C. ovalis* and related to such other varieties as *odorata, obovalis, hirsuta,* etc. In most respects the tree resembles *C. glabra,* but the small nut with a sweet kernel and the somewhat shaggy bark distinguish it from the true pignut hickory.

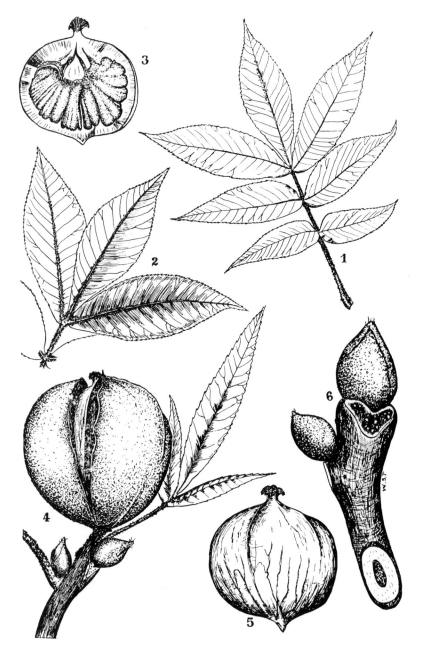

PALE-LEAF HICKORY

1. Leaf, upper surface, x ½.
2. Portion of leaf, lower surface, x ½.
3. Nut broken to show kernel anl shell, slightly enlarged.
4. Branchlet wtih maturing fruit, slightly enlarged.
5. Nut, slightly enlarged.
6. Terminal portion of thrifty twig, x 2.

PALE-LEAF HICKORY
Carya pallida, Engl. & Graebner

[*Carya villosa,* Schneider]
[*Hicoria pallida,* Ashe]
[*Hicoria villosa,* (Sarg.) Ashe]

The pale-leaf hickory, or hairy-leaved hickory, is a small tree usually 30' to 40' tall and 1' to 1½' in diameter but may rarely attain a height of 100' and a diameter of 2' to 3'. Trunk usually straight with little taper, ending in a narrow head composed of stout ascending branches in the upper portion, gradually becoming drooping below.

LEAVES—Alternate, compound, 7" to 15" long, with slender petiole covered with persistent clusters of rusty hairs mixed with silvery scales and having 5 to 9, but usually 7, leaflets. Leaflets lance-shaped, long pointed, tapering to a narrow or usually unequally rounded base, finely toothed on margins, pubescent and covered beneath with silvery scales when young, but at maturity light green and shiny above, pale and hairy (especially on the midrib and veins) beneath, the terminal leaflet nearly or truly sessile, 4" to 6" long and 1" to 2" wide, similar in size to the adjacent sessile lateral leaflets and twice the size of the lower pair of leaflets which seldom exceed 2" in length.

BARK—On old trees in this latitude, thick, dark gray, and much roughened by short deep fissures and flat topped, V-shaped, scaly ridges (Fig. 17); on young trunks smooth, light gray; on the slender twigs sometimes pubescent but usually smooth and reddish brown.

BUDS—Alternate, the terminal one about ¼" long, egg-shaped, covered by 6–9 scales, the outer ones reddish brown, slightly hairy on the tip and roughened by globules of resin.

FLOWERS—The male ones as scurfy pubescent drooping aments 5" to 7" long; the female ones solitary or in pairs, scaly, yellow.

FRUIT—October, pubescent, covered with minute yellow scales, ellipsoidal to obovoid or usually depressed globose and compressed, 1" to 1½" in diameter with husk ⅛" or less in thickness, splitting tardily to, or nearly to the base by 2 or 3 sutures, or occasionally remaining tightly closed. Nut, about 1" long or broad, light brown to white, compressed, obscurely ridged, with a thick, hard shell containing a brown, rough coated, sweet, kernel.

WOOD—Similar to other hickories in texture; heartwood brown; sapwood white. Used for the same purposes as the wood of other hickories.

RANGE AND DISTRIBUTION—From Cape May, New Jersey and Southern Delaware southward in the Piedmont Region and mountains to northern Florida, westward to eastern Texas and northward to southern Missouri, the mountains of Tennessee, Kentucky and West Virginia. Reported only from Kent and Sussex Counties in this State, where it is comparatively rare.

HABITAT—Prefers the rich, sandy soils of the Coastal Plain and Piedmont Regions, attaining its largest size in Virginia.

NOTES—The pale-leaf hickory may be distinguished from other hickories by the villous leaf stem (hence *Hicoria villosa*) and usually 7 narrow leaflets and by the characteristic thick rough bark on old trunks. The kernel is sweet and edible while that of the pignut *C. glabra,* which it most closely resembles, is usually bitter. In winter, the resin globules normally present on the outer bud scales, is an identifying characteristic.

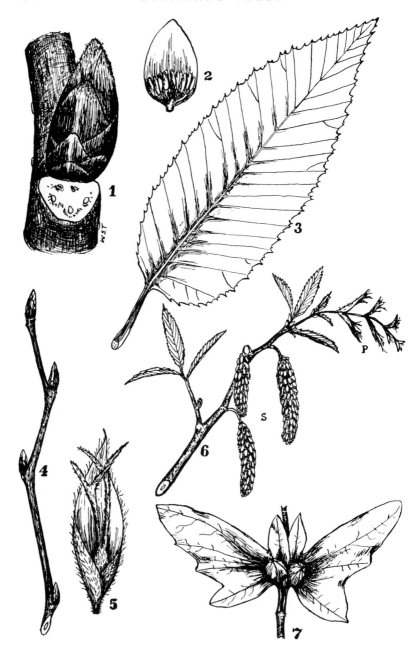

BLUE BEECH

1. Section of winter twig enlarged to show bud and leaf scar characteristics.
2. Single staminate (male) flower, enlarged.
3. Leaf, natural size.
4. Winter twig, x 2.
5. Single pistillate (female) flower, enlarged.
6. Branchlet with staminate flowers (s) and pistillate flowers (p), natural size.
7. Fruit, x 2.

BLUE BEECH
Carpinus caroliniana, Walter

GENUS DESCRIPTION—The genus *Carpinus* or hornbeam, is represented by about 20 species and varieties, all but one of which are native to Asia and Europe. Probably the best known of the European species is *C. betulus*, or English hornbeam, which, in Europe, is much used as an ornamental and hedge plant because of its ability to endure severe clipping. Description of the only American species follows:

The blue beech, also known as American hornbeam, water beech, and iron wood, is often a small bushy tree 10' to 25' tall and 4" to 6" in diameter, but may occasionally attain a height of 40' and a diameter of 1½' to 2'. Trunk generally short, inclined and clothed for about half its length with slender, zigzag, ascending branches and slender, tough, semi-pendulous branchlets, forming a wide spreading, rounded crown.

LEAVES—Alternate, simple, oblong with long acute apex and rounded or occasionally wedge shaped base, 2" to 4½" long, 1" to 1¾" wide; margins doubly serrate; brownish green and covered with long white hairs when they first unfold; at maturity thin and blue-green above; pale, with small tufts of white hairs in axils of veins beneath; turn yellow, scarlet or orange in autumn and often persisting in dried form until late winter; petiole about ½" long, slender, bright red when young; stipules small, ovate long pointed, hairy on the margins and often bright red beneath.

BARK—On young and old trunks, thin, smooth, blue-gray, often marked by lighter patches and bands and tightly fitting the contours, corrugations and fluted ridges of the hard wood beneath; on the very slender tough branchlets at first silky hairy and green, later smooth, shiny, reddish to purplish brown and dotted with small pale lenticels.

BUDS—Alternate, all axillary on the zigzag twig, long egg-shaped, slightly or strongly 4 angled, about ⅛" long, covered with 8–12, 4 ranked, red-brown scales which increase in size toward the apex and apex scales white hairy on the tips.

FLOWERS—April, with the leaves; the staminate (male) aments about 1½" in length when fully grown; the pistillate (female) ones ½"–¾" long with ovate hairy green scales and long hairy red styles, in terminal aments on the new growth.

FRUIT—In persistent crowded clusters on a 6" long, slender, pubescent, red-brown stem; the individual fruit consisting of a small, many angled, egg-shaped nut, partially enclosed by a 1" to 1½" long leaf-like, 3 lobed bract or involucre which is usually unequally lobed only on one margin.

WOOD—Diffuse-porous with conspicuous medullary rays; heavy, hard moderately strong and limber and possessed of exceedingly high resistance to shock; heartwood light brown; sapwood wide, white. Weighs about 45 pounds per cubic foot and when used for other than fuel is manufactured into levers, tool handles, spoons, bowls, and woodenware novelties.

RANGE AND DISTRIBUTION—New Hampshire to Minnesota southward to eastern Texas and northern Florida, reaching its greatest size in the southern and central portions of its range. Common throughout Delaware.

HABITAT—Prefers the deep moist or wet soils on the borders of streams and in swamps, hence the name "water beech."

NOTES—Because of its small size and limited use, the blue beech cannot be recommended for forestry purposes, but should be allowed to grow in those locations where other more valuable commercial species will not thrive. Ornamentally it is an attractive tree, especially in the autumn when its foliage is orange or scarlet in color. The small nuts are eaten by forest rodents and occasionally by birds.

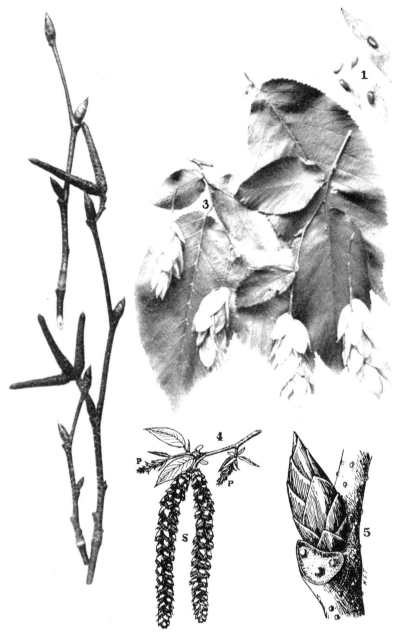

HOP HORNBEAM

1. Fruit and seed, x ½.
2. Branchlet with fruit, x ½.
3. Leaf, lower surface, x ½.
4. Branchlet with staminate flowers (s) and pistillate flowers (p), natural size.
5. Section of branchlet enlarged to show bud, lenticels and leaf scar.
Unnumbered: Three Winter twigs, one showing partially developed terminal staminate aments, natural size.

HOP HORNBEAM
Ostrya virginiana, (Miller) K. Koch

GENUS DESCRIPTION—The genus *Ostrya* is represented by 4 species distributed throughout the northern hemisphere of both the New and Old World. Of these, 2 are native to North America and one to Delaware. The other, western hop hornbeam, *Ostrya knowltonii* Coville, is limited to a small area in the Grand Canyon region of the Colorado River.

The hop hornbeam, also known as ironwood, leverwood, American hop hornbeam, and hardhack, is a small tree usually 20′ to 30′ tall and 12″ to 15″ in diameter, but may occasionally attain a height of 60′ and a diameter of 2′. Trunk usually straight with slender, wide-spreading branches often drooping at the ends, forming a broad open crown.

LEAVES—Alternate, simple, oblong-lanceolate with gradually tapering apex and rounded or broadly V-shaped base; margins sharply serrate and often doubly toothed toward the apex; at maturity thin, tough and dull yellow-green above; lighter and downy, especially in the midrib and in the axils of the veins, beneath; 3″ to 5″ long, 1½″ to 2″ wide; turn bright yellow in the fall. Stipules small and early deciduous.

BARK—On old and young trunks similar, thin, grayish brown and broken by narrow shallow fissures into loose, flat scales (Fig. 20); on the thin, tough, slightly zigzag twigs, at first light green and hairy, soon becoming smooth, shiny, dark red-brown, and marked by large leaf shoulders exposing a depressed leaf scar usually having 3 bundle scars within.

BUDS—Alternate, all axillary, usually distinctly divergent, about ¼″ long, ovate sharp pointed, covered by about 8 visible 4 ranked chestnut brown scales.

FLOWERS—The staminate (male) in April with the leaves, developing from the ¾″ to 1″ long 3 clustered dormant aments formed the preceding summer on a short stem at the end of twigs, lengthening in spring to about 2″; pistillate (female) flowers in erect aments at the tip of the new growth, ¼″ long, enclosed in a hairy, bladder-like bract.

FRUIT—In September, as a 1″ to 2½″ long pendant cluster resembling hops, light blue-green; nut small and flat, enclosed by the inflated sack-like involucre equipped at its base with stiff hairs which are irritating to a tender skin.

WOOD—Diffuse-porous with indistinct rays, very hard, strong, stiff, very high in resistance to shock, durable; heartwood light red-brown with thick white sapwood. Weighs about 51.6 pounds per cubic foot and used for levers, tool handles, mallets, fence posts, and woodenware articles.

RANGE AND DISTRIBUTION—Cape Breton Island to Minnesota and South Dakota southward to eastern Texas and Florida, reaching its largest size in the lower Mississippi region. Extremely rare in Delaware and probably native only in New Castle County. (Cr. Tatnall list of 1860.)

HABITAT—Prefers dry, gravelly ridges and uplands, often thriving under the shade of other trees.

NOTES—The names "hornbeam," "ironwood," etc., obviously owe their origin to word coinage designed to describe the wood as "hard as horn and strong as iron." Tests made in the U. S. Forest Products Laboratory disprove the popular conception that the wood of ironwood rivals the strength of steel, and reveal the fact that in most mechanical properties, the wood of the hickories is superior. Because of the special uses for which the wood of this tree may be employed, it deserves protection wherever it occurs, but it is too slow of growth to be recommended for reforestation planting. The "hop" name applied to the tree refers to the distinctive hop-like fruit. Being slow of growth, small of stature, and difficult to transplant, the tree is hardly suited to street or roadside planting, but is satisfactory as a lawn or border tree especially if it must endure the shade of other trees.

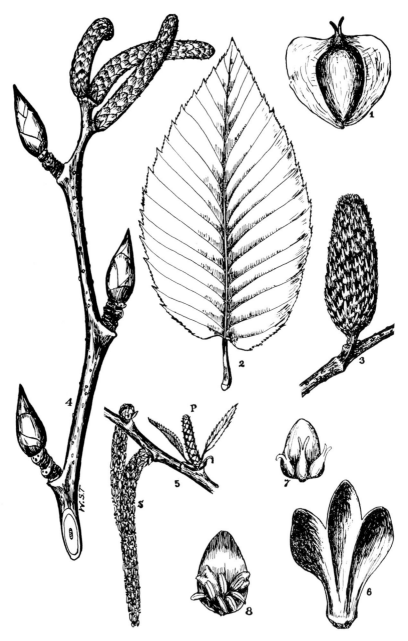

BLACK BIRCH

1. Seed, enlarged.
2. Leaf, natural size.
3. Fruit, natural size.
4. Winter twig with terminal staminate aments, x 2.
5. Portion of branch with staminate catkins (s) and pistillate spike (p), natural size.
6. A strobile scale, enlarged.
7. A single pistillate flower, enlarged.
8. A single staminate flower, enlarged.

BLACK BIRCH
Betula lenta, Linnaeus

GENUS DESCRIPTION—The genus *Betula* comprises about 30 species of trees and shrubs distributed over the northern hemisphere of the world. Of these, 12 to 15 are native to North America, only 9 of which normally attain tree size. Some authors credit Delaware with having 2 species, others with 4. The Edward Tatnall list of 1860 is reported by Dr. Robert R. Tatnall, of Wilmingtin to contain a record of yellow birch *B. lutea* on the western shore of Duck Creek and a record of gray birch *B. populifolia* Marsh, at Townsend. Dr. Tatnall is of the opinion that neither species is now native and accordingly are not described in this publication.

The black birch, also known as sweet birch, cherry birch, and birch (c) is a tree usually 50' to 60' tall and 1½' to 2' in diameter, but may occasionally attain a height of 80' and a diameter of 5'. In forest stands the trunk is usually straight but often forks at about two-thirds the total height with slender nearly horizontal branches and pendulous branchlets, to form a narrow conical crown.

LEAVES—Alternate, simple, occur singly on the new growth and in pairs on growth of previous years, ovate with more or less abruptly tapering apex and rounded or heart-shaped base; margins sharply and unevenly toothed; at first light green with sparse long white hairs above and coated below with long white hairs, later dark green above, pale yellow-green and with small tufts of white hairs in the axils of the prominent veins beneath; 2½" to 5" long, 1½" to 3" wide; petiole stout and short; stipules small, light green to white.

BARK—On old trunks black, broken into large thick, irregular plates; on young trunks and limbs, close fitting, smooth, shiny dark brown and marked by pale horizontally elongated lenticels; on the slender twigs at first light green and hairy, later reddish brown, smooth, and marked by numerous raised lenticel dots. Tender bark has a strong wintergreen flavor.

BUDS—Alternate, axillary, except spur buds of lateral shoots; about ¼" long, conical and covered by imbricated, ovate, acute tipped, red-brown, shiny scales.

FLOWERS—April, before the leaves, the staminate (male) flowers from ¾" long 3 clustered aments developed during the previous summer, elongating to 3" to 4" when fully developed; the pistillate (female) flowers on the twig below the staminate catkins or terminal on the short spur-like lateral branchlets, cylindrical, ½" to ¾" long, pale green.

FRUIT—An oblong or ovoid strobile or cone, 1" to 1½" long, erect, sessile, made up of 3 lobed and cupped brown scales and small winged nutlets; nut conical, pointed at the base, rounded at the apex, brown, and equipped with broad, thin wings.

WOOD—Diffuse-porous and rays indistinct, very heavy hard and strong with high shock resistance; heartwood dark red-brown; sapwood thin, yellowish. Weighs about 47 pounds per cubic foot and used for flooring, furniture, often as imitation for other woods such as mahogany, maple, walnut and cherry, and for woodenware novelties, veneer and fuel.

RANGE AND DISTRIBUTION—New Brunswick to Illinois, southward to Delaware and along the mountains to Georgia. Common in New Castle County but rare in Kent County and not reported from Sussex County in Delaware.

HABITAT—Prefers cool, moist, rich soils, but may be found on drier sites.

NOTES—Where the black birch grows, there are few who do not know it by the wintergreen flavor of its twig bark. The sweet birch oil distilled from the branches, bark and sapwood, is used in medicines and as a substitute for wintergreen oil used in flavoring confections, soft drinks, medicines, etc. Trees tapped in the spring of the year will yield large quantities of sugary sap which when fermented produces a tasty birch beer. Because the tree bleeds profusely when injured in early spring, it is unwise to attempt pruning at such times.

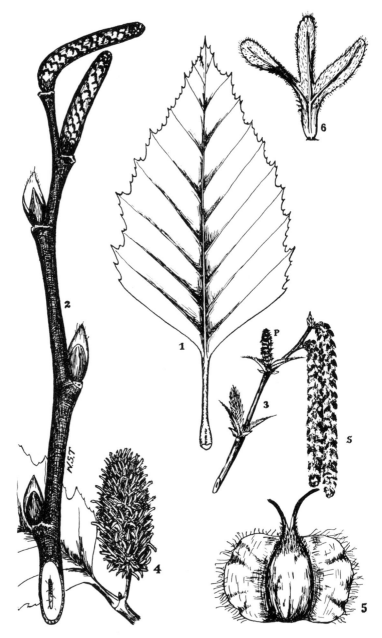

RIVER BIRCH

1. Leaf, natural size.
2. Winter twig, with terminal staminate aments, x 2.
3. Branchlet with staminate flowers (s) and pistillate flowers (p), natural size.
4. Fruit, natural size.
5. Seed, enlarged.
6. Strobile scale, enlarged.

RIVER BIRCH
Betula nigra, Linnaeus

The river birch or red birch (c) is a medium sized tree generally 30' to
50' tall and 1' to 2' in diameter but may occasionally attain a height of 90'
and a diameter of 5'. Trunks, even in dense stands, often included and divided
below the middle. Crown of young trees conical, open; of old trees broad,
irregular and picturesque.

LEAVES—Alternate, simple, singly on new shoots, in pairs on growth
of the previous season; 2" to 4" long, 1½" to 2½" wide, with broad V-shaped
base and gradually tapering apex; margins doubly serrate except the base
which is usually entire; light yellow-green and pubescent at first, becoming
thin, shiny and dark green above; pale green and sometimes pubescent on the
midrib, beneath. Petiole about ¾" long, slightly flattened and often fuzzy.

BARK—On old trunks dark red-brown, thick and broken into irregular
plate-like scales (Fig. 23); on young trunks and large limbs, broken into successive thin, tough, paperly layers which upon peeling back expose the orange
color of the under layer; on the slightly zigzag, slender twigs, at first green
and hairy, later smooth reddish brown and marked with pale horizontally
elongated pale lenticels.

BUDS—Alternate, ovate sharp pointed, about ¼" long, the outer bottom
scales shiny and bright chestnut brown, the inner and apex ones light reddish
brown and often velvety pubescent.

FLOWERS—About April before the leaves; the staminate from ¾" long
2 or 3 clustered aments formed the previous year, elongating in spring to 2"
to 3" long drooping catkins; the pistillate erect, from buds below the staminate
flowers, cylindrical, about ½" long.

FRUIT—May and June, as an erect, slender stalked, pubescent strobile
or cone, 1" to 1½" long, made up of 3 lobed, hairy scales and winged nutlets;
nutlet ovoid, about ⅛" long with apex pubescent and equipped with broad,
hairy margined, lateral wings.

WOOD—Diffuse-porous; rays indistinct; light, comparatively hard and
strong; heartwood light brown; sapwood thin, pale pink or yellowish. Weighs
about 36 pounds per cubic foot, and used for furniture, slack cooperage, basket
veneer, woodenware articles, turnery and fuel.

RANGE AND DISTRIBUTION—New Hampshire to Florida, west to
eastern Texas and northward to Minnesota. Common throughout the State.

HABITAT—Prefers stream banks and wet locations, hence the name "river
birch." Because of this habitat the tree invariably takes the full force of flood
waters and serves to protect stream banks from serious scouring.

NOTES—The name "red" as applied to this birch refers to the distinctly
reddish to orange appearance of the bark on the trunk and larger limbs. Its
ability to thrive on sterile soils makes it useful in erosion prevention, but is
hardly to be recommended in place of the black locust for such purposes. It
makes an attractive ornamental and several varieties developed for their lighter
colored bark, or leaf form and color are cultivated for the nursery trade.

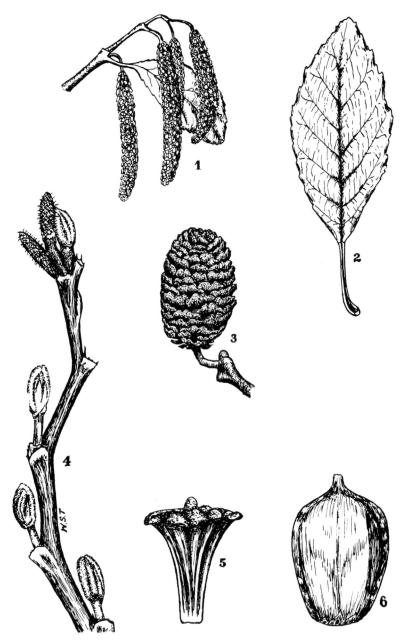

SEASIDE ALDER

1. Staminate flowering branchlet, natural size.
2. Leaf, natural size.
3. Fruit strobile, natural size.
4. Winter twig, with immature strobiles, x 2.
5. Strobile scale, enlarged.
6. Seed, enlarged.

SEASIDE ALDER
Alnus maritima, Nuttall

GENUS DESCRIPTION—The genus *Alnus*, or alders, comprises a small group of water loving shrubs and small trees occurring from sea level to high altitudes in both hemispheres of the world. Of the 20 known species, 9 are found in North America. Of the 6 which normally attain tree size, only one is native to Delaware. A shrubby species commonly known as smooth alder, *Alnus rugosa* Du Roi, is common throughout the State.

The seaside alder is a small tree which occasionally attains a height of 30' and a diameter of 4" to 5", but more often assumes the size of a large shrub. The trunk is usually straight and tall, ending in a small round topped head composed of small spreading branches and zigzag branchlets.

LEAVES—Alternate, oblong, 3" to 4" long, 1½" to 2" wide, usually blunt at the apex and wedge-shaped at the base; margins finely toothed and undulating; at maturity light blue-green and very lustrous above, lighter or yellowish and pale glandular dotted beneath; petiole stout, yellow and grooved above.

BARK—On old and young trunks smooth, slate gray (Fig. 25) on the zigzag twigs light green and hairy at first, becoming during their first winter dull light orange or reddish brown.

BUDS—Alternate, axillary on a short stalk, ovate, blunt pointed, dark red and coated with gray-brown velvet.

FLOWERS—In September, from catkins formed during the summer; the staminate (male) in 1½" to 2½" long, golden colored racemes from axils of upper leaves; the pistillate (female) ones at the same time, solitary usually in the axils of lower leaves on thrifty twigs but often appear to be terminal on lateral shoots, ¼" long, enlarging to fruit the following autumn.

FRUIT—September, a short stemmed oval cone or strobile, about ⅝" long and ½" in diameter, composed of thin shiny tipped scales and nutlets. Nutlets stubby bottle-shaped, with a thin narrow lateral ridge suggesting a wing.

WOOD—Diffuse-porous; rays distinct and prominent; light, soft, and moderately durable. Weighs about 31 pounds per cubic foot. Not commercially valuable.

RANGE AND DISTRIBUTION—Occurs only in the southern part of the Delmarva peninsula and a small area of the Red River valley in south central Oklahoma. In this State rare in Kent County but somewhat more common within its habitat in Sussex County.

HABITAT—Prefers the banks of streams and swamps within or close to tidewater and is rarely found in other than sandy peat soils.

NOTES—The seaside alder derives both its common and species name from its habitat in the Delmarva Peninsula, being usually close to tidewater or the sea. It differs from the other alders in many respects, particularly as to leaf glossiness and color in contrast to the usually dull surface and deeper color of shrubby forms, and in the time of blossoming which is in the autumn when most other trees are preparing for their winter rest. The chief characteristic distinguishing it from other alders in winter is found in the cones which are 2 to 3 times larger than the native shrubby species.

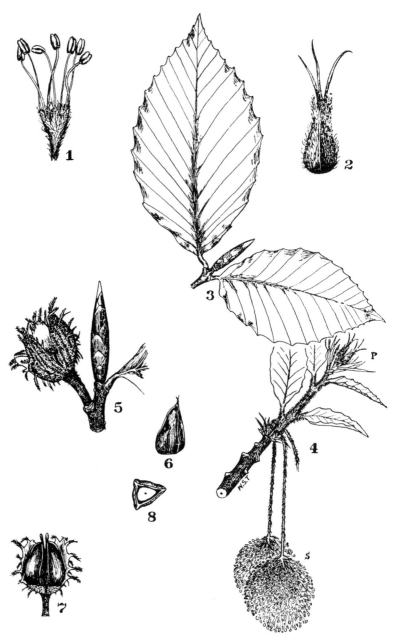

BEECH

1. Single staminate flower, enlarged.
2. Single pistillate flower, enlarged.
3. Leaves, x ½.
4. Branchlet with staminate flowers (s) and pistillate flowers (p), natural size.
5. Terminal bud and empty bur, natural size.
6. Seed, natural size.
7. Fruit with 2 lobes of bur removed, natural size.
8. Nut sectioned, natural size.

BEECH

Fagus grandifolia, Ehrhart

[*Fagus americana*, Sweet]

GENUS DESCRIPTION—The genus *Fagus* is credited with five species, three of which are native to China, one to Europe, and one to North America. Of the Old World species the European beech, *F. sylvatica*, L. and its varieties, copper beech, weeping beech, and cut-leaved beech are best known for their ornamental use in this Country.

The beech (c) is a tree usually 50' to 60' tall with a diameter of 1½' to 2' but may occasionally attain a height of 120' and a diameter of 4'. Trees in old growth stands are tall, with straight, little tapered trunk and small crown, but those of second growth stands are short of trunk, branch by 2 or more stems 20' to 30' above ground and are often clothed nearly to the ground with drooping lateral branches below, graduating to ascending branches in the top to form a broad symmetrical oval head. Reaches commercial maturity in 100 years or less but trees 300 years old are not uncommon.

LEAVES—Alternate, usually singly on new shoots, clustered on old growth and short lateral branches; ovate, sharp pointed, 3" to 5" long and half as broad; margins coarsely toothed with a vein terminating in each tooth; tough and leathery, lustrous light green above, yellow-green, lustrous and with tufts of white hairs in the axils of veins beneath; turn yellow in autumn and often persist in a dried condition until the following spring.

BARK—On young and old trunks alike, smooth, light gray; on the slender zigzag twigs lustrous, light yellow-brown, and marked by pale lenticels and the scars of the bud scales.

BUDS—Alternate, axilllary and terminal, the terminal ones slender, sharp pointed, ¾" to 1" long, covered by 10–20 chestnut brown scales having gray tips.

FLOWERS—April, when the leaves are about half grown; the staminate as globose heads 1" in diameter, on a slender hairy stem about 2" long; the pistillate usually in 2 flowered clusters on short stalks in the axils of upper leaves.

FRUIT—October; a stalked, prickle coated 4 valved bur about ¾" long containing 2 triangular, shiny coated, chestnut brown, nuts about ½" long, which contain a sweet edible kernel. In the northern portion of its range the tree appears to produce larger quantities of good nuts than it does in Delaware.

WOOD—Diffuse-porous, medullary rays prominent with less prominent intervening ones; hard, strong, with high shock resistance, not durable in contact with the soil, difficult to season; heartwood light reddish; sapwood thin, cream white. Weighs about 43 lbs. per cu. ft. and used for furniture, flooring, shoe lasts, carpentry tools, woodenware articles and fuel.

RANGE AND DISTRIBUTION—Nova Scotia to Wisconsin, south to Texas and Florida. Common throughout the State but more abundant in the northern portion.

HABITAT—Prefers rich bottomland soils but may be found on rich upland soils. Rarely found on soils containing lime and thrives under the shade of other trees.

NOTES—There are few people who do not know the beech tree and identify it by its smooth gray bark which, even in deep woods, will often show the disfiguring callus of pocket-knife carved initials or other inscribed characters. The triangular nuts are noted for their delicious flavor and are much prized as food for woods rodents, bears, wild turkey and other forest creatures. As an ornamental tree for lawn use, few hardwood trees are more beautiful than the beech but it is difficult to transport and usually grows slowly for several years afterwards if not carefully handled when replanted. The tree appears to be immune to lightning and according to Indian legend, one may seek its shelter during a thunderstorm without fear of being struck.

AMERICAN CHESTNUT

1. Summer branchlet with staminate and pistillate (p) flowers, x 1/3.
2. Fruiting branchlet, x 1/3.
3. Nuts and bur, x 1/3.
4. Winter twig, natural size.
5. Section of twig with bud and leaf scar, enlarged.
6. A pistillate flower, enlarged.
7. A staminate flower, enlarged.

AMERICAN CHESTNUT
Castanea dentata, (Marshall) Borkhausen

GENUS DESCRIPTION—The genus *Castanea* or chestnut, comprises 7 species and numerous varieties of nut bearing trees and shrubs widely distributed over the Northern Hemisphere of both the Old and New Worlds. Of the 4 species indigenous to the United States only 3 attain tree size. Two of these are native to Delaware. Of the Old World species the best known are the Italian chestnut, *C. sativa* Mill., the Japanese chestnut, *C. crenata,* Sieb. & Zucc., and the Chinese chestnut, *C. mollisima,* Bl. The Italian and Chinese species are quite often cultivated as orchard or ornamental trees in central and eastern U. S. Many of the latter species, introduced and distributed by the U. S. Dept. of Agriculture in Delaware about 1897, have grown successfully and, in addition to proving resistant to the chestnut bark disease *Endothia parasitica,* Anders, are prolific bearers of large nuts.

By those old enough to remember it, before the introduction of the chestnut bark disease, the American chestnut or chestnut (c) was a tree which usually attained a height of 60' to 80' and a diameter of 2' to 3' in a comparative short time. Trees 100' tall with a diameter of 4' to 6' were not rare. However, in the northeastern and Central Atlantic sections of the United States one is fortunate today in finding a sprout or stump shoot which does not show the telltale cankers of the blight before it has attained a height of 15' and a diameter of 3".

LEAVES—Alternate, oblong lanceolate, 6" to 9" long, 2" to 3" wide; margins coarsely incurve toothed with nearly parallel veins terminating in the tip of the tooth; at maturity dark green above and paler beneath.

BARK—On old trunks dark brown, fibrous, divided by broad shallow interrupted fissures into flat topped scaly ridges; on young trunks smooth greenish or purplish brown; on the somewhat angled and zigzag twigs, at first yellow-green soon becoming shiny reddish brown and marked by numerous small pale lenticels and small raised leaf bases exhibiting a broadly lunate leaf scar.

BUDS—Alternate, axillary, about ¼" long, ovoid, usually blunt pointed, covered by 2–3 chestnut brown, often fuzzy tipped scales.

FLOWERS—In June or July; the staminate aments 6" to 8" long with flower clusters closely spaced on numerous stout hoary stems; the pistillate flowers in globular involucres scattered near the base of upper aments also bearing staminate flowers, i.e. androgynous aments.

FRUIT—October; a globular spine covered bur 2" to 3" in diameter, which upon opening exposes 1 to 3, or rarely 5, shiny red-brown coated nuts containing a sweet edible seed.

WOOD—Ring-porous, with indistinct medullary rays; moderately hard and weak, splits readily, rich in tannic acid; heartwood reddish brown and very durable in contact with the soil; sapwood thin and cream colored. Weighs about 28 lbs. per cu. ft. and used for railroad ties, telegraph poles, posts, fence rails, interior finish, furniture, tannin extract and fuel. Because it snaps and cracks profusely with the attending shower of sparks, it is not safe to use in fire places without a protecting screen.

RANGE AND DISTRIBUTION—Maine to Michigan, southward in the mountains to northern Georgia and Mississippi. Common throughout the State, now, however, being confined to shrub-like growth by repeated attacks of the bark disease.

HABITAT—Prefers the medium moist soils but is not particular in either moisture or fertility requirements. It is, however, rarely found on limestone soils.

NOTES—In the mountains of North Carolina, Kentucky, and Tennessee there may be areas where the chestnut trees have not yet suffered the full effects of the chestnut bark disease, but the tree seems doomed to eventual extermination as a timber producing species. The capacity of the chestnut to reproduce by stump shoots, sprouts and seed has enabled it to survive repeated killings by the blight. In the opinion of the author this inherent tenacity of the species indicates that it will eventually, and by natural evolutional selection, develop resistance to the disease to the extent that fruit bearing trees will be common. How long this will take is beyond human estimation. It is, however, reasonable to assume that the eventual or climax type will have characteristics similar to the Asiatic species, which are blight resistant, and will not be the fast growing forest giant familiar to living generations.

The greatest tree diameter of record is for an Italian chestnut at the foot of Mt. Aetna in Sicily. It measured more than 60'. The largest chestnut tree on record in the State Forestry Dept. is for a tree which stood on the Sarah Ann White property about 6½ miles west of Felton. It measured 22'-2" in circumference at 4½' above the ground.

CHINQUAPIN

1. Autumn branchlet with fruit, x ½.
2. Winter twig, natural size.
3. Portion of twig enlarged to show bud and leaf scar.

CHINQUAPIN
Castanea pumila, Miller

The chinquapin (c) is a small tree which under the most favorable conditions may rarely attain a height of 50' and a trunk diameter of 3'. More often it is of shrubby growth and consists of clustered and much branching stems 6' to 12' tall. This latter form is more prevalent in this State.

LEAVES—Alternate, 3" to 5" long, 1½" to 2" wide, broader than those of the chestnut at apex and base and generally not as deeply serrate on the margins; at maturity thick firm, smooth and bright yellow-green above; silvery down-coated beneath.

BARK—On old and young trunks lighter in color than chestnut but otherwise similar. On the stout twigs at first light-green and woolly, later dull light reddish brown and roughened by numerous small wart-like lenticels and enlarged leaf bases exposing a large lunate leaf scar.

BUDS—Alternate, axillary, small, ovoid, blunt pointed covered with 2–3 pubescent red scales.

FLOWERS—Similar to chestnut but usually more abundantly produced.

FRUIT—October, a globular spine covered bur 1" to 1½" in diameter which upon opening, exposes 1 or rarely 2, lustrous, dark chestnut-brown coated nuts, containing a sweet edible seed.

WOOD—Similar in character to chestnut but harder and stronger; heartwood darker. Weighs about 32 lbs per cubic foot when air dry. Not of commercial importance in this latitude.

RANGE AND DISTRIBUTION—From southern New Jersey and Pennsylvania westward to Missouri, southward to Texas and Florida; reaching its maximum development in Texas and Missouri. Now rare in the State.

HABITAT—Prefers the drier sites but may be found on any but lime bearing soils.

NOTES—The chinquapin is somewhat more resistant to the chestnut blight than the American chestnut but because of its slow growth and limited distribution is perhaps more susceptible to extermination than the chestnut. Recently published American dictionaries give chinquapin as the preferred spelling. However U.S.D.A. Handbook No. 41 spells it chinkapin. Chincapin is also occasionally used. The name is derived from two words: *chinkwa* and *min* of Delaware Indian language.

Family: FAGACEAE
  Genus: QUERCUS

THE OAKS

Members of the genus *Quercus* are distributed over the Northern Hemisphere and mountainous parts of the tropics in both the Old and New Worlds. About 200 species have been described. Of these, some 55 are native to North America and 19 to Delaware. The numerous species are classified under 3 subgenera: Cyclobalanus, Lepidobalanus, and Erythrobalanus. Those classified under the first are all Asiatic and not considered herein; under the second are classified all the white oaks distinguished by acorns, maturing in one season, while the last includes the black oaks characterized by acorns maturing at the end of the second season.

The oaks in general are tall, massive long lived trees, but a few are distinctly shrubby and often occupy vast areas to the exclusion of most other tree species.

The **leaves** of the oaks are alternate, simple and lobed, dentate or rarely entire on the margins; evergreen or deciduous in autumn or die and remain attached to the branchlet until spring.

The trunk **bark** is usually close fitting, scaly or ridged and hard; has a high tannin content and sometimes used in tanning leather as is that of the native chestnut oak. The **buds** are lateral and terminal, the terminal one large, generally strongly 5 angled in the black oaks and surrounded by similar sized or smaller buds; scales 5 ranked, imbricated, and upon falling in summer leave a ring-like scar around the twig. The pith of the twig of most oaks is 5 angled or distinctly star-shaped. The **flowers** are monoecious; the staminate in slender, drooping catkins with 4–7 parted calyx and 4–12, usually 6, stamens; the pistillate solitary or in few flowered spikes in the axils of leaves on the new growth, each consisting of a 3 or occasionally 4 to 5 celled ovary surrounded by an involucre of imbricated bracts which at maturity, become the cup of the acorn. The **fruit** is a one seeded nut or acorn maturing in one or two years and surrounded at the base or sometimes nearly enclosed by the cup-like involucre. The seeds are usually bitter but in some species fairly sweet and edible. In many sections it is the practice to turn swine into the woods in autumn to fatten on the acorns or "mast." The acorns are also eaten by many forest creatures, particularly squirrels, bears and grouse. Early settlers used the roasted seeds as a substitute for coffee and the American Indians used them as food in various ways but usually dried and pulverized them to make flour.

When observed from the viewpoint of **wood** uses the genus becomes one of the most important in the tree world. The wood of most arborescent species is strong, tough, hard and, particularly in the white oaks, durable in contact with the soil. Possessed of such qualities it is highly valued for shipbuilding, construction, furniture, flooring, interior finish, truck bodies, tool handles, railroad ties, fuel and numerous other uses.

Members of the genus habit a variety of soils from sea level to altitudes of 7,000 or more feet and often occupy large areas to the exclusion of other tree species.

The oaks make attractive shade and ornamental trees and are valued for their form and foliage characteristics. Because young trees, especially those of the white oak group, develop a long strong tap root, they are difficult to successfully transplant. Consequently, propagation is best done by planting the acorns where the tree is wanted. Nurserymen follow a practice of transplanting oak trees often in order to discourage the tap root development and encourage the development of strong lateral roots.

Two of the most valuable of the European oaks are *Q. occidentalis* and *Q. suber* whose outer bark is the cork of commerce. Dye and tanning extract are manufactured from the galls caused by the punctures of insects which attack various oak species, in Europe. From others medical ingredients and surgery supplies are manufactured.

The silk oak of florists is *Grevillea robusta* and Jerusalem oak is *Chenopodium botrys*. Poison oak is *Rhus quercifolia* (Michaux) Steud., identified by its shrubby growth and thick leathery leaves which are pubescent beneath. It is occasionally found in Delaware.

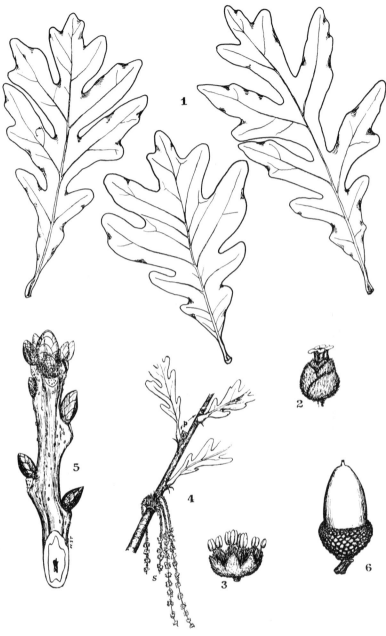

WHITE OAK

1. Leaves, x ½, the middle one characteristic of var. latiloba.
2. Single pistillate flower, enlarged.
3. Single staminate flower, enlarged.
4. Flowering branchlet with staminate catkins (s) and pistillate flowers (p), x ½.
5. Terminal portion of winter twig, x 2.
6. Fruit, natural size.

WHITE OAK
Quercus alba, Linnaeus

The white oak (c) is a tree usually 70' to 80' tall with a diameter of 2' to 3' but may occasionally exceed a height of 120' and a diameter of 7'. In forest stand the trunk is straight and usually clean for the greater portion of its length but in the open is short and branches by many large gnarled and twisted limbs to form a broad rounded head. Reaches commercial maturity in 75 years or less but trees 200 years old are common and individual trees 800 years old have been known.

LEAVES—Alternate, simple, 6" to 9" long, 2" to 4" wide, divided often nearly to the midrib by broad sinuses to form 7 to 9 forward pointing rounded lobes; when they first unfold bright red above and velvety pubescent beneath, becoming at maturity, thick, firm, smooth, and deep green above, pale and glaucous beneath; midrib and primary veins bright yellow, turn reddish in fall and upon dying often persist on the branchlet until spring. The variety *latiloba,* Sarg., which differs from the type in having leaves with shallower sinuses and broader lobes, is common in Delaware.

BARK—On old trunks gray and broken by narrow fissures into flat topped, scaly ridges, or occasionally broken into long broad irregular plates giving the tree a shaggy appearance; on young trunks similarly roughened but usually light gray and scaly; on the twigs, at first light green tinged with red and coated with loose pale hairs, becoming reddish-gray in winter and covered with glaucous bloom.

BUDS—Alternate, of varying broad forms, the terminal one about ⅛" long, egg shaped or globular, surrounded by a cluster of smaller ones; bud scales round tipped, reddish-brown.

FLOWERS—In May, when the leaves are about half grown; the staminate as 2" to 3" long hairy aments; the pistillate on a short stalk in the axils of leaves on the new growth with bright red stiles protruding from an involucre of hairy scales.

FRUIT—A sessile or short stalked acorn maturing in one season; nut ¾" to 1" long, ovoid to oblong, shiny chestnut brown at maturity, enclosed for about ¼ its length in the bowl-like cup which is covered by numerous imbricated scales, which are blunt pointed near the rim and knobby toward the base. Occasionally the nuts will start to sprout while still on the tree and upon falling attach themselves to the earth by partial development of the root. The acorns are an important item of food for forest mammals and birds.

WOOD—Ring-porous and pores filled with tyloses; medullary rays wide and continuous; strong, very heavy, hard, tough, and durable; heartwood light brown; sapwood nearly white. Weight 46.3 lbs. per cu. ft. and used for piling, ship building, tight cooperage, construction, interior finish, flooring, railroad ties, furniture, baskets, fish traps, and fuel.

RANGE AND DISTRIBUTION—Maine to Minnesota, south to Florida and Texas. Very common throughout Delaware.

HABITAT—Not particular as to soil fertility or moisture content but reaches its best development on the rich bottomlands of the lower Ohio basin. Tolerates shade.

NOTES—In summer the white oak is readily recognized by many distinguishing characteristics, chiefly that of the deeply incised and lobed leaves. In winter, the presence of the persistent, dry, purplish-brown leaves and bloom covered twigs with comparatively small buds, is characteristic.

Commercially the white oak is one of Delaware's most important hardwood trees, but being of slow growth and not subject to successful artificial reproduction, from a forestry standpoint, natural regeneration must be depended upon to supply future needs of this superior wood. Since trees developing from stump shoots or sprouts rarely produce high grade lumber, trees of seed origin should be encouraged in forest culture work.

Few trees in old age are more picturesque and truly handsome than the white oak. Its rugged and sturdy appearance gives one a feeling of stability and security not equalled in other native trees. However, because it is difficult to successfully transplant and at best is a slow grower, it is not popular as a tree for street and highway planting.

Many natural hybrid oak having the white oak as one of the parents, have been discovered and described. Of these, one known as saul oak *Q. saulii,* Schneider, has been found in Kent County, east of Smyrna.

OVERCUP OAK

1. Autumn branchlet with leaves and fruit, x ½.
2. Terminal portion of winter twig, x 4.

OVERCUP OAK
Quercus lyrata, Walter

The overcup oak, also known as swamp oak and swamp post oak is a tree which usually attains a height of 50' to 60' with a diameter of 1½' to 2' but may rarely attain a height of 100' and a diameter of 3'. Trunk straight but often dividing 20' to 30' above ground into many stems with semi-pendulous branches to form a symmetrical round topped crown.

LEAVES—Alternate, 7" to 10" long, 1" to 4" wide, varying greatly in depth of sinuses and shape of lobes, but sinuses generally noticeably angular and forming 5–9 round tipped, or ovate acute, lobes, 2 of which are usually more blunt and wider than the others; at maturity thin, firm, smooth and green above, white tomentose or rarely pale green beneath. Lobes are generally more angular than shown on the opposite page.

BARK—On old trunks similar to white oak and light gray tinged with red; on young trunks smooth, hard and gray; on the slender twigs at first green and hairy, later orange-brown, smooth and marked by minute pale lenticels.

BUDS—Alternate, globular, the terminal about ⅛" long in a cluster of smaller ones on the enlarged tip of the twig, covered with several pale brown scales.

FLOWERS—After the leaves; the staminate in slender hairy aments 4" to 6" long; the pistillate ¾" to 1" with scaly pubescent involucre, sessile or on a pubescent stalk.

FRUIT—An acorn maturing at the end of the first season, ¾" to 1" in diameter, sessile or borne on a stalk sometimes 1½" long; the nut globular or depressed globose, light brown with upper portion pubescent, enclosed for more than three-quarters of its length in a thin, hoary, yellow-brown cup, ragged and often split at the rim, thicker and warty toward the base.

WOOD—Similar in texture to white oak but heartwood a rich dark brown. Not distinguished from white oak on the market.

RANGE AND DISTRIBUTION—Southern New Jersey to Florida west to Missouri and Texas. Indigenous to lower New Castle, Kent and Sussex Counties where it is comparatively rare.

HABITAT—Prefers the banks of streams and moist soils at low altitudes. In Delaware observed only in such locations.

NOTES—The overcup oak derives its common name from the fact that the cup of the acorn often nearly completely covers the nut. This characteristic identifies it from all other oaks except the mossycup oak in which the cup is shorter, very thick and fringed at the rim with matted moss-like appendages. Because of its limited distribution the overcup oak is not commercially important but as an ornamental it is one of the best and deserves greater use than it now enjoys.

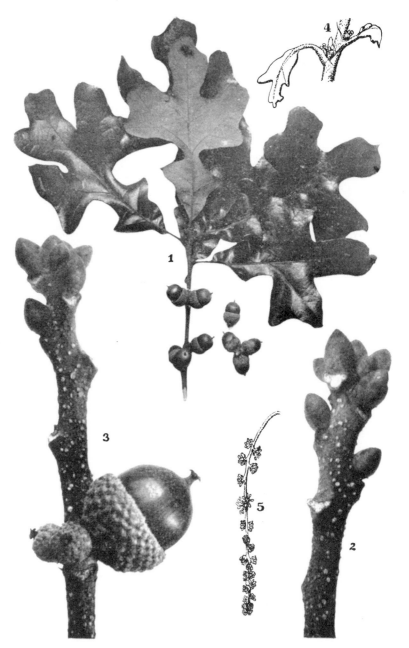

POST OAK

1. Fruiting branchlet and fruit, x ½.
2. Terminal portion of autumn twig, x 2.
3. Terminal portion of autumn twig with fruit and undeveloped fruit, x 2.
4. Portion of branchlet showing pistillate flowers, x ½.
5. Single staminate ament, x ½.

POST OAK
Quercus stellata, Wangenheim

The post oak is a medium sized tree, usually 50' to 60' tall and 1½' to 2½' in diameter but may rarely attain a height of 100' and a diameter of 5'. The trunk, in forest stands, is usually very straight with few gnarled lateral branches and short spreading branchlets forming a broad medium dense irregular head. Grows slowly and attains a great age. A tree on the property of Mr. Charles Rogers, near Shortly in Sussex County, measured 12'-8" in circumference in 1937.

LEAVES—Alternate, often clustered on the tips of twigs, 4" to 7" long, 3" to 5" wide, with broad rounded sinuses dividing the leaf into irregular lobes, usually 5, the opposite central ones being large and blunt or club-like; leathery in texture, deep dark green and shiny above; pale and rusty pubescent beneath. Often the dry leaves will persist on the branchlets during the winter, but this characteristic is more pronounced in other oak species.

BARK—On old trunks similar to white oak but darker, less scaly and more closely fissured and ridged (Fig. 32); on the young trunks and branches brownish gray, roughened by patches of thin curled scales; on the stout twigs at first light yellowish or orange, thickly covered with rusty tomentum and much roughened by enlarged leaf bases and numerous large, light colored, raised lenticels.

BUDS—Alternate, broadly ovate, the terminal bud in a cluster of similar sized ones, about ¼" long, blunt, covered with numerous overlapping, red-brown scales, wooly early but, by late winter, often shiny.

FLOWERS—About May; the staminate as slender yellowish green aments 4" to 5" long; the pistillate in the axils of leaves of the new growth, sessile or short stalked and wooly.

FRUIT—An acorn maturing at the end of the first season, usually sessile, singly, in pairs or clusters. Nut ½" to ¾" long, oval, slightly pubescent at the apex, longitudinally striate with light and dark brown bands, enclosed for about half its length in a thin, saucer-shaped cup, hairy within and light hoary tomentose on the scaly outer surface.

WOOD—Ring-porous; medullary rays wide and conspicuous; very heavy, very hard, moderately strong with high resistance to shock and high durability in contact with the soil; heartwood light gray-brown; sapwood thin, nearly white; weighs about 52 lbs. per cu. ft. and used for the same purposes as white oak. Recognized as a more durable wood for posts than white oak, and accounts for the common name "post oak."

RANGE AND DISTRIBUTION—Massachusetts to Oklahoma, south to eastern Texas and northern Florida. Common throughout the State.

HABITAT—Common on dry soils and uplands. Exhibits little preference for degree of soil fertility or consistency.

NOTES—In summer the post oak may be distinguished from all other oaks by its characteristic "Maltese cross" patterned, dark green shiny leaf with pubescent under surface. Microscopic examination of this pubescence reveals it to be star-like hence the *stellata* in its scientific name. In winter the light colored, rusty pubescent stout twigs, which are roughened by the enlarged leaf bases and abundance of raised circular lenticels, serve to distinguish it from all other oaks.

Ornamentally the post oak is a handsome tree and although it will grow on poorer soil than the white oak it grows slowly and is difficult to transplant successfully.

BASKET OAK

1. Fruiting branchlet, x ½.
2. Terminal portion of winter twig, x 2.

BASKET OAK

Quercus prinus, Linnaeus

[*Quercus michauxii,* Nuttall]

The basket oak (c) also known as cow oak and swamp chestnut oak, is a tree usually 60' to 70' tall and 2' to 3' in diameter but may often attain a height of 100' and a diameter of 6'. Trunk, in dense forest stands, often clean and without branches for 40' to 50' above ground and then branching by nearly upright branches to form a small symmetrical rounded crown. Trees, in the open, are elliptical and compact of form.

LEAVES—Alternate, 6" to 8" long, 3" to 5" wide, ovate to oblong-ovate, usually widest above the middle, tapering to a short apex and to a rounded or broadly wedge shaped base; margins coarsely and uniformly dentate with rounded lobes sometimes with glandular tips; at maturity thick, firm, or even leathery, dark green and shiny above, pubescent and pale green or more often silvery white beneath, turning dark crimson in fall; petiole about ½" to 1½" long.

BARK—On old trunks, light gray to white (Fig. 35); on young trunks and limbs scaly and whitish gray; on the stout twigs at first dark green and hairy later becoming orange-brown or bright red-brown and smooth.

BUDS—Alternate, those of the terminal cluster about ¼" long, ovate sharp pointed, covered by dark red, pale margined scales, slightly hairy at the apex.

FLOWERS—In May after the leaves; the staminate in slender hairy aments 3" to 4" long; the pistillate in few flowered clusters on a short, rusty, hair coated, stem.

FRUIT—Matures at the end of the first season; solitary or in pairs, sessile or short stalked; nut 1" to 1¼" long, ¾" to 1¼" in diameter, ovoid or elliptical, light brown with pubescent apex, enclosed for about a third of its length in a thick, broad, flat cup, red-brown and pubescent within, hoary on the outside and covered by regularly imbricated scales, their tips commonly forming the fringed rim of the cup; seed reasonably sweet and edible.

WOOD—Ring-porous, with wide prominent medullary rays, hard, moderately strong, tough but splits easily, durable in contact with the soil; heartwood light brown; sapwood thin, lighter. Weighs 47.7 lbs. per cu. ft. and used for the same purposes as white oak but seems to produce a better type of basket splint than the white oak, hence the common name "basket oak."

RANGE AND DISTRIBUTION—Central New Jersey to Illinois southward to Texas and Florida. Common throughout the State, but more abundant south.

HABITAT—Prefers stream borders, swamps, and low wet lands.

NOTES—Due to the similarity of leaf outline, the basket oak may sometimes be confused with the chestnut or rock oak, but the leaves of this tree differ from the latter in having a silvery under surface. Also the ashy-gray bark of this tree can hardly be mistaken for that of the chestnut oak which is very thick, hard, and broken into rugged ridges.

The basket oak when growing in the open is one of the most symmetrical and beautiful of oaks and when once seen in its full autumnal scarlet foliage is not soon forgotten. Unquestionably suited to ornamental use wherever it can be planted on suitably moist soils.

In evaluating the attributes of this tree the fact that the seeds are sweet and edible, and therefore constitute an item of food for forest rodents, should not be overlooked.

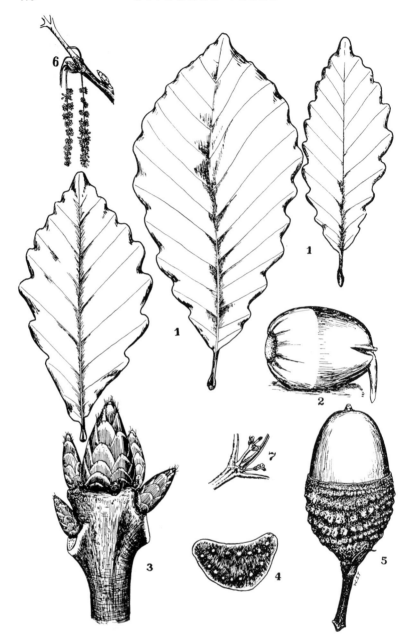

CHESTNUT OAK

1. Leaves, x ½.
2. Sprouting nut, natural size.
3. Terminal portion of winter twig, x 2.
4. Leaf scar, enlarged.
5. Fruit, natural size.
6. Portion of branchlet with staminate aments, x ½.
7. Portion of branchlet with pistillate flowers, x ½.

CHESTNUT OAK
Quercus montana, Willdenow

[*Quercus prinus,* Engelmann not Linnaeus]

The chestnut oak, also known as rock oak, rock chestnut oak, and tanbark oak, is a tree usually 50′ to 60′ tall and 1½′ to 2½′ in diameter but may occasionally attain a height of 100′ and a diameter of 6′ to 7′. Trunk, in dense forests stands, in valley soils tall and straight but trees on rocky slopes at higher altitudes often inclined, short and dividing at 10′ to 20′ into large gnarly limbs to form an open spreading crown.

LEAVES—Alternate, variable in form especially between lower and upper branches but usually oblong to lanceolate, 4½″ to 9″ long, 1½″ to 3″ wide; margins irregularly shallow indented with round tipped and forward pointing lobes; at maturity thick, firm, almost leathery smooth, and green above; pale green and very finely pubescent beneath; petiole, midrib and primary veins light yellow; turn light brown in autumn, and often persist into winter.

BARK—On old trunks and large branches ¾″ to 1½″ thick, deeply fissured into continuous, broad based and narrow topped ridges, brownish gray to dark gray with bottom of fissure showing a salmon to rusty-red color (Fig. 34); on young trunks and small branches, thin, smooth, often shiny and purplish gray; on the stout angular twigs at first purplish green with scattered hairs, becoming during the following winter smooth and orange or red-brown. The trunk bark is rich in tannin and is used in tanning leather.

BUDS—Alternate, ovate-conical, sharp pointed, often angled, those of the terminal cluster larger and about ½″ long; the imbricated bud scales light chestnut brown and often slightly pubescent toward the apex of the bud.

FLOWERS—In May when the leaves are partly developed; the staminate as hairy aments 2″ to 3″ long; the pistillate in pairs or groups on a stout pubescent stalk.

FRUIT—Matures at the end of the first season singly or in pairs on a short stout stalk; nut 1″ to 1½″ long, ⅝″ to 1″ in diameter, oval, or long pointed; shiny, bright chestnut brown, enclosed for half its length or less in a thin, bowl-like cup, pubescent on the inner surface, with exterior red-brown and roughened by knobby scales near the base; kernel moderately sweet.

WOOD—Ring-porous; medullary rays prominent; hard, strong, tough and durable in contact with soil; heartwood dark brown; sapwood lighter; weighs 46.7 lbs. per cu. ft. and when sawed into lumber and marketed, is not differentiated from white oak, otherwise used for fence posts, railroad ties, and fuel.

RANGE AND DISTRIBUTION—Maine to Indiana south to Mississippi and Alabama. In Delaware not as common as many other oaks, but most abundant north.

HABITAT—In Delaware not particular as to soil fertility or moisture, but elsewhere normally habits hillsides, rocky places and mountain tops to an altitude of 4500′ often comprising a high percentage of the tree growth in the latter environment. Reaches its maximum size in the Smoky Mountain region of the Allegheny Mountains. Prefers sunlight and is rather intolerant of shade.

NOTES—The chestnut oak leaves resemble those of the basket oak but differ from the latter in being green, less shiny on the upper surface and not having a silvery under surface. The distinctive rugged dark bark of the chestnut oak can hardly be confused with that of the basket oak or any oak of either the white or black oak group except saul oak, *Q. saulii* Schneider, which is believed to be a natural hybrid of this species and white oak, and extremely rare in Delaware. The tree probably derives its common name "rock oak" from its usual habitat in rocky places and from its rugged bark, or possibly from the wood which is often gnarly but actually in texture differs little from white oak. The bark is highly valued for its tannin content and even the sapwood contains a higher percentage of tannin than most oaks.

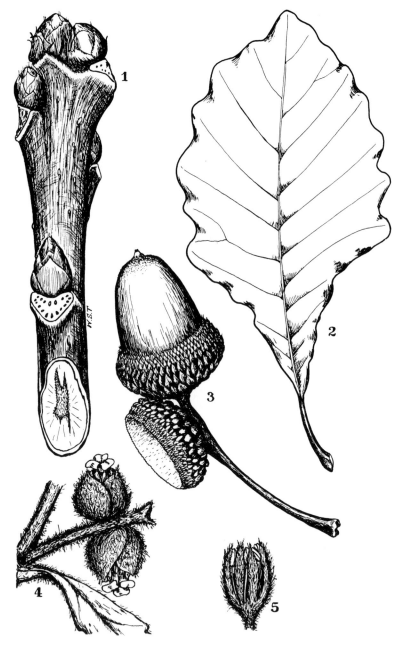

SWAMP WHITE OAK

1. Terminal portion of winter twig, x 4.
2. Leaf, natural size.
3. Acorn fruit, natural size.
4. Portion of branchlet with pistillate flowers, enlarged.
5. A single staminate flower, enlarged.

SWAMP WHITE OAK
Quercus bicolor, Willdenow
[*Quercus platanoides,* Sudworth]

The swamp white oak is a tree usually 60' to 70' tall with a trunk diameter of 2' to 3' but may rarely attain a height of 100' and a diameter of 8'. Trunk, in dense forest stands, tall and continuous but in the open has a short thick trunk with upper branches ascending, graduating to drooping ones below, to form a round tipped open head.

LEAVES—Alternate, simple, oblong or obovate in outline, 5" to 6" long, 2" to 4" wide; margins coarsely dentate with lobes acute or rounded and short; at maturity thick, firm, dark green and shiny above; pale green or more often silvery white and finely hairy beneath. Turn a distinctive bright red-brown in autumn and persist for awhile but usually deciduous by December.

BARK—On old trunks thick, yellowish gray, broken by narrow deep fissures into long continuous flat topped, ridges composed of small appressed scales (Fig. 33); on young trunks and large branches, reddish brown, appearing ragged and unkept by reason of the irregularly separating paper-like scales which upon peeling back expose the greenish inner bark; on the stout twigs, yellowish to light reddish brown, smooth and marked by scattered pale raised lenticels.

BUDS—Alternate, broadly ovate, the terminal less than ¼" long, covered by overlapping chestnut brown scales which are often hairy toward the apex of the bud.

FLOWERS—In May, before the leaves are well developed; the staminate in hairy aments 3" to 4" long; the pistillate solitary or in clusters on a long stem in the axils of leaves.

FRUIT—An acorn maturing in one season, solitary, in pairs, or in clusters on an unusually long stem (1½" to 4"); nut ovoid, light chestnut brown, usually hairy at the top, ¾" to 1¼" long, enclosed for about a third its length in a deep cup, which is hairy inside and wooly outside, with scales thickened or knobby near the base, thinner and often fringed at the rim.

WOOD—Diffuse-porous; medullary rays conspicuous; very strong, very stiff, very hard with very high resistance to shock; similar in other respects to white oak and not distinguished from it in the market. Weight 47.7 lbs. per cu. ft.

RANGE AND DISTRIBUTION—Maine to southern Minnesota, south to Oklahoma and West Virginia. Most abundant in New York State. In Delaware frequent in its natural habitat, particularly along streams emptying into Chesapeake Bay, but nowhere abundant. Rather common in the vicinity of Iron Hill, in New Castle County.

HABITAT—Prefers rich soils and wet locations such as stream banks and swamps, as indicated by its common name.

NOTES—An additional descriptive common name for this oak might be the scaly limbed oak in that the exfoliating bark on the young limbs is a distinguishing characteristic present at all times of the year. In summer the larger leaves which are usually broadest above the middle and taper abruptly to the tip and gradually to the base, are characteristic. In autumn the long stemmed acorns are distinctive. This tree would appear to be the "black sheep" of the white oak group in that it is slow of growth, and adapted only to rich moist soils. A fair sized specimen of this species stands (1938) within the right-of-way of the State road along the south slope of Iron Hill about one mile west of Cooch's Bridge.

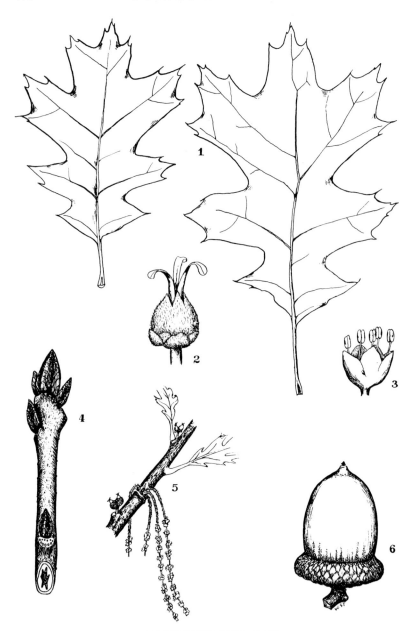

NORTHERN RED OAK

1. Leaves, x ½.
2. Single pistillate flower, enlarged.
3. Single staminate flower, enlarged.
4. Winter twig, x 2.
5. Branchlet with staminate and pistillate flowers and first season acorns, x ¼
6. Fruit, natural size.

NORTHERN RED OAK
Quercus borealis maxima, (Marshall) Ashe

[*Quercus rubra,* Du Roi not Linnaeus]

This variety of the northern red oak (c) is a tree usually 60' to 70' tall with a trunk 2' to 3' in diameter but may occasionally attain a height of 150' with a trunk 3' to 5' in diameter. Trunk, in dense forest stands, clean with small crown; in the open, often short with 45° ascending branches forming a broad symmetrical crown.

LEAVES—Alternate, variable but usually broadly ovate, 5" to 9" long, 4" to 6" wide, usually divided about half way to the midrib, by wide oblique sinuses, into 11 or few as 7, 2–6 (usually 3) bristle tipped forward pointing lobes; at maturity firm, smooth dull green, with yellow or red midribs above; pale yellow-green and smooth or sometimes with tufts of rusty hairs in the axils of veins, beneath; petiole 1" to 2" long, yellow or red. Often remain on the tree in dried condition during the winter.

BARK—On old and large trunks thick, broken by wide shallow fissures and rather continuous, flat topped ridges, the top of the ridges light gray and smooth, the fissures darker and rough (Fig. 29); on young trunks smooth and slate-gray; on the twigs, smooth dark red or reddish brown during the first winter.

BUDS—Alternate, ovoid, angled, narrowing gradually to a sharp apex, those of the terminal cluster about ¼" long and covered with numerous overlapping, glossy chestnut brown scales.

FLOWERS—In May when the leaves are partly developed; the staminate in 4" to 5" long hairy aments with greenish 4–5 lobed calyx and 4–5 stamens longer than the calyx; the pistillate on short smooth stalks, with 3 strap-like bright green stigmas protruding from a brown hairy involucre.

FRUIT—An acorn maturing at the end of the second season; solitary or in pairs, sessile or on a short stout stalk; nut ¾" to 1¼" long, ½" to ¾" in diameter, light red-brown often with a coating of bloom or pubescence which will rub off; enclosed only at the base in a flat saucer-shaped cup covered with closely appressed reddish brown, sometimes fuzz coated scales. The large nut with rounded apex and flat base is the most distinguished characteristic of this variety. The white nut meat is very bitter and therefore not important as food for squirrels.

WOOD—Ring-porous, with conspicuous medullary rays, heavy, hard, strong, not durable in contact with the soil; heartwood reddish; sapwood thin, light colored. Weighs 41.2 lbs. per cu. ft. and used for interior finish, construction, railroad ties, furniture and fuel.

RANGE AND DISTRIBUTION—"Northern range not fully determined. To be looked for—from western New York" (Sudworth) to southern Michigan, Kansas and Nebraska southward to Mississippi and Georgia. Common throughout Delaware but most abundant north.

HABITAT—Requires well drained soil and will not grow in wet situations. Intolerant of shade.

NOTES—The range of the true northern red oak *Q. borealis,* Michaux f. is reported to approach Delaware no closer than Erie County, Pennsylvania hence the description here applies specifically to the large leaved and large fruited form of the species so common in northern New Castle County. It may be distinguished from other members of the black oak (or red oak) group by the red petiole and midrib of the broad leaf. The smooth gray tops of the ridges of the bark of large trees and the light salmon color of the inner bark are distinguishing characteristics.

From a forestry standpoint this oak is one of the few hardwoods that lends itself to successful artificial reforestation practice. It is probably the fastest growing of the commercially valuable oaks, which attribute, in conjunction with the dense foliage and red autumn coloration, makes it attractive as an ornamental. This species was used in what is believed to be the oldest forest planting of oaks in Delaware, which was established in 1910 on P. R. R. lands near Middletown and is regarded as one of the best of such plantings in the East.

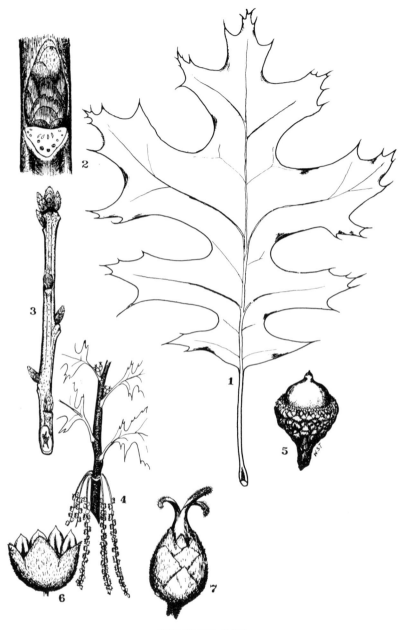

SCARLET OAK

1. Leaf, natural size.
2. Portion of winter twig, enlarged to show bud and leaf scar.
3. Winter twig, natural size.
4. Branch with staminate (bottom) and pistillate (top) flowers, x ½.
5. Fruit, x ¾.
6. Single staminate flower, enlarged.
7. Single pistillate flower, enlarged.

SCARLET OAK
Quercus coccinea, Muenchhausen

The scarlet oak is a tree usually 60' to 80' tall and 2' to 3' in diameter, but may occasionally attain a height of 150' and a diameter of 4'. Trees, in forest stands, have a small open head, but those in the open have a broad shallow crown of numerous slender branches ascending above, horizontal in the middle and descending below.

LEAVES—Alternate, broadly oval in outline, 3" to 6" long, 2½" to 4" broad, deeply divided by broad circular sinuses into 5 to 9 bristle tipped lobes, at maturity thin and firm, bright green, smooth and very shiny above; paler less shiny and often having tufts of rusty hairs in the axils of veins beneath; turn brilliant scarlet in the autumn. Leaf stem slender, round and 1½" to 2½" long. Often persist in dried form during late fall and winter.

BARK—On old trunks intermediate between the ruggedness of black oak and the smoothness of red oak, gray-brown with salmon to gray colored inner bark; on young trunks and limbs thin, smooth, and greenish gray; on the slender twigs, reddish or grayish brown and covered with numerous small pale lenticels.

BUDS—Alternate, those of the terminal cluster about ¼" long, elliptical, dark reddish brown and covered with white pubescence from the middle to the apex.

FLOWERS—In May when the leaves are about half grown, the staminate in slender pubescent catkins 3" to 4" long; the pistillate on a short pubescent stalk in the axil of leaves on the new growth.

FRUIT—An acorn maturing at the end of the second season, sessile or short stalked, solitary or in pairs. Nut ½" to 1" long, ovoid, light reddish brown or occasionally striped, enclosed for one-half its length in a deep tapering-based cup, light brown on the inner surface, and covered on the outside with closely imbricated, somewhat glossy red-brown scales which at the rim form a saw-tooth fringe.

WOOD—Ring-porous, with conspicuous medullary rays; very strong, very heavy, very hard and coarse grained; heartwood reddish, with thick light colored sapwood. Weighs 46 lbs. per cu. ft. and when sound is usually marketed as red oak.

RANGE AND DISTRIBUTION—Maine to Minnesota south to Oklahoma and Georgia, being most abundant at the north and on mountain tops. Common throughout Delaware.

HABITAT—Shows little preference for soil fertility or moisture, but reaches its maximum size in fertile dry soils of slopes and mountain tops. It is intolerant of shade.

NOTES—In summer the scarlet oak may be distinguished from the red and black oak, which it more closely resembles, by the deep rounded sinuses of the glossy leaves. In winter the fuzzy tipped dark red-brown buds are characteristic.

Commercially the tree is of minor importance because the wood is inferior to that of other oaks and it is rare that the lumberman finds a good sized tree of this species in which the heartwood has not been weakened or destroyed by fungous disease.

It is occasionally planted as ornamental for the bright scarlet autumn coloration of the leaves, but is hardly to be recommended for street or shade tree use because of its marked susceptibility to attacks of wood destroying fungi.

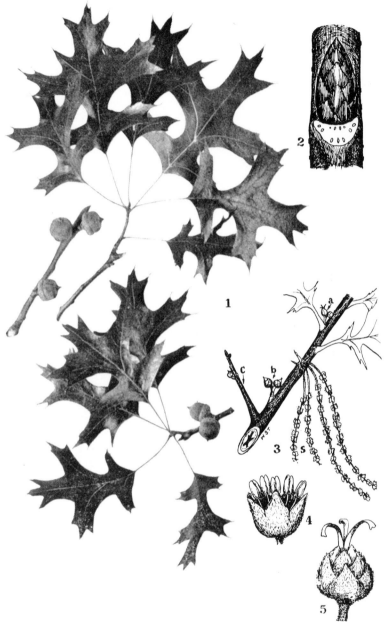

PIN OAK

1. Autumn branchlets and fruit, x ½.
2. Portion of winter twig enlarged to show bud and leaf scar.
3. Branchlet with staminate flowers (s) pistillate flowers (a), immature acorns of previous season (b) and pin (c), x ½.
4. Single staminate flower, enlarged.
5. Single pistillate flower, enlarged.

PIN OAK

Quercus palustris, Muenchhausen

The pin oak is a tree usually attaining a height of 50' to 60' and a diameter of 1' to 2' but may occasionally attain a height of 120' and a diameter of 5'. The tree develops a central straight trunk, which tapers uniformly from the base to the tip, and has a distinctly pyramidal crown composed of numerous slender branches ascending in the top, horizontal in the central portion and usually conspicuously drooping near the base. Reaches commercial maturity in 60 years or less, but trees 150 years old are common.

LEAVES—Alternate, ovate in outline, 4" to 6" long, 2" to 4" wide, divided nearly to the midrib by deep sinuses into 5 to 7, or rarely 9 lobes which terminate in 3 or 4 sharp tips; at maturity thin, firm, dark green and shiny above; light green, smooth, and usually with tufts of pale hair in axils of veins beneath; gradually turn deep scarlet in late fall and often persist in dried form during the winter.

BARK—On large old trunks, dark gray-brown, comparatively smooth but broken by shallow fissures and narrow low flat ridges (Fig. 30); on young trunks smooth, lustrous, brownish green; on the slender, tough, twigs hairy at first, later smooth, shiny and dark red, grayish brown or gray-green and marked by numerous pale lenticel dots.

BUDS—Alternate, those of the terminal cluster about ⅛" long, ovoid sharp pointed, prominently or obscurely 5 angled, covered with numerous imbricated light brown scales, the margins of which may sometimes be minutely round toothed or hairy.

FLOWERS—In May with the leaves; the staminate in 2" to 3" long hairy aments; the pistillate on short velvety stems in the axils of upper leaves.

FRUIT—An acorn, maturing at the end of the second season, solitary or in pairs, sessile or on a short stalk. Nut semi-spherical, about ½" long, brown to dark red-brown striate with lighter colored stripes, enclosed only at the base by a very thin flat saucer-shaped cup, dark red-brown inside and covered outside by light brown scales having dark margins. Kernel yellow and very bitter.

WOOD—Ring-porous, with conspicuous medullary rays, heavy, hard, strong, but not durable in contact with the soil; heartwood light brown with thin lighter sapwood. Weighs 43.2 lbs. per cu. ft. Used for piling, railroad ties, and interior construction. Usually marketed as red oak.

RANGE AND DISTRIBUTION—Massachusetts to Wisconsin south to Oklahoma, Tennessee and North Carolina. Most abundant and of its largest size in New Jersey, Delaware and Ohio. Common throughout Delaware.

HABITAT—Prefers the edge of swamps and deep rich lowlands along streams, but may be found on Coastal Plain uplands and moist mountain slopes.

NOTES—Because of its fibrous root development and general absence of a tap root, the pin oak is not difficult to transplant. In youth its symmetrical pyramidal crown, rapid growth and bright red autumn foliage make it one of the most handsome and desirable of the oaks for ornamental use.

The word "Pin" in the common name of this oak refers to the short thorn-like branchlets which are characteristic of the tree. Note C of No. 3 on the opposite page. The specific name *palustris* is derived from the Latin word palus, meaning swamp or wet place and refers to the usual habitat of the species.

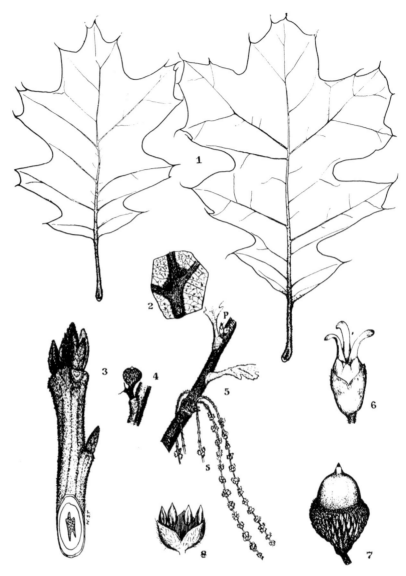

BLACK OAK

1. Leaves, x ½.
2. Section of the under side of a leaf, enlarged.
3. Portion of a thrifty winter twig, natural size.
4. Immature acorn, x ½.
5. Branchlet, with staminate flowers (s) and pistillate flowers (p), x ½.
6. Single pistillate flower, enlarged.
7. Fruit, x ½.
8. Single staminate flower, enlarged.

BLACK OAK
Quercus velutina, Lamarck

The black oak, also known as yellow bark oak and quercitron, is a tree usually 60' to 70' tall and 2' to 3' in diameter, but may occasionally attain a height of 150' with a diameter of 4'. Trunk usually tapers only slightly from the ground to the deep narrow or wide open crown composed of slender ascending branches. Attains commercial maturity in 80 years or less but trees 200 years old are comparatively rare.

LEAVES—Alternate, ovate or obovate in outline, normally 5" to 6" long, and 3" to 4" wide, divided by deep or shallow sinuses into 7 lobes which usually terminate in 3 or more bristle tips; when they unfold, bright crimson and covered with scattered white hairs above and thick white velvet below; becoming, at maturity, dark green, smooth and shiny except on the midrib above; pale or yellowish green with tufts of rusty hairs in the axils of veins and tomentum on the midrib beneath; in autumn gradually turning yellow-green and brown. Extremely variable in form and size of leaf.

BARK—On old trunks thick, very dark gray to black, rough, and broken by closely spaced short fissures into thick blocks or broken ridges (Fig. 27); inner bark is bright orange yellow; on small young trunks and branches smooth and very dark gray or brown; on the stout twigs during the first season, rusty or scurfy tomentose soon becoming smooth, reddish, and roughened by ridges extending down from the enlarged leaf bases.

BUDS—Alternate, ovoid, strongly angled, often fluted, rather blunt pointed, with numerous imbricated scales thickly covered with yellowish or gray down, those of the terminal cluster about ½" long.

FLOWERS—In May before the leaves are half grown; the staminate in numerous tomentose aments 4" to 6" long; the pistillate on short tomentose stalks.

FRUIT—An acorn maturing at the end of the second season, sessile or short stalked, solitary or in pairs; nut varies from oblong to hemispherical but is more often of the latter shape, ½" to rarely 1" long and broad, with a stout apex tip surmounted by a black spear-shaped vestige of the stigma, light brown, often striate with darker bands and coated with rusty tomentum; enclosed for about half its length in a thick bowl-like or saucer-shaped cup, red-brown inside and covered on the outside with thin, acute, hoary scales which are closely appressed at the base of the cup but at the rim are free at the tip and form a border of several saw-toothed rings.

WOOD—Ring-porous, with conspicuous medullary rays; heavy, hard, strong, not tough and not durable in contact with the soil; heartwood light brown; sapwood lighter. Weighs 43.9 lbs. per cu. ft. and used for furniture, interior finish and construction, but mostly as fuel. Usually marketed as red oak.

RANGE AND DISTRIBUTION—From southern Maine to Ontario and Nebraska, southward to Texas and Florida, being quite abundant throughout its range. Attains its largest size in the Ohio River Valley. Common throughout Delaware.

HABITAT—Prefers dry gravelly uplands and, in the southern Appalachian Mountains, ascends to altitudes of 4000'. A poor land species, not tolerant of shade and strongly tap rooted.

NOTES—The black oak may be distinguished from other native oaks at all times by the bright yellow inner bark. In winter, the large gray tomentose buds are distinctive. Except for its ability to thrive on poor soils it has little merit as an ornamental tree. The bark is rich in tannic acid and is sometimes used in tanning leather. Prior to the introduction of better dye materials the inner bark was the source of a yellow dye known as quercitron, hence one of its common names. The common name "black" applied to this oak refers to the distinctive blackness of the bark in contrast to that of other oaks.

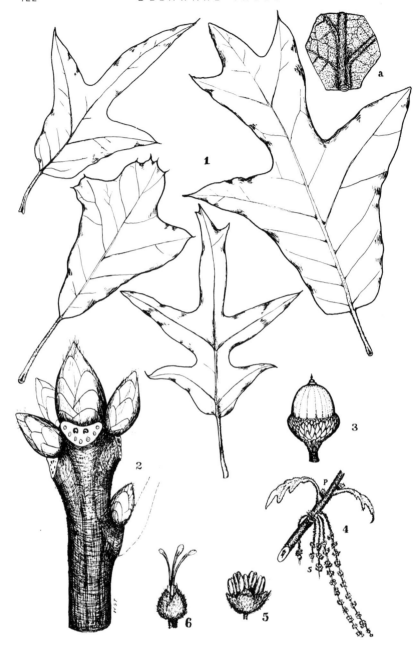

SOUTHERN RED OAK

1. Leaves. x ½; the ones on the left more typical of the var. *latiloba;* a—section of leaf, under side.
2. Section of winter twig, x 3.
3. Fruit, natural size.
4. Portion of branchlet with staminate flowers (s) and pistillate flowers (p), x ½.
5. Single staminate flower, enlarged.
6. Single pistillate flower, enlarged.

SOUTHERN RED OAK

Quercus falcata, Michaux

Quercus rubra, Linnaeus

[*Quercus digitata,* Sudworth]

The southern red oak, also known as Spanish oak and turkey oak, is a tree usually 70' to 80' tall and 2' to 3' in diameter, but may sometimes attain a height of 120' and a diameter of 4½'. Trees, in forest stands, have a tall straight trunk with few stout branches forming a broad open crown. In the open, the trunk is short and clothed with stout spreading branches to form a broad rounded crown. Reaches commercial maturity in 80 years or less, but trees 200 years old are not rare.

LEAVES—Alternate, 6" to 9" long, 4" to 5" wide, ovate or obovate in outline, with 3, 5 or 7 lobes, the terminal lobe usually linear-lanceolate and entire or further divided into short bristle pointed teeth; at maturity dark green and shiny above; dull green and coated with pale or rusty tomentum especially on the midrib and veins, beneath. Very variable in shape and size, and often characterized by a pronounced drooping from the slender, slightly flattened, petioles. Often persist in dry form on the tree in winter.

BARK—On old trunks, about 1" thick, divided by shallow fissures into low, broad, dark gray or brown, scaly ridges (Fig. 26); on young trunks thin with shallow dull red fissures and dark gray ridges; on the stout twigs at first coated with sticky buff colored tomentum which is usually deciduous by the first winter disclosing a dull reddish brown or dark gray colored bark. Rich in tannic acid and formerly used in tanning and occasionally in medicine.

BUDS—Alternate, ovoid, sharp pointed, usually not angled—the terminal one about ¼" long, covered with bright chestnut brown scales, slightly pale pubescent, or also with a few long hairs toward the apex of the bud.

FLOWERS—In April-May when the leaves are partly developed; the staminate in pubescent aments 4" to 5" long; the pistillate on stout hairy stalks with long dark red stigmas.

FRUIT—An acorn maturing at the end of the second season, sessile or usually short stalked; nut globose or elliptical, about ½" long and broad, buff to dark red-brown, striate and usually coated below the apex; enclosed at the base, or for not more than a third of its length, in a thin urn-shaped or sometimes flat saucer-shaped cup, light red-brown inside and covered outside with buff colored velvety scales.

WOOD—Ring-porous, with conspicuous medullary rays, heavy, hard, medium strong, coarse grained, not durable in contact with the soil; heartwood light red; sapwood lighter. Weighs 43.1 lbs. per cu. ft. and used for the same purposes as northern red oak and usually not distinguished from it in the market.

RANGE AND DISTRIBUTION—Southeastern Pennsylvania and southern New Jersey to southeastern Missouri, south to eastern Texas and Florida. Common throughout Delaware but most abundant south.

HABITAT—Prefers dry uplands and well drained soils.

NOTES—The southern red oak is distinguished from other members of the black or red oak group by the peculiarly shaped leaves which often appear to droop on the twigs and are gray-green or rusty velvet coated on the under surface. The largest tree of this species recorded by the State Forestry Department measured 17.3' in circumference breast high in 1933. It is situated on the south shore of Broad Creek west of Portsville in Sussex County. The variety *triloba* of Ashe, is comparatively common in Delaware and is characterized by sparse foliage composed mostly of 3 lobed leaves. It is of inferior form and size—seldom attaining a height of more than 30' in this latitude.

BLACKJACK OAK

1. Autumn branchlet with leaves, mature and immature (i) fruit. x ½.
2 Terminal section of winter twig. x 2.

BLACKJACK OAK

Quercus marilandica, Muenchhausen

The blackjack oak, also known as jack oak and barrens oak, is a tree usually 20' to 30' tall with a diameter of less than 1', but may rarely attain a height of 60' and a diameter of 3'. Trunk, when a single stem, short and stout, with stout contorted branches forming an irregularly shaped but usually round compact head.

LEAVES—Alternate, simple, broadly obovate in outline, 6″ to 7″ long and broad, with margins entire or dentate at the apex to form usually 3 or rarely 5 broad prickle tipped lobes; at maturity thick, firm and leathery; dark rich yellow-green and very shiny above, golden yellow tomentose beneath, sometimes becoming at length, smooth and yellow-green with broad yellow midrib and short, stout petiole.

BARK—On old and young trunks thick, black and roughly broken by deep fissures into irregular rectangular blocks or plates; on the branches dark brown or gray; on the stout twigs coated at first with thick, pale brown tomentum, ultimately becoming smooth and brown or gray.

BUDS—Alternate, ovate, distinctly angled, sharp or blunt pointed and covered with rusty tomentose scales with longer hairs at the tip of the bud; terminal bud ¼″ to ½″ long.

FLOWERS—In May when the leaves are about half developed; the staminate in 2″ to 4″ long, hoary aments; the pistillate on short rusty pubescent stalks.

FRUIT—An acorn maturing at the end of the second season, singly or in pairs on a short stalk; nut ovoid or globular and with prominently spiked apex, about ¾″ long and broad, light brown and often striate with greenish bands, dull coated and inclosed for a third to two-thirds its length in a thick urn-shaped, light brown cup, downy on the inside and covered outside by large loosely imbricated, hoary scales at the base, which grow smaller toward the top and form a broad rim composed of many rows of upright tips.

WOOD—Ring-porous; medullary rays conspicuous; heavy, hard, strong, not durable in contact with the soil; heartwood dark brown with thick light colored sapwood. Weighs 45.6 lbs. per cu. ft. and generally used only for fuel.

RANGE AND DISTRIBUTION—From Long Island and Staten Island, N. Y. to Nebraska, south to Texas and Florida. Most abundant and of its largest size in Arkansas and eastern Texas. Common throughout Delaware, but more abundant in Sussex County.

HABITAT—Usually occurs on poor, dry, sandy or clay soils, and is quite intolerant of shade.

NOTES—The fact that blackjack oak often habits vast areas of sterile soils known as barrens accounts for the common name "barrens oak." The rich yellow-green shiny foliage makes it one of the handsomest of oaks for ornamental use.

Numerous natural hybrids of this tree, with *Q. phellos, Q. nigra, Q. imbricaria, Q. texana* and *Q. velutina* occurring over extensive and local areas, have been classified.

WATER OAK

1. Autumn branchlet with mature and immature (i) fruit, x ½.
2. Winter twig, x 2.

WATER OAK
Quercus nigra, Linnaeus

[*Quercus aquatica,* Walter]

The water oak is a tree which, in Delaware, usually attains a height of 20' to 30', with a trunk diameter of less than 9", or rarely a height of 60' and a diameter of 2½'. Further south in its range it may attain a height of 80', with a trunk 3½' in diameter. In this latitude the trunks are often in clusters, slightly inclined and clothed for most of their height with numerous slender tough branches and short branchlets forming a round topped crown.

LEAVES—Alternate, oblong—obovate, 1½" to 3" long, 1" to 2" wide, extremely variable in size and shape, but widest near the apex, entire and rounded or acute and shallowly 3 lobed on the tip, or divided by 2 deep sinuses and shallow sinuses to form 3 to 7 acute tipped lobes; at maturity thin, leathery, deep blue-green and smooth above; pale green and often with tufts of rusty hairs in the axils of the prominent veins beneath; petiole stout, short and flattened.

BARK—On old trunks ½" to ¾" thick, hard and broken by shallow fissures pinkish tinged in the bottom, to form irregular flat red-brown ridges with ashy gray tops (Fig. 28); on young trunks and branches light or dark gray and smooth; on the slender, stiff twigs, smooth dull red, and marked by pale lenticels and enlarged leaf bases exhibiting a semi-circular leaf scar. Bark of old and even young trees blotched with light gray and often supporting many species of lichens, mosses, liverworts, etc.

BUDS—Alternate, ovate with an acute or blunt tip, strongly or slightly angled and covered with imbricated dull red-brown scales pubescent at the tip of the bud.

FLOWERS—In May when the leaves are about half developed; the staminate in 2" to 3" long red hairy aments; the pistillate on short hairy stalks.

FRUIT—An acorn maturing late in the second season, usually solitary, but clustered on the twig, sessile or short stalked; nut hemispherical or ovoid, ⅜" to ¾" long and broad, shiny light or dark brown and striate, usually enclosed only at the base in a thin, saucer-shaped cup, silky inside and covered outside by small, dull buff colored, but darker margined scales.

WOOD—Ring-porous, with conspicuous medullary rays; heavy, very hard when dry, strong, close grained and tough; heartwood dark with white sapwood. Weighs 44.5 lbs. per cu. ft., difficult to season and is mostly used for fuel. The wood of dead branches is so hard and close grained that axes and other cutting tools may easily be chipped or broken when struck into it.

RANGE AND DISTRIBUTION—Delaware to Missouri, south to Texas and Florida. Common in the southern part of Delaware.

HABITAT—Prefers rich bottom lands adjacent to streams and swamps, but may also be found on sandy uplands or dry locations.

NOTES—Delaware's largest water oak situated on the south side of the Bridgeville-Woodenhawk state highway, about 1½ miles northwest of Bridgeville was removed to make way for roadway widening in 1958. It measured 10.9' in circumference, breast high (4½'), in 1933. Because this species rarely develops a tap root and is easily transplanted it is often used as a highway, street and ornamental tree in the southern states. In our latitude, however, it is generally regarded as a weed tree of the forest, but charcoal made from the wood is reputed to have promise as an absorbent for use in gas masks.

WILLOW OAK

1. Autumn branchlet with fruit, x ½.
2. Terminal portion of winter twigs, the one on the left with immature acorns, natural size.
3. Single staminate flower, enlarged.
4. Single pistillate flower, enlarged.

WILLOW OAK
Quercus phellos, Linnaeus

The willow oak, also known as peach oak, water oak, and swamp oak, is a tree usually 50' to 70' tall and 2' to 3' in diameter, but may occasionally attain a height of 100' and a diameter of 4'. Trunk straight, tapering to a conical, round topped, open crown composed of ascending limbs and slender descending or drooping branches clothed with numerous spur-like branchlets. Attains commercial maturity in 70 years or less, but trees 150 years old are common.

LEAVES—Alternate, narrowly elliptical or lanceolate, 2½" to 5" long, ½" to ¾" broad, with entire wavy or undulating margins and bristle tip; at maturity light green, glabrous, semi-glossy and roughened by veinlets above; dull pale green and with conspicuous slender yellow midrib beneath; petiole stout and short.

BARK—On old trunks thin, close fitting, dark gray or nearly black, generally quite smooth but sometimes broken by shallow light brown fissures into irregular plates and often covered at the base with abundant lichen and other thallophytic organisms (Fig. 31); on young trunks smooth, shiny and greenish or grayish brown; on the slender twigs shiny, dark red-brown.

BUDS—Alternate, ovoid with acute pointed tip, the terminal one about ¼" long, conical, not or slightly angled and covered with overlapping smooth, dark chestnut-brown scales having darker, toothed or wavy margins.

FLOWERS—In May with the leaves; the staminate in slender yellow aments 2" to 3" long; the pistillate with 3 bright red stigmas and brown hairy involucre on a short smooth slender stem.

FRUIT—An acorn, maturing at the end of the second season, usually solitary on a short stalk or sessile. Nut hemispherical or globular, ½" long and broad, buff colored and velvety coated; appearing to sit on the thin saucer-shaped, pale brown, rust coated cup.

WOOD—Ring-porous with conspicuous medullary rays, heavy, moderately strong, hard, coarse grained, bends readily; heartwood light brown; sapwood thin white. Weighs 46.5 lbs. per cu. ft. and used for piling, general construction, boat building, wagon fellies and uses where the bending qualities are valued. Usually marketed as red oak and sometimes as bending oak.

RANGE AND DISTRIBUTION—Staten Island, N. Y. to eastern Missouri, south to eastern Texas and Florida, generally confined to low altitudes. Attains its largest size and is most abundant in the lower Mississippi Valley. Common throughout the State.

HABITAT—Prefers wet places, but may occur on sandy uplands.

NOTES—The willow oak derives its name from the willow-like leaves and branchlets, and may be distinguished from all other native oaks by these characteristics. It is rather satisfactory as a shade and ornamental tree, but is subject to the attacks of insects which cause the development of unsightly galls and knobs on the limbs and branchlets. The largest tree of this species on record in the State Forestry Department was reported in 1932 and measured 16' in circumference breast high at that time. It is situated on the "Knight" farm east of Dover in Kent County.

A Bartram oak, *Q. heterophylla.* Michaux fils, at Townsend Station is reported in the Edward Tatnall list of plants in New Castle County published in 1860 to have been "detected by Thomas Meehan, June 18, 1860." Other *Quercus* species recorded in the Tatnall list as found in New Castle County but rare, even then, are: yellow oak or chinquapin oak, *Q. muhlenbergii* Engelmann and the dwarf chinquapin oak, *Q. prinoides* Willdenow. Reports of existing natural specimens or stands of any of these species in the State will be appreciated by the State Forestry Dept.

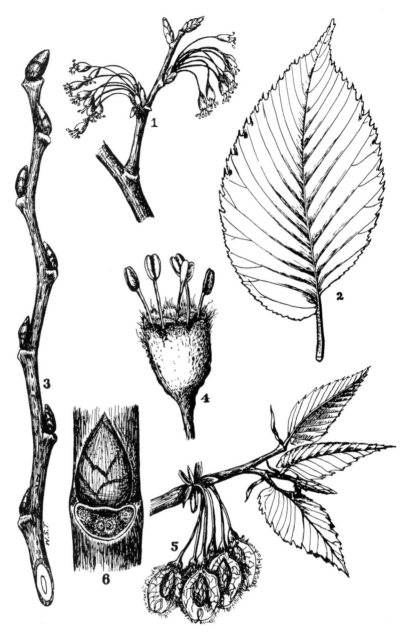

AMERICAN ELM

1. Section of flowering branchlet, natural size.
2. Leaf, x 2/3.
3. Winter twig, natural size.
4. Single flower, enlarged.
5. Fruiting branchlet, natural size.
6. Portion of winter twig, enlarged.

AMERICAN ELM
Ulmus americana, Linnaeus

GENUS DESCRIPTION—The genus *Ulmus*, or elms, comprises about 18 species of trees, or rarely shrubs, distributed over the Northern Hemisphere in the Old World, and in the New World east of the Rocky Mountains. Of these, 6 are native to North America and 2 to Delaware. The wood of most species is heavy, hard and tough, and the inner bark of some species is used medicinally, made into a meal and used as food, or furnishes a fiber use in the manufacture of cloth, bags, rope, etc. Most species enjoy limited or extensive use as shade or ornamental trees. Of the foreign species planted in this Country the English elm, *U. campestris*, and recently the northern Asiatic species *U. pumila*, *U. parvifolia* and *U. japonica* with common names such as Chinese elm, Siberian elm and Japanese elm are probably the most popular.

The American elm, also known as white elm (c), gray elm and water e'm, is a tree 70' to 80' tall with a diameter of 2' to 4', but may sometimes attain a height of 120' and a diameter of 11'. Trunk usually wide buttressed with short or tall trunk dividing into many large outward arching branches and drooping branchlets to form a broad umbrella-shaped crown. Reaches commercial maturity in 80 years or less, and rarely exceeds 150 years of age.

LEAVES—Alternate, ovate, obovate or oblong, acute at the apex and uneven at the base with one side rounded; 3" to 5" long, 1" to 3" wide; margins doubly toothed with incurved teeth; at maturity dark green and smooth or rough to the touch above; pale green and delicately pubescent or smooth below, with a narrow midrib and nearly parallel veins.

BARK—On old trunks thick, ashy gray, or gray-brown and divided by more or less continuous furrows into continuous, usually flat topped, ridges and small oblique connecting ridges; on young trunks similarly fissured but darker; on the slender, slightly zigzag twigs, at first green and pale pubescent, later becoming smooth, reddish brown and marked by scattered inconspicuous lenticels and large elevated semi-circular leaf scars exhibiting the ends of 3 or 4 fibro-vascular bundles.

BUDS—Alternate, axillary, the leaf buds, on the upper portion of thrifty twigs, ovate with acute sharp pointed apex and flattened, particularly on the twig side, 1/8" to 1/4" long; the flower buds larger and occur on spur branchlets and below the leaf buds; both types covered by 6–10 overlapping red-brown scales having darker margins.

FLOWERS—In early spring before the leaves and before those of most other trees, from lower buds on lateral twigs, clustered, each on a 1" long thread-like drooping stem; they are perfect, and composed of green styles and bright red anthers enclosed by a 7–9 lobed calyx, pubescent on the outside, green at the base, shading to light red at the hairy margin.

FRUIT—Clusters of oval samara, maturing as the leaves are unfolding, each about 1/2" long, born on a slender stem and consisting of an oval flat seed surrounded by a membranous wing, hairy on the margin and deeply notched at the apex. Fruit is abundantly produced but unless it falls on moist soil and soon germinates, the seed dries and loses its viability.

WOOD—Ring-porous, with very fine medullary rays; the pores in spring wood large, usually in a single row; those in the summer wood small, grouped into several wavy bands. Wood heavy, hard, coarse but tough and difficult to split; heartwood light brown; sapwood lighter. Weighs 45.3 lbs. per cu. ft. and used for wheel hubs, saddle trees, hockey sticks, cooperage and ship building.

RANGE AND DISTRIBUTION—Newfoundland to North Dakota, south to Texas and Florida. Most abundant and of its largest size northward. Common in Delaware.

HABITAT—Prefers moist rich soils but will grow satisfactorily when planted on drier and less fertile sites.

NOTES—The American elm, because of its rapid growth, ease of transplanting and stately form, makes perhaps the most popular street, highway and shade tree in northeastern United States. The discovery of several dying elm trees on the streets of Cleveland and Cincinnati, Ohio, in 1930, and investigation of the cause led to identification of the malady as the Dutch elm disease, which was first discovered in the Netherlands in 1919. Until control of spread of infection is assured, the planting of elms in, or in proximity of, the infected area with any thought of permanency, appears unwise. Despite the erection of drastic control and eradication measures the disease has since spread over most of the eastern U. S. The vectors of the disease are the European and American elm bark beetles.

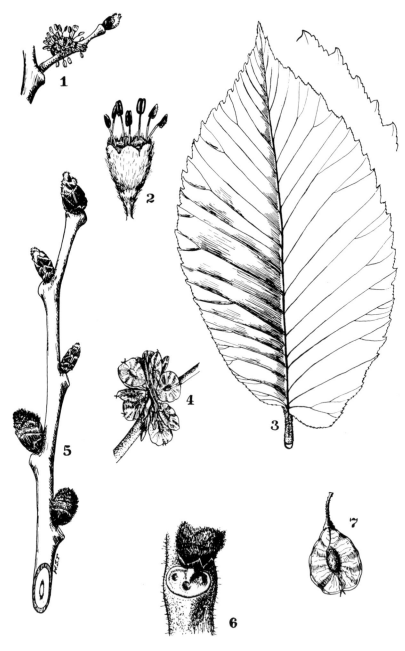

SLIPPERY ELM

1. Flowering branchlet, x ½.
2. Single flower, enlarged.
3. Leaf, natural size, with margin detail enlarged.
4. Fruit cluster, x ½.
5. Winter twig, x 2.
6. Portion of winter twig showing leaf scar, enlarged.
7. Fruit, natural size.

SLIPPERY ELM
Ulmus fulva, Michaux

The slippery elm, also known as red elm and moose elm, is a medium sized tree, 40′ to 60′ tall and 1′ to 1½′ in diameter, but may rarely attain a height of 80′ and a diameter of 2½′. Trunk is usually longer than American elm, with irregularly spaced spreading branches and branchlets.

LEAVES—Alternate, 5″ to 7″ long, 2″ to 3″ wide, ovate with unevenly rounded base and long acute tip; margins doubly toothed; at maturity thick, firm, often creased at the midrib, dark green and much roughened by minute spines above; green and pale pubescent, especially on the narrow midrib and in the axils of the nearly parallel veins, beneath; turn dull yellow in autumn.

BARK—On old and young trunks, thick, dark reddish brown and broken by shallow fissures into more or less continuous plated ridges; inner bark white, thick, mucilaginous and fragrant; on the stout, slightly zigzag, round twigs at first pubescent and light green, later ash-gray or brownish gray and roughened by minute spines and by enlarged leaf bases exhibiting a smooth surfaced oval leaf scar, having 3 or 4 depressed bundle scars.

BUDS—Alternate, axillary, stand away from the twig; the leaf buds on the upper portion of the twigs, ovoid, blunt pointed, about ¼″ long; the flower buds nearly globular about ½″ long, both covered by very dark reddish brown velvety and furry tipped scales—the fur on the leaf buds sometimes orange in color.

FLOWERS—Very early in spring, in crowded clusters, each on a short slender stem, perfect, with green, hairy 5–9 lobed calyx enclosing dark red anthers and reddish purple, white haired stigmas.

FRUIT—Maturing when the leaves are nearly half grown, in dense clusters, each a short stout stalked oval samara, ½″ to ¾″ broad, the rusty pubescent coated seed surrounded by a thin membrane-like wing, thickened, wavy and naked on the margins.

WOOD—Ring-porous, the 3 or more rows of large and conspicuous pores in the spring wood forming a broad band; medullary rays rather indistinct; heavy, hard, coarse grained, strong, but splits easily; heartwood dark brown to red and durable in contact with the soil; sapwood thin, lighter colored. Weighs 45.3 lbs. per cu. ft. and used for posts, railroad ties, sill timbers, wagon wheel hubs, agricultural implements, automobile truck bodies, slack cooperage, sporting goods articles and fuel.

RANGE AND DISTRIBUTION—Valley of the St. Lawrence River to North Dakota, south to Texas and Florida. Most common in the St. Lawrence valley and the central portion of its range. In Delaware common north, but rare south.

HABITAT—Prefers rich limestone soils and lowlands in proximity of streams, but sometimes ascends rocky hillsides to altitudes of 2000′. Does not form pure stands.

NOTES—The name "slippery" elm applied to this tree owes its origin to the thick fragrant and mucilaginous (slippery), inner bark which is sometimes used as a substitute for chewing gum. It is often used medicinally for the relief of throat irritations and inflammations, as a fever remedy and for poultices. The name "red" applied to this elm undoubtedly refers to the color of the heartwood, while the designation "moose" elm refers to the fact that in the northern portion of its range moose feed on the branchlets.

The slippery elm may be distinguished from the American elm in summer by the rough surfaced larger leaves and comparatively horizontal branchlets, and in winter by the light colored bark and dark fuzzy buds of the twigs. The tree has little merit as an ornamental, and like other species of elm, is not immune to the Dutch elm disease.

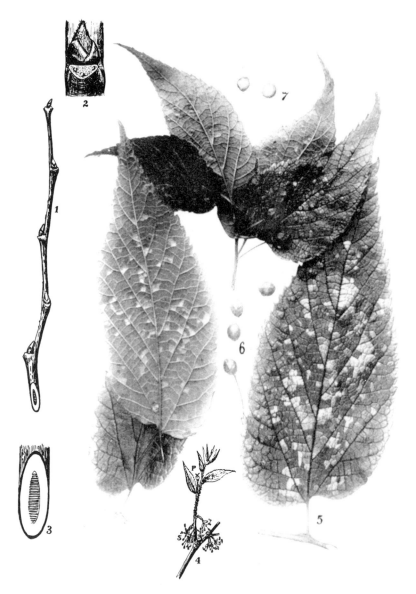

HACKBERRY

1. Winter twig, natural size.
2. Portion of winter twig, showing leaf scar and bud, enlarged.
3. Portion of twig showing chambered pith, enlarged.
4. Branchlet with staminate flowers (S) and fertile flowers (P), x ½.
5. Branchlet and assorted leaves, x 2/3.
6. Fruit, x 2/3.
7. Fruit sectioned, x 2/3.

HACKBERRY

Celtis occidentalis, Linnaeus

GENUS DESCRIPTION—The genus *Celtis* comprises about 50 species distributed through-out the Northern Hemisphere of the world. Of these, 6 species are native to North America and 1 to Delaware.

The hackberry (c) also known as sugarberry, nettle tree, hack tree and hoop ash, is a tree which in this latitude usually attains a height of 30' to 40' with a diameter of 1' to 2', but may rarely attain a height of 120' with a diameter of 4'. Trunk usually inclined and branches 10' to 15' above the ground by large contorted spreading limbs and often drooping branches to form a broad, deep, irregularly rounded crown, often exhibiting several "witches brooms." Of rapid growth and comparatively short life.

LEAVES—Alternate, 2½" to 3½" long, 1½" to 2" wide, ovate or ovate-lanceolate, with long pointed apex and unevenly, obliquely rounded base; margins, except at or near the base, coarsely toothed; at maturity thin, rough-ened by sunken veins and veinlets, green and often with lighter splotches above; dull green with prominent midrib, veins and veinlets beneath.

BARK—On young and old trunks thick, gray, smooth and more or less covered by irregularly spaced and shaped corky or hard projections; on the very slender zigzag twigs at first light green, pubescent and marked by pale conspicuous lenticels, soon becoming dark red-brown and semi-lustrous. Pith of twigs is usually light gray-green and chambered.

BUDS—Alternate, usually less than ⅛" long, flattened and appressed to the twig, broadly triangular with blunt tip and covered by a few chestnut brown scales, the upper ones often slightly pale pubescent.

FLOWERS—In May, of three kinds—staminate, pistillate and perfect—the staminate in clusters on short drooping stems on the lower part of the new growth each with 5 parted, light green calyx and yellow anthers; the perfect flowers (or the rare pistillate ones) in the axils of leaves on the upper part of the new growth each with 5 parted, bowl-like, hoary calyx inclosing short stalked anthers and cleft recurving stigma.

FRUIT—Matures in September and October, and often remains attached by its long slender stem into winter; a berry-like globular drupe about ¼" in diameter, with thin semi-hard, dark purple, shiny skin and dark orange tasty flesh, surrounding a thick shelled nutlet containing a pale brown seed. The flavor of the fruit has been compared to sweetened coffee.

WOOD—Ring-porous, with pores in summer wood in tangential wavy bands and with distinct broad and narrow medullary rays; heavy, soft, coarse, durable, but not strong; heartwood and sapwood not usually distinguishable, cream or white in color. Weighs 45.5 lbs. per cu. ft. and used for fence posts, furniture, woodenware articles, carving and fuel.

RANGE AND DISTRIBUTION—With its varieties (Sargent) believed to be transcontinental, but rare in New England and west of the Rocky Moun-tains. Common throughout the State but usually singly or scattered.

HABITAT—Seems to prefer rich moist soils, but is also found on dry sandy or gravelly uplands where it develops a more buttressed base. Survives well in regions of little and periodic rainfall such as the "Dust Bowl" of the western plains.

NOTES—The hackberry is extremely variable in leaf form and texture and size of fruit, seeming to be effected by latitude, soil and moisture. Its chief identifying characteristics lie in the chambered pith and peculiar corky warts of the trunk bark. The usually present deforming witches' brooms and abnormal swellings of twigs and buds, are the result of gall insect stings.

It enjoys extensive use as a shade and ornamental tree in warmer regions of the United States and in Europe, but is not necessarily an attractive tree for such purposes. It probably enjoys such popularity because of the ease of successfully transplanting it and the rapid growth it makes.

The fruit is eaten by birds and animals, and when ripe the pulp constitute7 a sweet agreeable morsel for human consumption.

RED MULBERRY

1. Thrifty winter twig, natural size.
2. Fruit, natural size.
3. Leaf, x ½ and leaf forms in miniature.
4. Spike of pistillate flowers, natural size.
5. Single pistillate flower, enlarged.
6. Single staminate flower, enlarged.
7. Branchlet with staminate flower spikes, x ½.

RED MULBERRY
Morus rubra, Linnaeus

GENUS DESCRIPTION—the genus *Morus*, one of 3 genera in the family *Moraceae*, comprises about 9 species of trees and shrubs distributed over the New World as far south as western South America, and in Asia and the Indian Archipelago of the Old World. Of the 2 species indigenous to North America only one is native to Delaware. The white mulberry, *M. alba*, L., early introduced into this Country from Asia, has become as widely distributed in the State as the native species.

The red mulberry is a tree usually 40' to 50' tall, with a diameter of 1' to 2', but may occasionally attain a height of 70' and a diameter of 4'. Trunk of forest trees tall and with few branches, but in the open is generally short and vested with stout contorted branches forming a broad round topped head. Sometimes attains an age of 150 years.

LEAVES—Alternate, 3" to 7" long, 2½" to 6" broad, heart-shaped or sometimes shaped like a mitten, or divided by deep rounding nearly opposite sinuses into 3 lobes; the margins coarsely or finely serrate with callous teeth; at maturity dark bluish green and smooth or rough and corrugated by the deeply sunken veins above; pale green, pubescent and roughened by the prominent orange colored midrib, primary veins and connecting veinlets beneath. The stout petioles when cut or broken exude a milky sap.

BARK—On old and young trunks thin, gray-brown, broken by shallow fissures into more or less continuous irregular scaly plates; on the stout, slightly zigzag, twigs at first dark green and pubescent becoming by winter, buff colored and marked by stipule scars and enlarged leaf bases exhibiting a depressed leaf scar.

BUDS—Alternate, all axillary, ¼" to ½" long, ovoid, sharp pointed, divergent and inclined, covered by several greenish brown shiny scales.

FLOWERS—In May with the unfolding of the leaves; staminate (male) and pistillate (female) usually on separate branchlets, but sometimes male flowers occur with the female ones on the spike; the male catkins 2" to 2½" long on a drooping hairy stalk; the female ones in 1" long, oblong spikes on a hairy drooping stem.

FRUIT—Ripen from June to August, blackberry like, 1" to 1½" long, ¼" to nearly ½" in diameter, suspended on a ¾" long drooping stem. When fully ripened they are dark purple in color, soft, juicy, very sweet and edible.

WOOD—Ring-porous, with pores in spring wood in a wide zone and those in the summer wood minute, in groups of 3–6; medullary rays prominent; rather hard and strong, odorless and tasteless; heartwood yellowish brown becoming red-brown on exposure; sapwood thin white; weighs 36.7 lbs. per cu. ft. and used for posts, tight cooperage, furniture and boat building.

RANGE AND DISTRIBUTION—Massachusetts to Minnesota and South Dakota, south to Texas and Florida. Most abundant and of its largest size in the central portion of its range. Moderately common but nowhere abundant in the State.

HABITAT—Prefers rich moist soils and hilly lowlands. It tolerates shade.

NOTES—The red mulberry is hardly to be recommended for forestry or street tree use, but where its dropping fruit would not be objectionable such as on a large lawn, or as a field or fence row tree, it makes an attractive ornamental tree. The ripened fruit attracts many birds, the neighborhood children and the adults too.

Because the pores in the wood usually contain tyloses (pore sealing membranes or crystals) the wood makes an excellent tight cooperage wood suited to the manufacture of barrels for liquids which will not bear the discoloring effect or taste and odor of other cooperage woods.

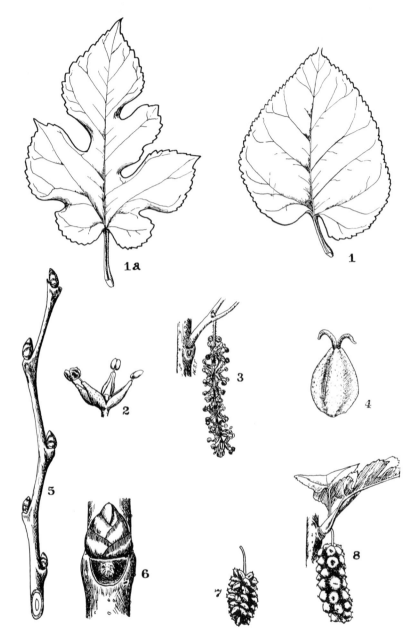

WHITE MULBERRY

1. Usual leaf, x ½.
1a. A leaf form not uncommon. x ½.
2. Single staminate flower, enlarged.
3. Spike of staminate flowers, natural size.
4. Single pistillate flower, enlarged.
5. Winter twig, natural size.
6. Portion of twig, enlarged to show bud and leaf scar.
7. Pistillate flower spike, natural size
8. Fruit, natural size.

WHITE MULBERRY
Morus alba, Linnaeus

AUTHOR'S NOTE: The white mulberry, a native of Asia, was introduced into eastern America during Colonial days in a fruitless attempt to establish the silk industry on this Continent and has since become naturalized in many places.

The white mulberry, sometimes called shiny leaved mulberry and the silkworm mulberry, is usually a small tree 15′ to 25′ tall with a trunk less than 1′ in diameter, but may sometimes attain a height of 50′ and a trunk diameter of 2′ or more. Trunk usually short with a broad round-topped deep head composed of stout ascending branches and numerous slender branchlets.

LEAVES—Alternate, simple, broadly oval or heart-shaped, 2″ to 4″ long, 2″ to 3″ wide, but extremely variable in size and in the number and shape of lobes; margins coarsely or rarely finely round toothed; at maturity thin, glossy yellow-green, slightly corrugated by the sunken midrib, veins and veinlets above; smooth, light green and marked by prominent light yellow midrib veins and veinlets beneath; petiole light yellow, 1″ to 1½″ long and grooved above.

BARK—On old and young trunks thin, yellow-brown, broken by shallow fissures into rough, firm, flat topped, often interlacing ridges; on the slender zigzag twigs, reddish or pale grayish yellow and marked by yellow lenticels and enlarged leaf bases exposing a semi-circular leaf scar. The tender bark contains a milky, sticky sap.

BUDS—Alternate, all axillary, divergent, broadly ovoid, slightly flattened and covered with broad semi-glossy, red-brown scales having darker margins.

FLOWERS—In May or June, male and female separate or occasionally with individual male flowers mixed with the female ones on the same tree, the male catkins 1″ to 2″ long, on a drooping, slightly pubescent stem; the female flowers in short catkins, rarely 1″ long.

FRUIT—July and August; a blackberry-like cyndrical cluster of drupes, ½″ to occasionally 1″ long, when ripe, greenish white, violet or rarely light purple, very sweet and edible. Like its American relative the fruit is borne in abundance and is a tasty morsel for birds, poultry, beasts, and humans.

WOOD—Ring-porous, the pores in the spring wood large and forming a narrow band, those in the summer wood small and grouped to form wavy tangential bands; medullary rays distinct; heavy, hard and durable; heartwood yellow-brown with distinct satiny sheen; sapwood cream or white, but yellows on exposure. Not commercially important in this Country.

RANGE AND DISTRIBUTION—A native of northern China and Japan. Rather commonly established in waste places, along fence rows and roads in Delaware.

HABITAT—Prefers rich upland soils and appears intolerant of shade.

NOTES—There are many ornamental and horticultural varieties of the white mulberry. Of the former, the most popular in the East is Teas' weeping, which originated from a chance seedling of the Russian mulberry, *M. alba tatarica,* L. The Russian mulberry is strongly recommended for planting for wind breaks and hedges in the "Dust Bowl" of the Plains because of its ability to withstand extremes of temperature and drought. Of the varieties cultivated on the Pacific coast for the fruit, the varieties of black mulberry *M. nigra,* appear to be the most popular.

The silkworm mulberry is *M. multicaulis,* Perr. by some botanists classified as a variety of *M. alba,* and is one of the 10 trees in the world considered most valuable to civilization.

The paper mulberry, a native of eastern Asia, has escaped cultivation and become naturalized in many parts of eastern United States and to some extent in this State. It is a large shrub or small tree with large mulberry-like, dull gray-green tomentose leaves and corrugated semi-lustrous purplish gray bark. It is best known botanically as *Broussonetia papyrifera,* Vent.

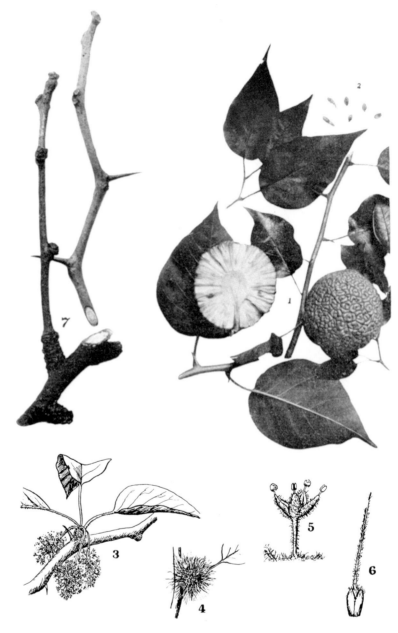

OSAGE ORANGE

1. Leafy branchlets and fruits, x ¼.
2. Seeds, x ¼.
3. Staminate flowering branchlet, x ½.
4. Pistillate flowering branchlet, x ½.
5. Staminate flower, enlarged.
6. Pistillate flower, enlarged.
7. Young (right) and old branchlet. natural size.

OSAGE ORANGE
Maclura pomifera, Schneider

[Toxylon pomiferum, Raf.]

GENUS DESCRIPTION—The Osage orange is the sole representative of the genus *Maclura* or *Toxylon*. It is native only in Oklahoma and Texas, but having been much planted elsewhere as a hedge plant and escaped from cultivation, is now naturalized in many localities.

The Osage orange, also known as bow-wood, mock orange, dye-wood orange, Osage apple and hedge orange, is usually a medium sized tree 15' to 25' tall with a trunk diameter of less than 1' but may sometimes attain a height of 60' and a trunk diameter of 3'. Trunk generally stout and divided 8' to 10' above ground into stout arching branches and tough branchlets drooping or ascending by several arcs or graceful bends to form a deep rounded crown.

LEAVES—Alternate, 3" to 5" long, 2" to 3" wide, ovate with acute apex; margins entire or wavy; shiny and light green above, pale beneath; petiole slender; stipules minute and early deciduous.

BARK—On old trunks ¾" to 1" thick, dark yellow-brown, divided by deep fissures into rough interlacing ridges; on the zigzag twigs greenish yellow. The season's branchlets on young trees, except near the tip, are armed with stout sharp axillary spines ¼" to 1" long, but the lateral or second year branchlets, developing from buds on the twig at the base of spines, are usually unarmed. The bark of twigs when cut exudes a milky acrid sap.

BUDS—Alternate, all axillary those on the first year twigs on the tip above the leaf scar, but those on the spiny portion at the base of and beside the spine, both depressed globose, covered by a few red-brown scales and partially covered by the twig bark; those in the staminate flower—leaf buttons on the lateral twigs, minute or invisible.

FLOWERS—In June when the leaves are about half grown, staminate (male) and pistillate (female) on separate trees; the staminate ones, from old wood buds, in globular racemes about ¾" in diameter on slender pubescent drooping stems 1" to 1½" long; the pistillate in dense globular heads ¾" to 1" in diameter on short stalks, axillary on the new growth.

FRUIT—Ripens in October; a yellow-green orange-like fruit 4" to 6" in diameter composed of the union of many fleshy drupes containing oblong, compressed, light chestnut brown thin shelled nutlets (seed). The fruit is saturated with milky juice which is acrid and turns black and sticky on exposure.

WOOD—Ring-porous, with inconspicuous medullary rays; heavy, very hard, tough, flexible and exceptionally durable, but splits rather easily; heartwood golden yellow and darkens on exposure; sapwood thin, light brown; weighs about 48 lbs. per cu. ft. and used for fence posts, wheel-stock, insulator pins, furniture, turnery, or anywhere that a hard durable wood of its character is required.

RANGE AND DISTRIBUTION—Truly native only from southern Arkansas and Oklahoma to Dallas, Texas but before the introduction of wire fencing was extensively planted as a hedge plant throughout the Country. It has become naturalized in some localities in Delaware.

HABITAT—In its natural range, prefers rich bottomlands but will grow on most any soil.

NOTES—The names "Osage" and "bow wood" as applied to this tree originated from the uses made of it by the Osage Indians, while the other names refer either to the orange like fruit, a particular quality of the wood or the use of the tree as a hedge plant. It is regrettable that in losing favor for the last named purpose farmers have destroyed it when, by a bit of judicious pruning, individual plants could be trained to tree form and serve as living fence posts or produce post wood. In durable qualities, when in contact with soil, few if any native woods are superior but when seasoned, it is so hard that wire staples are driven into it with difficulty and edge tools used in cutting or working it are quickly dulled or easily broken.

The bark, especially that of the scaly orange roots, contains moric and morintannic acid, sometimes used in tanning leather or as a dye.

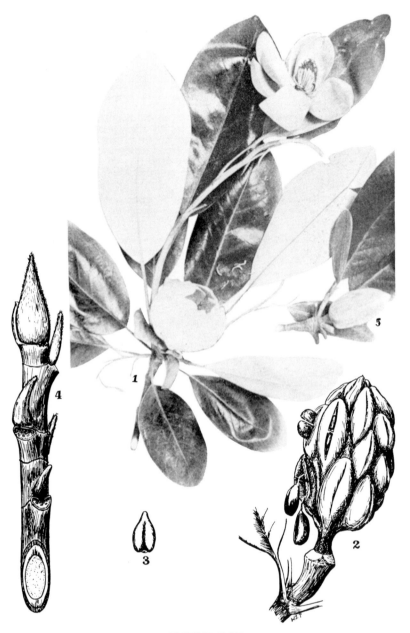

SWEET BAY

1. Branchlet with flowers and leaves, x ½.
2. Fruit with suspended seeds, natural size.
3. Seed with pulp removed. x 2.
4. Winter twig. x 2.

SWEET BAY

Magnolia virginiana, Linnaeus

[*Magnolia glauca*, Linnaeus]

GENUS DESCRIPTION—The genus *Magnolia* is named in honor of Pierre Magnol, a seventeenth century French botanist. It comprises about 35 species scattered over southern and eastern Asia, Central and North America. Of these, 7 are native to the United States and one to Delaware.

The sweet bay, also known as swamp magnolia, glaucous magnolia, laurel magnolia and beaver tree, is a large shrub or small deciduous or semi-evergreen tree 20' to 30' tall with a trunk 6" to 9" in diameter, but further south in its range may occasionally attain a height of 75' and a trunk diameter of 3'. Trunks often in clusters, inclined, slender and having a few slender branches and branchlets forming an irregular open crown. Often only a many stemmed shrub.

LEAVES—Alternate, oblong or elliptical, 3" to 6" long, 1½" to 3" wide; margins entire; medium thick; at maturity deep green and shiny above, glaucous white bloom coated and sometimes velvety pubescent especially on the midrib beneath; in exposed locations in the North deciduous by December or earlier, but in deep swamps, sheltered situations and further south they may persist until spring.

BARK—On old and young trunks smooth, gray or ashy gray; on the stout or slender twigs, at first light green and downy, soon smooth and coated with glaucous bloom, becoming purplish and eventually gray. Twigs conspicuously marked by encircling stipule scars and crescent-shaped, sunken leaf scars. Pith large, white.

BUDS—Alternate, ¼" to ¾" long, the lateral ones curved, conical; the terminal larger, ovoid with long acute tip, covered by successive white silky coated, light green scale-stipules.

FLOWERS—In late spring and during summer to August, solitary on the new growth, very fragrant, globular, about 2½" across, each complete and composed of 3 pale sepals, 6 to 9 cream white incurving petals, numerous purple based linear stamens and pistils clustered in a central group.

FRUIT—September–October, a knobby light green bloom coated cone-like aggregation of capsules which upon splitting open on the back and drying, force out the glossy bright red coated seeds which are suspended for a time by a web-like thread; the nutlet enclosed within the soft milky flesh of the seed is about ¼" long, pear-shaped, with a central crease and thin shell. Birds and rodents feed on the seed.

WOOD—Diffuse-porous, with distinct medullary rays; soft, brittle and coarse grained; heartwood (if any) light reddish brown; sapwood very thick, cream white; weighs about 31 lbs. per cu. ft. Used for cheap lumber, basket veneer, wood turnery and sometimes for paper pulp.

RANGE AND DISTRIBUTION—Imperfectly determined but probable from Massachusetts along the coast to Georgia and westward through the Gulf states to Arkansas. Common within its habitat throughout the State.

HABITAT—Prefers swamps and moist soils, but may sometimes occur on upland sandy soils.

NOTES—Where the sweet bay grows, there are few who do not know it by the sweet (oftimes sickening sweet) fragrance of its blossoms, the spicy taste of the tender bark of twigs and the deep rich green shiny leaves with glaucous white under surface. Commercially the species is not greatly important, but it is an attractive ornamental, suited primarily to lawn planting. Numerous ornamental varieties and hybrids have been developed. Propagation is by seed sown in the fall which, however, may not germinate until the second year.

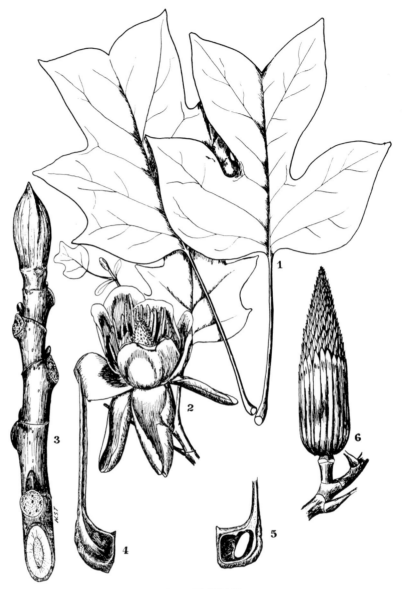

TULIP TREE

1. Leaf types, x ½.
2. Flowering branchlet, x ½.
3. Winter twig, x 2.
4. A seed carpel or samara. natural size.
5. Section of samara showing seed. natural size.
6. Seed cone, x ½.

YELLOW POPLAR
Liriodendron tulipifera, Linnaeus

GENUS DESCRIPTION —Paleobotanists have found that, prior to the Ice Age, there were several *Liriodendrons* but only 2 species, one in America and one in China, have survived the evolution of the ages. The latter is *L. chinensis,* Sarg.

The yellow poplar (c) or tulip tree, also known as white wood (c) tulip poplar, hickory poplar and sap poplar, is a most stately tree, usually 50' to 70' tall with a trunk 2' to 3' in diameter, but may rarely approach 200' in height with a trunk diameter of 9' to 10'. The largest diameter recorded for this species is 16', for a tree in Francis Cove in Western North Carolina. In favorable forest environment the trunk is tall, very straight, with slight taper and without limbs for the greater portion of its height, terminating in a small pyramidal or rounded crown. Young trees in the open are pyramidal in form but in old trees the crown is broad, thin and rounded. Reaches commercial maturity in 50 years or less, but may occasionally attain an age of 250 years.

LEAVES—Alternate, orbicular in outline, 5" to 6" long and broad, truncate at the apex with deep opposite sinuses forming 3 broad lobes, or the basal ones further divided by one or more broad sinuses; thin smooth and green above; paler beneath; petioles long, smooth and slender. Turn bright yellow in fall and deciduous over a brief period.

BARK—On old trunks thick, gray and broken by wide light colored fissures into round tipped intercepting ridges (see Fig. 4.); on young trunks smooth and purplish gray or characteristically roughened and white spotted gray; on the stout twigs green or purplish green, covered with glaucous bloom and marked by orbicular leaf scars, narrow, twig encircling stipule scars and scattered pale lenticels.

BUDS—Alternate, the terminal ½" to ¾" long, oblong, constricted at the base, somewhat flattened, the lateral ones smaller often evidently stalked, each covered with two, striate purplish bloom covered stipular scales which, at their meeting margins, often form a ridge over the apex and sides of the bud. Each stipular scale encloses succeeding right and left opening leaves, and scales which, after releasing the leaves, enlarge to about 2" in length and 1" in width before deciduous.

FLOWERS—In June on the new growth after the leaves, 1½" to 2" deep and broad, tulip-shaped, perfect, with 3 downward curving greenish petal-like sepals, 3 greenish cream colored petals exhibiting a circular basal orange area, numerous linear stamens and a central pistil cone.

FRUIT—September, 1½" to 3" long, a faded yellow "cone" formed of imbricated woody samaras in the enlarged base of which are enclosed the one or two seeds, if any. Less than 15% of the samara contain viable seed, and when planted rarely result in more than 5% germination.

WOOD—Diffuse-porous, with inconspicuous rays; usually soft, light, not durable, straight grained and easily worked but in some parts of Delaware, especially from trees on high ground, is hard tough and with twisted grain, contributing the name "hickory poplar"; heartwood greenish; sapwood wide, white; weighs 26.6 lbs. per cu. ft. and used in construction, interior finish, furniture, paper pulp, basket veneer, boat building, tobacco hogsheads, cigar boxes, kitchen ware and for numerous other purposes.

RANGE AND DISTRIBUTION—Massachusetts to Missouri, south to Louisiana and Florida. Reaches its maximum size and distribution in the Ohio basin and the coves of the Smoky Mountains. Common throughout Delaware.

HABITAT—Prefers deep rich moist, but well drained soils. Likes sunlight, is intolerant of shade, and does not thrive in lime bearing soils.

NOTES—The stately, clean, yellow poplar (from the color of the heartwood), or tulip tree (from the tulip like blossom), can hardly be mistaken for any other native species. Because the wooden package industries in this and neighboring states use large quantities of the wood, the supply of marketable timber of this species in the State is rapidly approaching exhaustion. In view of the anticipated shortage and the fact that it grows rapidly on suitable sites, it is strongly recommended for reforestation purposes. In comparative commercial value it ranks with pine and gum. Ornamentally, it is suited to lawn and park planting but, because of its sensitivity to transplanting and acute soil preferences, it is reservedly recommended for city street or highway use.

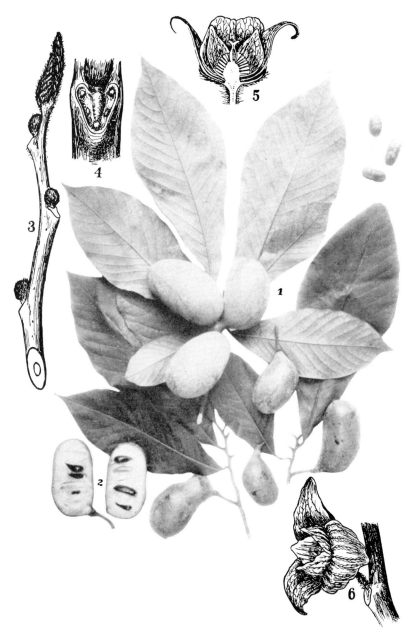

PAWPAW

1. Branchlet with mature leaves, fruit and seed, x ¼.
2. Fruit sectioned, x ¼.
3. Winter twig, natural size.
4. Portion of winter twig enlarged to show leaf scar.
5. Section of flower, natural size.
6. Flower, natural size.

PAWPAW
Asimina triloba, Dunal

GENUS DESCRIPTION—The genus name *Asimina* is Latinized from the Indian name *asmin* for the tree. It is represented by 8 species indigenous to eastern North America, only one of which attains tree size. Description of this one follows.

The pawpaw (or papaw as sometimes spelled), sometimes called custard apple, false banana, and wild banana, —— banana with the name of the state as the first word of the binomial, is generally a large shrub or small tree. When a tree it may sometimes become 40' tall with a trunk diameter of less than 12".

LEAVES—Alternate, but usually crowded toward the ends of the twigs, obovate-lanceolate, 6" to 12" long and half as broad, broadest above the middle; margins entire; at maturity thin and green above; pale green and with prominent midrib and veins beneath; turn dull yellow in autumn.

BARK—On old and young trunks, thin, brown, usually smooth or slightly irregularly broken into plates (Fig. 24); on the slightly zigzag slender twigs, at first greenish brown and pubescent, later smooth, light brown and marked by enlarged nodes exhibiting a characteristic triangular leaf scar with a large raised bundle scar at each point, with a smaller one intervening.

BUDS—Alternate, the terminal and lateral leaf buds larger than the flower buds; the terminal one ½" to ¾" long, often curved, without covering, being composed of enfolded miniature leaves which are covered with dense dark red-brown silky pubescence; the flower buds axillary, spherical, about ⅛" in diameter, velvety dark brown.

FLOWERS—Develop from the flower buds in April–May, with the leaves; solitary on a short hairy stalk, perfect, at first green becoming at maturity 1¼" to 1¾" across with 3 purplish red outer petals and 3 lighter colored erect and shorter inner petals, inclosing stamens and pistils. They have a disagreeable odor.

FRUIT—September, resembles a miniature sausage balloon, 3" to 5" long, 1" to 2" in diameter with tough skin, light green and bloom covered early but when ripe, is dark brown. The creamy white or orange-yellow pulp is sometimes sweet and edible, other times unpalatable. The shiny, hard coated, brown seeds imbedded in the pulp are about 1" long and ½" wide. Occasionally offered in fruit markets.

WOOD—Ring-porous tending toward diffuse-porous; medullary rays distinct; soft, weak, coarse grained and spongy; heartwood light greenish yellow; sapwood yellow. Uses, if any, unknown.

RANGE AND DISTRIBUTION—New Jersey and western New York to Nebraska, southward to Texas and Florida. Most common and often forming pure thickets in the Mississippi valley. Present in all counties of the State but nowhere common.

HABITAT—Prefers protected moist locations such as borders of streams and swamps. Is tolerant of shade and seems to prefer it. Aside from the odd shaped and colored blossoms, and the tropical-like appearance of the foliage, the pawpaw has little to recommend it as an ornamental. Horticulturally it has its merits for those who like the fruit.

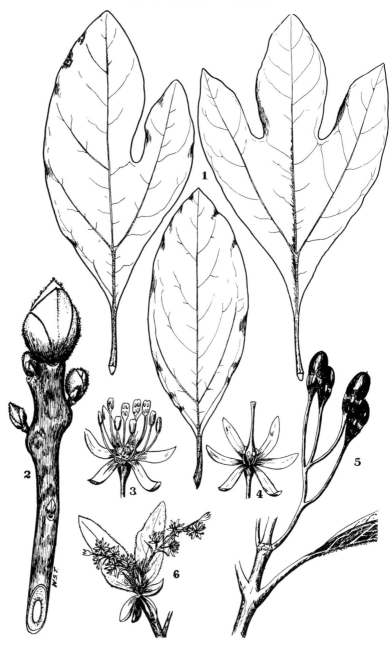

SASSAFRAS

1. Leaves, x ½.
2. Winter twig, natural size.
3. Single staminate flower, enlarged.
4. Single pistillate flower, enlarged.
5. Fruit cluster, natural size.
6. Flowering branchlet, x ½.

SASSAFRAS
Sassafras albidum (Nutt.) Nees

GENUS DESCRIPTION—The genus *Sassafras* is represented by 3 species in the Northern Hemisphere of the world, only one of which, described herein, is native to the United States. Another representative of the family **Lauraceae**, (the red bay, *Persea borbonia*, Spreng) was recorded by Thomas Nuttall in 1809 as occurring in the Great Cedar Swamp area of Sussex County. Despite subsequent search by many botanists it was not rediscovered until 1941 by W. S. Taber, who supplied herbarium material to the Society of Natural History of Delaware. The genus *Lindera* formerly *Benzoin* is also a member of this family and is represented in Delaware by the spice bush, *L. benzoin* (L), which also possesses spicy aromatic bark and fruit, extracts of which are used as ingredients of some medicines.

The sassafras sometimes called sassafrac or saxifrax is most often observed as a small tree, but may occasionally attain a height of 80' and a trunk diameter of 6' with a few large but short contorted branches and stout branchlets forming an irregular picturesque crown.

LEAVES—Alternate, simple, obovate in general outline, 4" to 6" long; margins entire and without lobes or with one, two, or rarely 5 lobes; densely pubescent at first but at maturity green and smooth above; paler and sparingly pubescent on the prominent midrib and veins beneath.

BARK—On old trunks thick, red-brown and divided by deep fissures into converging and separating rugged flat topped ridges (see Fig. 3); on young trunks red-brown, thin and similarly roughened; on the slender twigs light yellow-green and pubescent at first soon becoming darker green or red-brown and smooth. The inner bark of twigs is mucilaginous and possesses a strong spicy flavor not greatly unlike that of orange peel.

BUDS—Alternate, ovoid, covered with few sparingly pubescent light green scales, each often having a prominent central ridge; the terminal bud ¼" to ¾" long—much larger than the lateral buds and having usually 3 closer fitting scales.

FLOWERS—In April with the unfolding of the leaves, the male and female usually on different trees, rarely perfect, both in 2½" long drooping few flowered racemes, on slender pubescent pedicels, both flowers about ¼" across with 6, yellow, lanceolate, calyx lobes.

FRUIT—September and October; a shiny dark blue berry (drupe) about ⅜" long borne on the thickened calyx end of the long stem, which is often orange or bright red in color. The fleshy pulp covering the light brown seed is aromatic and spicy. Birds and animals feed on the berries.

WOOD—Ring-porous; medullary rays very fine; comparatively soft, brittle, quite aromatic and often with a taste, very durable in contact with the soil; heartwood dull orange-brown; sapwood thin, lighter; weighs about 31 lbs. per cu. ft. and used mostly for fence posts and rails, but sometimes for furniture, interior finish and occasionally as cabinet wood. Not commercially important as lumber but often sold as chestnut which it closely resembles.

RANGE AND DISTRIBUTION—Southern Maine to Michigan and Kansas, south to central Texas and central Florida, in the South often ascending to elevations of 4000'. Very common throughout Delaware in woods, along fence rows and abandoned fields.

HABITAT—Seems to prefer sandy soils but is not demanding in its requirements.

NOTES—The sassafras tree is principally noted for the tender bark of the roots which when gathered in late winter and steeped in water makes a pleasant tasting beverage known as "sassafras tea." Oil distilled from the tender bark and roots is used to flavor medicines, soft drinks, confections and as an ingredient of perfumes, especially that used in some soaps. Shavings of the wood of the roots are sometimes used as a perfume in linen closets, bureau drawers, pillows, etc. The leaves are occasionally used to flavor soups and food.

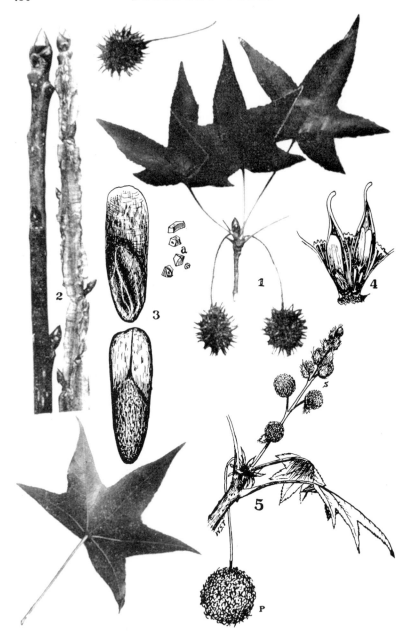

RED GUM

1. Leafy branchlet with fruit, x ½.
2. Winter twig, natural size.
3. Either side of winged seed and abortive seed (a), enlarged.
4. Section of unopened cone with seed, x 2.
5. Flowering branchlet; (S) staminate flowers, (P) pistillate flowers, natural size.

RED GUM
Liquidambar styraciflua, Linnaeus

GENUS DESCRIPTION—The genus name *Liquidambar* is derived from the coupling of the Latin word *liquidus,* fluid, and the Arabic word *amber* alluding to the fragrance of the sap of the tree. It is represented by fossil species and 3 living species in the world, 2 of which are Asiatic and one American.

The red gum (c) or sweet gum, also known as sap gum (c) white gum, star-leaved gum, hazelwood (c), satinwood (c), liquidambar and alligator tree, is a tree usually 50' to 75' tall with a trunk 1' to 2' in diameter, but may occasionally attain a height of 150' and a trunk diameter of 5'. The trunk in forest stands is tall with a central stem and few side branches forming a small oval head. The crown of young trees in the open is deep and pyramidal in form. Attains commercial maturity in 50 years or less, but trees 300 years old are occasionally found.

LEAVES—Alternate, 6" to 7" long and broad, like a six-pointed star with the bottom point missing hence "star leaved gum"; margins finely round toothed; bright green and shiny above; tufts of pale hairs in the axils of veins beneath; when crushed emit a fragrant resinous odor; turn brilliant or mottled shades of red, yellow or purple in autumn; petiole long and slender.

BARK—On old trunks thick, gray, corky and broken by deep fissures into round topped scaly ridges (see Fig. 37); on young trunks correspondingly roughened and light gray; on the stout twigs glossy, yellow-brown and marked by numerous pale conspicuous lenticels and raised leaf scars, often becoming during the second year equipped with parallel wing-like corky projections which, during succeeding years, may become as much as 1" high or broken into warty ridges, hence, "alligator tree."

BUDS—Alternate, the terminal one about ½" long, ovoid, broad pointed and covered by several yellowish or light red-brown shiny scales.

FLOWERS—In April when the leaves are about half developed, male and female on the same tree, the male ones in globular green heads on a hairy stalked raceme 2" to 3" long, terminal on the new growth; the seed producing ones globular, ½" to ¾" in diameter on a long hairy drooping stem from the axils of upper leaves.

FRUIT—Matures in October and often persists until early the following year; a shiny red-brown, beak covered, globular ball, 1" to 1½" in diameter, each composed of united woody capsules which upon ripening open at the surface to permit the escape of the 5/16" long winged seed which are mottled black or dark brown. Capsules contain many sawdust-like abortive seeds.

WOOD—Diffuse-porous, with distinct medullary rays; heavy, hard, with interlocking close grain and satiny luster; heartwood of old trees, in the southern part of its range, rich red-brown with darker streaks, but in this latitude reddish or greenish; sapwood very wide, white; weighs about 36 lbs. per cu. ft. and used in many kinds of wooden packages, furniture, flooring, interior finish, as an imitation for many costly woods, wood pulp, ice cream spoons, medical and hospital sticks and numerous other purposes. Ranks third in production among American hardwoods and in Delaware ranks with pine in commercial value.

RANGE AND DISTRIBUTION—Southern Connecticut to eastern Missouri, south to eastern Texas, Central America and Guatemala. Most common and of its largest size in the Mississippi basin and the lowlands of the south Atlantic and Gulf states. Common throughout Delaware.

HABITAT—Prefers deep rich soils adjacent to streams and in swamps covered by water for a part of the year, but will survive on drier sites. Is very intolerant of shade and, therefore, is usually found in pure even-aged stands occupying abandoned fields or following clear cutting.

NOTES—The word "red" in one of the common names of this tree may allude either to the red colored heartwood or the brilliant fall coloration of the foliage, either of which is distinctive. The word "sweet" probably refers to the fragrant odor of the sap which in warmer latitude may exude at an injury in the bark and coagulate in gobs of resin or "gum" storax. The liquid storax of commerce is derived from *L. orientalis* Mill., a native of Asia Minor. Although the tree in natural habitat usually develops spreading spur roots and is difficult to successfully transplant from the woods, nursery grown trees when handled with a ball of earth around the roots are quite readily moved. It makes a very attractive street, roadside and lawn tree. It is an excellent reforestation tree but because it is not easily transplanted as a seedling, nature will have to be depended upon to regenerate new forests of this valuable tree. The seed does not germinate until the second year.

In this latitude the tree is commonly the host for the American mistletoe, *Phoradendron flavescens.*

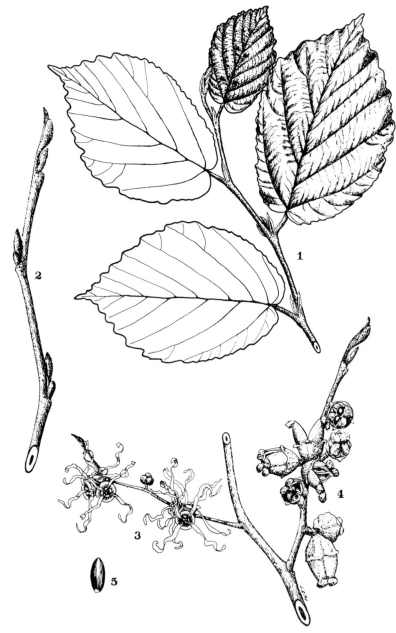

WITCH HAZEL

1. Branchlet with leaves, natural size.
2. Winter twig, natural size.
3 & 4. Autumn branchlet with flowers (3), and fruit (4), natural size.
5. Seed, natural size.

WITCH HAZEL
Hamamelis virginiana, Linnaeus

GENUS DESCRIPTION—*Hamamelis* is represented by 4 species, 2 in China and Japan and 2 in eastern North America. *H. macrocarpa* is native only in the South and is arborescent. The other, which may occasionally attain tree size, is described below.

The witch hazel or spotted alder is generally a shrub in this region but may occasionally attain tree form and a height of 25′ and a diameter of 14″.

LEAVES—Alternate, oval, acute or rounded at the apex, uneven at the base with one side rounded, 4″ to 6″ long, 2″ to 2½″ broad; margins wavy and unevenly toothed above the middle; when they unfold, covered with pubescence rough to the touch especially beneath; at maturity thick, tough and dull green above; lighter green and lustrous, but with pubescence on the prominent midrib, veins and veinlets beneath; turn bright yellow in autumn.

BARK—On old trunks fairly thick, smooth, and scaly, yellowish brown with lighter blotches (Fig. 38); on young trunks smooth, yellowish; on the slender zigzag twigs, at first coated with rough pubescence, becoming by the first winter nearly smooth, yellowish brown and marked by white lenticel dots, hence "spotted alder."

BUDS—Alternate, naked, the terminal one larger sickle-shaped, covered with buff or gray pubescence and corrugated by the primary veins of the immature scale-leaves.

FLOWERS—Develop in October and November from three-clustered axillary buds on a short stalk formed during the summer, each perfect, with long strap-like yellow petals enclosed with stamens and pistils in a three-lobed involucre.

FRUIT—October and November with the flowers, in 2s or 3s on a common stalk, each ½″ long, consisting of a dull-yellowish brown cylindrical rough coated woody capsule which, upon splitting open with an audible report, expels or actually shoots the shiny hard coated brown seeds for some distance. The actual expulsion is brought about by the pressure of the hard lining of the seed cavity on the seed which becomes a propulsive force when the lining splits open.

WOOD—Diffuse-porous, with barely visible medullary rays; heavy, hard, very close grained; heartwood, if any, reddish; sapwood wide white; weighs about 42 lbs. per cu. ft. but is of no commercial value.

RANGE AND DISTRIBUTION—New Brunswick and Quebec to Iowa, south to Louisiana and northern Georgia. Attains its greatest size in the Smoky Mountain region. Common as a large shrub in Delaware.

HABITAT—Prefers rich moist soils and shady places along streams and cool ravines but may sometimes be found on drier uplands where the water table is not deep.

NOTES—At one time the bark and leaves of this species were distilled to produce an extract used in medicines primarily for external application, and may occasionally still be used for such purposes. The chief interest in the witch hazel lies in the fact that it is one of the few trees in the world which blossom in the fall of the year often after the leaves have fallen and at the time the fruits from the previous year's blossoms are maturing.

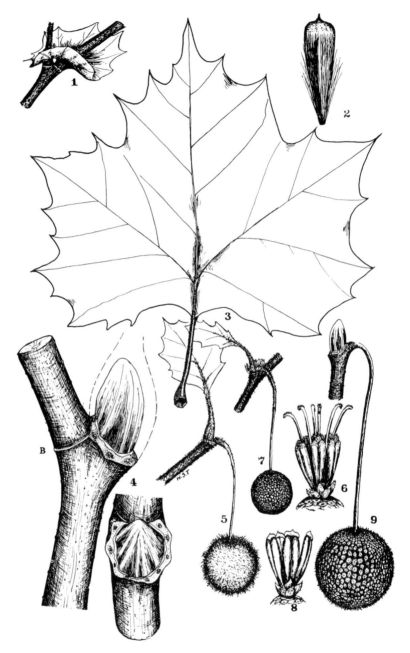

SYCAMORE

1. Section of twig showing stipule, natural size.
2. Seed, enlarged.
3. Leaf, x ½.
4. Sections of winter twig, showing bud leaf scar and stipule scar (B), enlarged.
5. Staminate flower head, natural size.
6. Staminate flower, enlarged.
7. Pistillate flower head, natural size.
8. Pistillate flower, enlarged.
9. Section of twig with fruit, natural size.

SYCAMORE
Platanus occidentalis, Linnaeus

GENUS DESCRIPTION—The genus *Platanus* is the single representative of the family and comprises 6 or 7 species in North America, Central America and Asia. Only one of these is native to Delaware. The London plane believed to be a hybrid between *P. orientalis* and *P. occidentalis* is much planted as a shade and ornamental tree in the temperate parts of the United States. It is generally called oriental plane and given the name *P. orientalis.* The true *P. orientalis* is, however, rarely cultivated in the United States.

The sycamore (c), also commonly called buttonwood, American plane (tree) and buttonball, is a large tree usually 70' to 125' tall with a trunk 3' to 4' in diameter, but may occasionally attain a height of 170' and a trunk diameter of 11'. Trunk usually divided or branching by long contorted limbs and branchlets to form a wide spreading open irregular crown. Attains commercial maturity in 50 years or less, but trees 300 years old have been found.

LEAVES—Alternate, 4" to 7" long and broad, broadly ovate with 3 to 5 lobes and numerous broad teeth; thin firm and bright green above; pale green and wooly below at first, but at maturity usually retaining pubescence only on the midrib and veins; petiole round, stout, with abruptly enlarged hollow base covering the developing bud; the conspicuous twig encircling stipules about 1½" across with toothed margins.

BARK—On very old trunks, thick, irregularly broken by shallow fissures into flat loose plated light gray-brown ridges; on young trunks and branches exfoliates in thin light brown patches exposing a white under bark which later becomes deep green giving the tree a distinctive splotched white and green appearance; on the medium stout, zigzag, ridged twigs, at first green and pubescent, later smooth, light brown, enlarged at the nodes and marked by leaf scars encircling the bud, twig encircling stipule scars and numerous small pale lenticels.

BUDS—Alternate, in late fall often covered by the remnant of the petiole, divergent from the twig, ⅛" to ⅜" long, dome-shaped, covered by 3 scales, the outer one reddish and glossy, the middle one green and sticky with resinous gum and the inner one silky pubescent. Botanically the tip bud is not a terminal one but it appears to be such.

FLOWERS—In May with the leaves, the male and female on different stalks on the same tree; both minute, in dense spherical heads on a long stalk, the male heads about ¾" in diameter, dark red, axillary; the female ones terminal, green or reddish green and about 1" in diameter.

FRUIT—October, but often persist as late as the following spring in light brown spherical head attached by a stem 3" to 6" long, each 1" to 1¼" in diameter and composed of many achenes about 2/3" long.

WOOD—Diffuse-porous, with broad conspicuous medullary rays; heavy, hard and splits with difficulty but is neither strong nor durable; heartwood reddish; sapwood thin white; weighs 30.4 lbs. per cu. ft. and used in furniture, interior finish, woodenware articles, butchers blocks, tobacco boxes, broom handles, cutlery handles, kitchen utensils, etc.

RANGE AND DISTRIBUTION—Maine to eastern Nebraska south to Florida and eastern Texas, most common and of its largest size in the Ohio and Mississippi basins. Common along streams in Delaware but more abundant north.

HABITAT—Prefers the rich moist soils of stream banks and the borders of swamps, but will grow on drier sites. It is intolerant of shade.

NOTES—It is difficult to distinguish between young trees of the American sycamore and the London plane for the differences are not prominent. Generally, however, the trunk bark of the London hybrid is darker in both the green and white splotches. Too, it is not as susceptible to attacks of the defoliating and twig cankering fungus disease *Gloeosporium* as is the native species. London planes of fruit bearing age may be easily identified by the fruits which occur in 2s or rarely 3s on a single stem, while those of the American species occur singly or rarely in pairs.

Of all the North American deciduous trees, the sycamore probably attains the most massive proportions and greatest height. A tree in Worthington, Indiana, reported in 1915, measured 42.2' in circumference and records of the oriental species show that it may attain a diameter of 40'. A large sycamore which stood on the Garrett property at the corner of Delaware Avenue and West Streets, Wilmington measured 14.5' C.B.H. in 1935. After the tree was felled in 1937, a count of the annual rings in a section taken at about 10' from the ground was made. It showed 167, indicating an age of about 171 years.

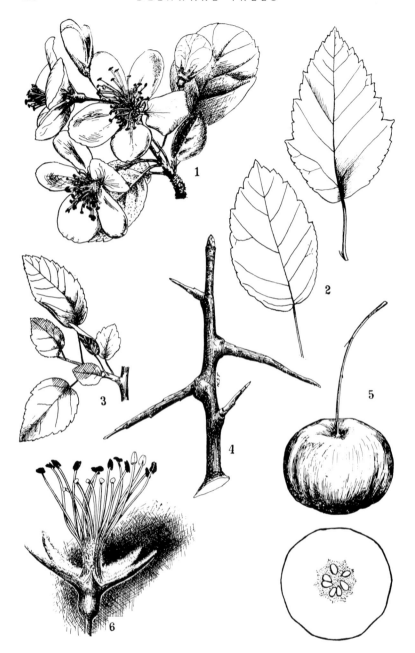

AMERICAN WILD CRAB APPLE

1. Flowering branchlet, natural size.
2. Leaves, x ½.
3. Spur-like leafy branchlet of the season, natural size.
4. Lateral winter twig, natural size.
5. Fruit and section of fruit, natural size.
6. Flower with petals removed, enlarged.

AMERICAN WILD CRAB APPLE
Malus coronaria, (L.) Miller

[*Pyrus coronaria,* Linnaeus]

GENUS DESCRIPTION—Early botanical authorities generally treated the genus *Pyrus* as including all pomaceous fruiting plants such as pears, apples, chokeberries, mountain ashes, quinces, etc. However, the present trend is to break this large and important genus into its subdivisions and raise them to genus classification; thus *Pyrus* retains the pears; *Malus* absorbs the cultivated and wild apples; *Sorbus* includes the mountain ashes, while *Cydonia* and *Aronia* are reserved for the quinces and chokeberries respectively. Accordingly *Malus* becomes a genus of great economic importance with representatives cultivated in most temperate regions of the world.

The American wild crab, sweet crab or garland tree, is a small tree sometimes 30' tall with a trunk rarely over 14" in diameter. Generally forms thickets but when in the open has a broad rounded crown composed of rigid, more or less horizontal, contorted branches bearing many short spur-like branchlets.

LEAVES—Alternate, simple, quite variable in outline ranging from elliptical on the older branchlets to triangular on the new vigorous ones, 2" to 4" long and often nearly as broad, margins sharply and often doubly toothed and lobed; at maturity thin, smooth, dark green and with grooved midrib above; paler, glabrous and with prominent midrib beneath; petiole slender usually tinged with red; turn yellow in autumn before falling.

BARK—On old trunks thin, broken into narrow longitudinal red-brown persistent plates; on young trunks appears ragged and shredded by reason of separating in paper-thin strips and rolls; on the slender vigorous shoots red and hoary tomentose at first, becoming reddish gray by the end of the first winter and deep purplish by the end of the second year, developing short stout spur-like laterals which are sometimes spinose tipped.

BUDS—Alternate, the terminal one on vigorous shoots ⅛" to ¼" long with sharp tip but otherwise rather blunt, covered by 4 to 8 bright red, shiny imbricated outer scales. Lateral buds long acute and sharp tipped.

FLOWERS—In April–May when the leaves are nearly full grown, borne in 3 to 6 flowered clusters on the new growth, each on a slender smooth pedicel, fragrant, 1¼" to 1½" across, with 5 club-like, rose-white petals irregular on the apex margin and gradually or abruptly narrowing to a long or short claw, with numerous stamens shorter than the petals, 5 styles united and set with white hairs near the base, within a 5 lobed calyx the lobes of which are acute and white pubescent above. Flowers resemble those of the cultivated apples but are usually more fragrant and more abundantly produced.

FRUIT—October but often remain on the tree through the winter without rotting, apple-like, depressed globose about 1" high and 1" to 1½" broad, pale green, or yellow-green with a waxy surface when fully ripened, fluted on the bottom and retaining the calyx lobes of the flower, very acid; stem long and slender; seed brown and shiny.

WOOD—Diffuse-porous; heavy, moderately soft, close grained; heartwood red-brown; sapwood thick yellow. Not commercially important in this State.

RANGE AND DISTRIBUTION—Western New York and southern Ontario to Iowa, southward to northern Texas and northern Georgia. Local in New Castle County, rare in Kent and not observed in Sussex County of this State.

HABITAT—Prefers the rich moist soils of stream banks and cool hillsides; in the mountainous portions of its range, sometimes found at elevations of 3,000'.

NOTES—The American wild crab apple closely resembles other *Malus* species in many of its characteristics. Generally, however, it may be readily distinguished by the thin leaves and characteristic spur-like branchlets. In autumn the fragrant fruit with ribbed calyx end and persistent calyx lobes is also characteristic. Although the fruits are occasionally used in making jellies and preserves, the chief value of the species appears to lie in the ornamental beauty of the abundantly produced fragrant blossoms.

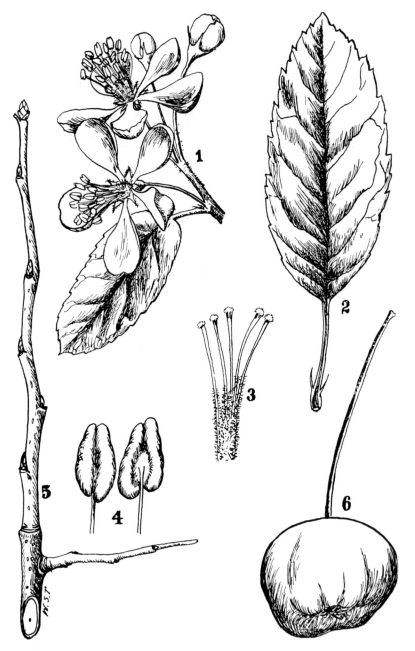

SOUTHERN CRAB APPLE

1. Flowering twig, x 2.
2. Leaf, natural size.
3. Style cluster, enlarged.
4. Anther showing filament attachment enlarged.
5. Winter twig, natural size.

SOUTHERN CRAB APPLE

Malus angustifolia (Ait.) Miehx.

(Pyrus angustifolia, Ait.)

The southern crab apple, or narrow-leaved crab apple is a small tree, occasionally 30' tall often with more than one main trunk in this latitude, generally less than 6" in diameter with slender rigid branches forming a broad ragged head characteristic of wild apple trees.

LEAVES—Alternate, simple, variable in shape between top and bottom of the tree, but generally narrower and smaller than in *M. coronaria;* margins double-toothed, and often lobed; at maturity leathery dull green on the upper surface and light green on the lower, often hairy at least on the midrib and veins, 1" to 3" long, 1½" to 1¾" wide, with stout ¾" long petiole tinged with red.

BARK—Apple tree-like, but on old trunks and twigs similar to *M. coronaria* (p. 157).

BUDS—Alternate, the terminal one on vigorous shoots, short, blunt, covered with 4 to 8 chestnut brown shiny scale which are lightly pubescent near the base.

FLOWERS—In April–May, about 1" in diameter in 3–5 flowered clusters (cymes) on the new shoots, each on a slender ¾" to 1" long slender usually smooth pedicel, very fragrant, petals 5, pink or rose colored, smooth on the outer surface, covered with hoary tomentum on the inner surface with elliptical shaped body constricted gradually into a long claw; stamens shorter than the petals; styles 5 united near their base, villose below middle.

FRUIT—October, depressed globose, yellowish, about 1" in diameter, often lop-sided, hard and quite persistent.

WOOD—Diffuse-porous, hard, close grained, reddish brown, sapwood thick, yellow. Weight per cu. ft. about 43 lbs.

RANGE AND DISTRIBUTION—Coastal Plain Delaware "to northwestern Florida west to Louisiana northward to Arkansas, Tennessee and southern Illinois," according to U.S.D.A. Check List (Handbook No. 41). First observed by the author in eastern Kent County 1946, but possibly present in Sussex along coast and estuaries, but not reported.

HABITAT—Seems to prefer moist heavy soils.

NOTES—The narrow-leaved crab apple resembles other wild apple species so closely that its presence in Delaware may easily have escaped observation. Possibly the most distinguishing characteristic is the color of the blossom being usually pink to rose, and the leathery consistence of the mature leaf. However, the petals are so quickly deciduous that its beauty is soon lost and the attacks of cedar rust disease so damaging to the foliage and fruit as to discourage its use as an ornamental.

SHAD BUSH

1. Fruiting branchlet, natural size,
2. Winter twig, x 2.
3. Fruit in section, enlarged.
4. Flower in section, enlarged.
5. Flowering branchlet, natural size.

SHAD BUSH
Amelanchier arborea (Michx. f.) Fernald
[*Amelanchier canadensis,* (L.) Medicus]

GENUS DESCRIPTION—*Amelanchier* comprises many species of small trees and shrubs in the temperate regions of the world. Of the some twenty species found in North America only 3 are arborescent. Of the 2 indigenous to Delaware only the one described below is arborescent. *A. laevis* Wieg. Allegheny service berry is shrubby.

The shad bush or serviceberry, also known as juneberry, shadblow, and service tree, is a small tree often 20' to 25' tall with a trunk 4" to 6" in diameter, but may rarely attain a height of 50' to 60' and a trunk diameter of 1½'. Trunk, in this region, often inclined, crooked and terminates in a small rounded crown composed of small contorted branches and slender branchlets.

LEAVES—Alternate, but ususally grouped at the tips of twigs, ovate to ovate-oblong, 2½" to 4" long, 1" to 2" wide; margins finely serrate with forward pointing acute teeth; covered with thick silky white tomentum when they unfold, but by mid-summer smooth, dull bluish green above and paler green beneath.

BARK—On old and young trunks slate or reddish gray, thin, hard; that on young trunks narrowly and slightly fluted which in older trees has a tendency to fissure; on the slender slightly zigzag twigs at first covered with long white pubescence but soon smooth red-brown or purplish, enlarged at the nodes and marked by inconspicuous leaf scars and numerous small dark raised lenticels.

BUDS—Alternate, long conical, the terminal one about ½" long and usually larger than the lateral ones, covered by several scales which increase in size toward the tip, the bottom ones greenish and the upper ones pale red with a dense marginal fringe of long white hairs.

FLOWERS—In early spring before or as the leaves are unfolding, in glabrous racemes 2½" to 5" long, each flower about 1" across, perfect, composed of a 5 parted green calyx hairy on the upper surface, 5 white narrowly oblong petals, numerous stamens and 5 styles united below.

FRUIT—In June (hence juneberry), in raceme-like clusters, berry-like, reddish purple and bloom covered when ripe, about 1/3" in diameter, pulpy, sweet and edible and containing small seeds.

WOOD—Diffuse-porous, with numerous indistinct rays; heavy, hard, strong and close grained; heartwood reddish, sapwood wide white, but turns light brown on exposure; weighs about 48 lbs. per cu. ft. and although difficult to season is occasionally used in turnery and sometimes made into poles and shafts when, because of the high polish and lustre possible, it may be called "lancewood."

RANGE AND DISTRIBUTION—Quebec to southeastern Nebraska, southward to Louisiana and Alabama. Probably attains its largest size in New York, Pennsylvania and Ohio. Common throughout Delaware.

HABITAT—Prefers moist soils, but not particular and, although reaching arborescent size more often when in the open, it appears to be quite tolerant of shade.

NOTES—The "shad" in the common names applied to this tree no doubt owes its origin to the time of blossoming, which closely corresponds with the run of spawn shad.

In spring its mass of white bloom make it one of the most conspicuous trees of the woods and by the less observant is sometimes believed to be dogwood, which, however, blooms later in the spring.

It makes a very attractive ornamental tree and deserves more use for such than it now enjoys. Despite the fact that the wood has practically no commercial value it is reputed to be tougher and stronger than white oak. Purely for the fruit which is readily eaten by man, bird and beast this tree deserves retention in Delaware woodlands.

COCK-SPUR THORN

1. Autumn leaves and fruit, x ½
2. Winter twig, natural size.
3. Flowering branchlet, x ½.

COCK-SPUR THORN
Crataegus crus-galli, Linnaeus

GENUS DESCRIPTION—The genus *Crataegus* or Hawthorns is represented by an increasing number of both arborescent (197) and shrubby (100) species in the world, occurring mainly in eastern North America and by a few in the Rocky Mountains and Pacific Coast regions. Of these indigenous to Europe and Asia probably the best known in the United States is English hawthorn, *C. oxyacantha*, L., and its varieties, which since their introduction early in the history of the Country, have escaped cultivation and became naturalized in many localities. Identification of the various species (in the language of the times) is "an awful headache" and is extremely difficult, even for the professional dendrologist. For this reason only one easily identified native species is described here. A list of other species reported as native to Delaware is included on the following pages.

The cock-spur thorn, also known as New Castle thorn, thorn apple, cock-spur hawthorn and red haw, is a small tree which occasionally reaches a height of 30' with a trunk diameter of 8' to 12'. Trunk short, often slightly inclined, with broad umbrella-like crown composed of stout branches and numerous more or less matted branchlets.

LEAVES—Alternate, distinctly obovate or elliptical, usually 1" to 4" long and a third as broad but larger on the ends of thrifty branchlets; margins often entire below the middle, but sharply, finely and often glandular toothed above the middle; tinged with red when they unfold but at maturity thick, leathery, shiny and dark green above; pale green beneath, with prominent midrib, and primary veins within the cellular structure of the leaf.

BARK—On old trees gray or slightly reddish and scaly; on young trunk and limbs gray or light brown; on the slender, tough, zigzag twigs, smooth light brown or ashy gray. Spines of twigs straight or slightly curved (hence cock-spur thorn) 2" to 4" long purplish brown mottled with gray; becoming on the branches and trunk as much as 8" long with shorter lateral spines.

BUDS—Alternate, the terminal one about ⅛" long, ovate blunt pointed and covered by several thick, broad, shiny red scales; the lateral buds smaller and often located at the base of a thorn.

FLOWERS—In June when the leaves are fully developed; arranged in corymbs, each flower about ⅝" across, perfect, with 5 white petals, 10 stamen with light red anthers and usually 2 styles.

FRUIT—Matures in September and October and persists on the tree with little change often until the following spring; globose or slightly oblong, about ½" long, dull red and sometimes covered by glaucous bloom, marked at the apex by the persistent calyx lobes, and composed of a yellowish pulp surrounding 2 small, ¼" long, hard coated nutlets which are rounded at the ends and ridged on the back.

WOOD—Diffuse-porous with inconspicuous medullary rays, heavy hard close grained; heartwood reddish brown; sapwood white; weighs about 45 lbs. per cu. ft. Not commercially valuable.

RANGE AND DISTRIBUTION—Southern Canada near Montreal to Michigan and southward to western North Carolina. In Delaware very common in New Castle county, hence the common name—New Castle thorn. Local in Kent and Sussex counties.

HABITAT—Prefers rich well drained soils in waste places in the open such as fence rows and the borders of forests.

NOTES—Three varieties of this species are found in the vicinity of Wilmington. The variety *pyracanthifolia*, Ait., is identified by narrower leaves having pubescence on the upper side of the midrib when young, and by smaller flowers and smaller bright red fruit. It is quite common in eastern Pennsylvania and northern Delaware.

The variety *oblongata*, Sarg., identified by bright red oblong fruit sometimes nearly 1" in length and containing nutlets which are acute at the ends, was at one time common in the northern part of the State but is now rapidly being cut out of its old locations along farm fence rows.

The variety *capillata*, Sarg., is identified by thinner leaves and by the flower stalks set with long hairs and fruit of the type but with 1 or rarely 2 nutlets. It is found in the northern part of the State.

NOTES ON OTHER SPECIES OF CRATAEGUS

In 1898 the number of recognized and cataloged species of *Crataegus* was less than 25 but so many new species have been described that botanists have found it convenient to classify them under no less than 22 groups. For a more complete treatment of the complicated situation attending the identification of the hawthorns the student is referred to the notes on the matter appearing in the "Check List of Native and Naturalized Trees of the United States," issued by the U. S. Department of Agriculture Forest Service as Agriculture Handbook No. 41.

A favorite reference on arborescent species of *Crataegus,* familiar to the author, is found in "Manual of Trees of North America" by Charles Sprague Sargent, published by Houghton Mifflin Co., New York City.

The following listing of species is from Elbert Little Jr.'s listing in Agriculture Handbook No. 41 above referred to and includes only those reported to be indigenous to, or naturalized in, Delaware.

C. canbyi, Sargent. Distinguished by leaves smaller than *C. crus-galli* but with conspicuous midrib and veins beneath and with petiole red below the middle and bearing scattered dark red glands. The fruit is larger than the type and is depressed at the stem, has bright red juicy flesh and 3 to 5 chestnut brown nutlets.

Dotted thorn, *C. punctata,* Jacquin. Distinguished by red fruit marked by scattered white dots or yellow fruit (var. *aurea* Ait.). Nutlets 5, about ¼″ long. The variety appears to be more common in the vicinity of New Castle where it indicates former extensive use as a hedge plant.

C. pruinosa (Wendland) K. Koch. The range of this species extends from southwestern Vermont to Central Illinois, southward to Kentucky and northern Delaware. Distinguished by broad double serrate blue-green leaves and large subglobose fruit which is lustrous purplish red when fully ripe. Nutlets 5, acute at the apex, narrow at the base. The spines are 1″ to 1½″ long and straight.

C. pennsylvanica, Ashe
C. rubella, Beadle
C. uniflora, Muenchhausen

The hawthorns, as a group, make very attractive ornamentals and are particularly useful in border planting. The popularity of a species or variety is usually based on a single prominent feature of the plant such as the foliage, the abundance and beauty of blooms, or size color and abundance of fruit.

AMERICAN WILD PLUM

1. Branchlets with leaves and fruit, natural size.

AMERICAN WILD PLUM
Prunus americana, Marshall

GENUS DESCRIPTION—The genus *Prunus* includes the almonds, peaches, cherries and plums, and is consequently regarded as one of the 10 most important and valuable of tree genera. It comprises about 120 species of trees and shrubs generally distributed and quite common over most of the Northern Hemisphere of the world. Of the 30 or less species native to North America, the great majority (22) are small trees. Three of these are credited as native to Delaware. Several species and many varieties, mostly of foreign origin, are cultivated in this country for their fruit and for ornamental uses. The wild black cherry is about the only species that produces wood of commercial importance.

The American wild plum, also known as wild yellow plum, red plum and wild plum is a small tree or large shrub rarely attaining a height of more than 35′ and a diameter of 1′. Trunk short and usually divided a short distance above ground into several spreading limbs with pendulous branchlets forming a broad rounded crown.

LEAVES—Alternate, oval, oblong or obovate, 2″ to 4″ long and 1″ to 1¾″ wide, generally broadest at or above the middle, tapering to an acute apex and gradually to a narrow or rounded base; margins sharply and often doubly toothed; at maturity thick, dark green, somewhat glossy, and roughened by the sunken midrib, veins and veinlets above; pale green and roughened by the conspicuous midrib veins and veinlets beneath; petiole short and rarely with glands near the leaf blade above.

BARK—On old trunks dark reddish brown and broken into long thin persistent plates; on young trunks smooth gray-brown; on the moderately stout twigs at first light green, soon becoming orange-brown and marked by kidney-shaped leaf scars showing 3 conspicuous bundle scars; the lateral twigs, spur-like or spinescent.

BUDS—Alternate, all axillary, conical and sharp pointed, less than ¼″ long, covered by triangular brown scales, often hairy on the margins and imbricated in rows.

FLOWERS—In April-May with the leaves in 2 to 5 flowered umbels, each perfect, about 1″ across with white petals constricted into a red claw, numerous stamens and a stubby pistile within a 5 parted calyx having white pubescence on the upper surface of the lobes. Odor of flowers unpleasant.

FRUIT—Matures in late summer (in this latitude about August), a globose or slightly elongated drupe, about ¾″ long, with tough skin, orange-red when fully ripe and usually devoid of bloom; flesh orange-yellow, about ¼″ thick surrounding a compressed oval nearly smooth surfaced pit; edible but tart and occasionally used in making jelly.

WOOD—Diffuse-porous with visible medullary rays; heavy, hard, strong close grained and with conspicuous luster; heartwood dark reddish brown; sapwood lighter; weighs about 45 lbs. per cu. ft. Not commercially important.

RANGE AND DISTRIBUTION—From Massachusetts, Michigan and Montana, southward to New Mexico, Texas and Florida. Now comparatively rare and local in Delaware and probably most common in New Castle county.

HABITAT—Along fence rows, edges of woods, stream banks, edges of swamps and waste places, but seems to prefer moist or wet soils.

NOTES—Without either fruit or flowers present the American wild plum is difficult for the layman to identify. However, the spur-like lateral twigs and absence of a truly terminal bud are identifying winter characteristics. The chief value of the species lies in the abundance of white flowers produced in spring and consequent ornamental use. The Chickasaw plum, *P. angustifolia* Marshall, which occasionally attains tree size, is naturalized in Sussex county. It is identified by trough-like lance-oblong, shiny leaves usually less than 2″ long which are very finely toothed on the margins, and by the thin skinned bloom coated or shiny red fruit which is quite tasty when fully ripe. Its wide distribution in the eastern states is credited to the eastern Indians who supposedly traded the fruit with the Chickasaw tribes and planted the seed near their camp sites. The European Damson plum *P. domestica* L. has escaped cultivation in a few places in Delaware. It is identified by its blue fruit. For reference to the native beach plum *P. maritima,* see p. 235.

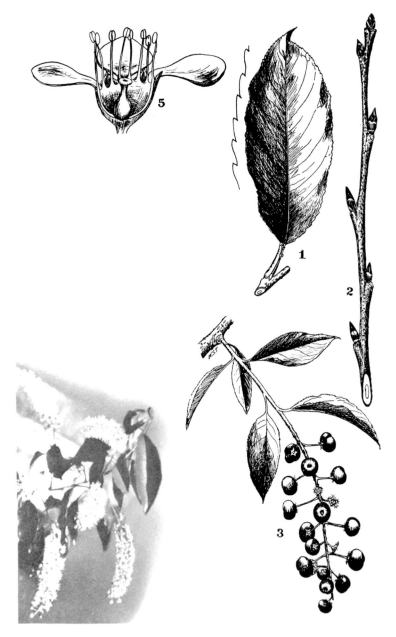

WILD BLACK CHERRY

1. Leaf, x ½ with margin detail, enlarged.
2. Winter twig, natural size.
3. Fruiting branchlet, x ½.
Unnumbered. Flowering branchlet, x ¼.
5. Single flower, sectioned to show detail, enlarged.

WILD BLACK CHERRY
Prunus serotina, Ehrhart

The wild black cherry also known as rum cherry, cabinet cherry, cherry (c) and wild cherry is a tree usually 50' to 60' tall with a trunk 1' to 2½' in diameter, but may occasionally attain a height of 100' and a trunk diameter of 5'. In forest stands the trunk is usually straight with little taper and clean for the greater portion of its length, ending in a small shallow crown. The trunk of open grown trees is generally short and the crown broad and irregular. Reaches maturity in about 60 years but trees 200 years old are not uncommon.

LEAVES—Alternate, lance-oblong or oblong with acute apex and tapering or broadly V-shaped base, 2" to 5½" long, 1" to 1½" wide; margins finely callous incurve toothed; thick and somewhat leathery, dark green and shiny above, paler beneath; petiole short and often furnished with conspicuous glands above.

BARK—On old trunks thin, very dark brown or black, broken into irregular plates (Fig. 22); on young trunks thin, shiny dark brown and marked by numerous horizontal pale lenticel bands; on the slender twigs during the first winter, lustrous light reddish gray and marked by numerous pale lenticels. Bark, especially of twigs, bitter and with a distinguishing hydrocyanic acid odor.

BUDS—Alternate, ovate or conical and sharp pointed, about ¼" long, covered with 4 to 6 visible scales, reddish brown at the bottom and green or light gray on the margins, often covered with a webby film.

FLOWERS—April to June, when the leaves are about half grown, in many drooping racemes 4" to 6" long, each perfect, ¼" across, with 5 white petals numerous stamens and expanded stigma.

FRUIT—Ripens from early to late summer in drooping raceme-like clusters, each drupe 1/3" to ½" in diameter, depressed globose and slightly lobed, dark purplish or nearly black when ripe, with a thin skin and juicy dark purple tart flesh, enclosing a thin-shelled oblong stone.

WOOD—Diffuse-porous with pores more abundant in spring wood and often plugged with dark red gum; rays distinct; moderately heavy, hard, close grained, with conspicuous silver grain on quarter finished surfaces, seasons well and is very durable in contact with the soil; heartwood rich light red-brown; sapwood thick, lighter. Weighs about 36 lbs. per cu. ft. and used for furniture, woodenware articles and turnery.

RANGE AND DISTRIBUTION—Nova Scotia to Florida and westward to Lake Superior, North Dakota, southward to western Texas. Common throughout Delaware.

HABITAT—Prefers rich deep soils but will thrive on poorer soils. Is generally tap-rooted and seems to prefer sunlight.

NOTES—The identifying characteristics of wild black cherry are quite generally known but the best of these is the hydrocyanic acid taste of the twig bark. This bitterness probably led to the early discovery of the medicinal value of the bark and extracts of it are now used in both home and commercial medicines of the tonic and sedative kinds. The tree has fallen into ill repute in regions where horticulture is a prominent part of agricultural pursuits in that it is an unwilling host of the tent caterpillar, the fall web-worm, and other insects and diseases which also attack cultivated fruit trees. Where its presence does not constitute a menace to horticulture, it deserves to be encouraged as a timber tree because of its rapid growth and the value of the wood it produces.

The tender shoots and leaves of this species are to cattle what candy is to a child but are usually fatal to them if eaten in large quantities when in a wilted condition. Therefore the farmer in brushing out fence rows or ditch banks where the species occurs, should exclude cattle from the area after the first day, unless he is willing to risk the loss of some of the herd. There appears to be no antidote for its poisonous effects on cattle.

REDBUD

1. Portion of twig with red fruit, x ½.
2. Leaf, x ½.
3. Winter twig, natural size.
4. Portion of twig enlarged to show leaf scar and bud.
5. Flowering branchlet, natural size.

REDBUD
Cercis canadensis, Linnaeus

GENUS DESCRIPTION—The 8 species of the genus *Cercis* are confined to the Northern Hemisphere of the world. Two of the 3 species found in North America attain tree sizes; only one of which is native to Delaware.

The redbud or judas tree occasionally attains a height of 50′ and a trunk diameter of 12″ but generally is much smaller. In the forest the trunk is tall and the crown small and round topped but open grown trees have a short trunk and broad spreading rounded crown.

LEAVES—Alternate, broadly heart-shaped, 3″ to 5″ in either dimension; margin entire and often slightly turned down and undulating; green, often lustrous and wrinkled along the 5 to 7 nerves above; pale dull green and with tufts of hairs in the axils of the nerves beneath; petiole 2″ to 5″ long, round, abruptly enlarged at the base and at the apex.

BARK—On old trunks, dark brown thin and broken by shallow fissures into flat topped plated ridges; on young trunk smooth grayish brown or dark red-brown; on the slender zigzag twigs shiny, light red-brown and marked by minute light colored lenticels and pale heart-shaped leaf scars exhibiting 3 fibro vascular bundle scars.

BUDS—Alternate, all axillary, the leaf buds on the upper portion of the twigs very small, dark red, triangular flattened and appressed to the twig; the flower buds larger, often situated above the leaf buds on the lower part of the twig, and in clusters on the branches and trunk, globular, covered by several small basal scales and 2 large outer red scales and pubescent pinkish inner scales.

FLOWERS—Borne in great abundance in March or April before the leaves, or as the leaves are appearing, in clusters of 4 to 8 on short stems, each perfect, pea-blossom-like, deep pink, about ½″ long.

FRUIT—A thin short stemmed pod 2½″ to 3″ long, ½″ wide, borne in clusters, light green and fully formed by midsummer, later turning light reddish brown before splitting open to release the 2 to 6 small olive brown oval seed. Often persist well into the winter.

WOOD—Ring-porous, heavy, hard, close grained; heartwood rich dark red-brown; sapwood lighter; weighs about 40 lbs per cu. ft. Not commercially important.

RANGE AND DISTRIBUTION—Delaware River in New Jersey westward through southern New York, southern Ontario to southern Minnesota, southward to Delaware and along the Allegheny foothills to western Florida, eastern Texas and Sierra Madre Mts. of Mexico. Extremely rare naturally in Delaware and probably owes its presence more to escape from cultivation than to natural distribution. Believed truly native only in lower New Castle County, but may occur along the Brandywine Creek and Delaware River.

HABITAT—Prefers the rich moist soils of stream banks and ample sunlight but is also found on drier sites and in the shade of deep woods.

NOTES—The chief importance of the redbud lies in the ornamental value of its beautiful and abundantly produced flowers. The foliage of open grown trees is likewise ornamental for they are tinged with red early and often copper tinged in late summer. The name "judas tree" alludes to a legendary supposition that Judas hanged himself on such a tree, but is difficult to correlate with the size the tree attains or its nativity to North America alone. Besides, it attaches an unsavory reputation to one of the most beautiful of American trees.

BLACK LOCUST

1. Winter twig, natural size.
2. Section through twig enlarged to show imbedded bud structure.
3. Fruit cluster, x ½.
4. Section of branchlet with leaf and flower raceme, x ½.
5. Single seed, enlarged and (a) seed showing attachment to pod, natural size.

BLACK LOCUST
Robinia pseudoacacia, Linnaeus

GENUS DESCRIPTION—The genus *Robinia,* named in honor of two 16th century French botanists with the family name of Robin, is represented by 7 species of leguminous trees and shrubs occurring in North America. Of these, 3 are arborescent anl only one established widely in Delaware. The clammy locust *R. viscosa* is occasionally seen as a shrub in ornamental plantings but rarely escapes for long because its mass of pink blossoms are so attractive as to cause it to be returned to cultivation.

The black locust (c) also known as yellow locust, false acacia, post locust, pea flowered locust and common locust, is a tree usually 40' to 50' tall with a trunk 12" to 20" in diameter but may rarely attain a height of 80' and a trunk diameter of 4'. In forest stands the trunk is tall and clean for the greater portion of its length, ending in a shallow open crown. Open grown trees branch nearer the ground and have an oblong, irregular, medium dense, crown.

LEAVES—Alternate, compound, 8" to 14" long with 7 to 9 leaflets arranged oppositely or nearly so, on a slender grooved petiole; leaflets short stalked mostly oblong, 1" to 2" long with entire margins; at maturity very thin and light blue-green above, paler beneath. Each leaflet is attended by a minute early deciduous stipule on the leaf petiole.

BARK—On young and old trees similar but thicker on the latter, rugged, deeply furrowed into long interlacing round topped ridges with smaller connecting ridges; on the zigzag round ridged or fluted twigs, at first light green, soon becoming light reddish brown and armed at the nodes with 2 stout persistent spines guarding the hidden bud.

BUDS—Alternate, all axillary, hidden beneath the light brown or grayish leaf scar and usually not visible until the approach of spring—sometimes termed the "monkey faced bud."

FLOWERS—May, in 4" to 5" long drooping, loose racemes, each flower resembling that of the common garden pea in shape and size, but usually cream white in color, about 1" long, and containing an abundance of very fragrant nectar from which the bees make an excellent honey.

FRUIT—Matures in late autumn and often persists in dried form on the tree until spring; a 3" to 4" long, thin brown bean-like pod borne in clusters along a common stem, the pods splitting open along the edges to release the 4 to 8 small yellowish brown kidney-shaped hard coated seeds contained therein. The seed is reputed to be an item of quail food which may have aided to some extent in its rapid distribution beyond its natural range.

WOOD—Ring-porous, with minute and medium sized medullary rays; heavy, very hard, with high resistance to stress but splits rather easily; extremely durable in contact with the soil; heartwood yellowish brown; sapwood thin, yellowish white; weighs about 45 lbs. per cu. ft. Used for posts, insulator pins, tree nails, sill timbers, in turnery and for fuel.

RANGE AND DISTRIBUTION—Mountains of central Pennsylvania south to northern Georgia and westward to Arkansas and Oklahoma, now widely naturalized throughout the United States east of the Rocky Mts. and in Europe. Common as a naturalized species throughout Delaware but more abundant north.

HABITAT—Prefers rich moist soils and plenty of sunlight but will grow on poor, even sterile, soils and under the shade of other trees.

NOTES—The black locust is not a native Delaware species, but is well enough distributed that it appears to be so. Epidemically, the tree is subject to attacks of the Locust Leaf Miner, a small white worm that feeds on the chlorophyll of the leaflets often with the result that defoliation results in late summer (August). In this latitude, however, the attack is seldom fatal and the tree puts out a new set of leaves. It is also attacked by the locust borer, an insect which burrows in the twigs and branches causing a characteristic enlargement and weakening of the organ at the point of attack. Despite these enemies the black locust continues to be the one tree that can be depended upon to produce the most durable fence post in a shorter time than any other native or introduced species. Moreover, its ability to thrive on, and improve, sterile soils and, in doing so, to develop extensive root systems that prevent and arrest erosion, makes it one of the most valuable of erosion control plants. A variety known as shipmast locust, because of the tall straight stem it develops, is recognized and cultivated on Long Island, N. Y. For some 260 years this strain has been kept pure by propagation from root cuttings only.

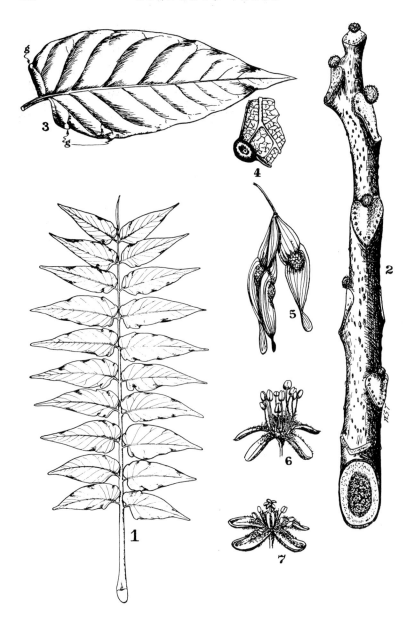

AILANTHUS

1. Leaf, x ⅛.
2. Winter twig, natural size.
3. Upper surface of leaflet showing gland locations (g), x ½.
4. Section of lower surface showing gland, enlarged.
5. Fruit, natural size.
6. Single staminate flower, enlarged.
7. Single pistillate flower, enlarged.

AILANTHUS
Ailanthus altissima (Miller) Swingle

[*Ailanthus glandulosa,* Desfontaines]

GENUS DESCRIPTION—The genus name *Ailanthus* is taken from the native name *Ailanto* meaning Tree of Heaven. The 8 or 9 species are all Asiatic. The species here described was introduced into this Country at Philadelphia about 1760 and has since rapidly spread and become naturalized in many parts of eastern United States.

The ailanthus, also known as Chinese sumac, stinking chun and tree of Heaven, is a very rapid growing tree usually 50' to 60' tall with a trunk 2' to 2½' in diameter, but may occasionally attain a height of 100' and a trunk diameter of 4' or more. Trunk moderately tall with outward arching branches and with few stout branchlets to form a symmetrical deep rounded crown.

LEAVES—Alternate, compound, 1½' to 3' long with 13 to 41 short stalked leaflets on a stout, wide based, petiole; leaflets ovate-lanceolate, 3" to 6" long with long acute apex and rounded or squarish base; margins usually entire above the middle, but with a few rounded teeth or notches from about the middle to the base; at maturity dull light green and sparsely hairy above, lighter green and shiny or lightly bloom covered and often with large raised circular glands near the tips of the notches of the leaflets.

BARK—On very old trunks thin, close fitting, broken by white ragged shallow fissures into greenish gray flat ridges; on young trunks quite smooth with diamond shaped markings of yellowish gray or light buff color; on the stout twigs yellowish green or reddish green, bloom coated and marked by numerous light colored lenticels and large heart-shaped leaf scars marked by numerous marginal bundle scars. Pith large, brown.

BUDS—Alternate, all axillary, small, globular, in the indented top of the leaf scar with several silky coated grayish or reddish brown scales, the outer pair large and nearly covering the bud.

FLOWERS—June, in terminal panicles 1' or more in length on the new growth when the leaves are nearly fully developed, male and female flowers on separate trees; the individual flowers small, greenish white.

FRUIT—September, and often persisting until the following year in dense panicled clusters with 1 to 5, spirally twisted, 1½" to 2½" long, oblong samaras on a stem, the circular compressed seed bearing portion borne centrally in the samara.

WOOD—Ring-porous, with conspicuous medullary rays; comparative light, hard, coarse grained; heartwood pale yellow; sapwood thick, lighter. Has possibilities as a pulp wood, but rarely used for commercial purposes.

RANGE AND DISTRIBUTION—Native of China. Naturalized locally throughout the State and eastern United States.

HABITAT—There appears to be no soil from moist to dry, poor or rich where this tree will not grow. It thrives in open sunlight and persists under dense shade, withstands smoke and gas and suffers little from low temperatures.

NOTES—The ailanthus, although called the tree of heaven as a result of the interpretation and application of its native name, is more a description in reverse of this tree. The disagreeable odor of its flowers and leaflets, especially those of the staminate tree, is said to aggravate catarrhal infection and for that reason should not be allowed to grow near human habitation. Although the tree grows very rapidly and in rare instances use of the pistillate trees warranted, it has so many objectionable features that its eradication in Delaware would appear to be a commendable public undertaking. Producing seed in great abundance and reproducing readily from suckers and root shoots, it soon takes over any site on which it is allowed to get a foothold.

STAGHORN SUMAC

1. Autumn branchlet with leaves and fruit, x 1/3.
2. Winter twig, natural size.

STAGHORN SUMAC
Rhus typhina, Linnaeus

[*Rhus hirta* (Linnaeus) Sudworth]

GENUS DESCRIPTION—The genus *Rhus* comprises more than 100 species distributed over most of the world. Only 4 of the 16 or 18 species in the United States attain tree size. Three of these are native to Delaware. The smooth sumac *R. glabra* L. is a shrubby species, common in the State. Of the foreign species introduced into this country the smoke tree, *R. cotinus*, and its varieties are rather common in gardens and on lawns. Several Old World and tropical species supply tanning materials and the juice of a poisonous Chinese species is used in the manufacture of black lacquer.

The staghorn sumac or hairy sumac in this latitude is a shrub or small tree attaining a height of 10' to 20' and a trunk diameter of 4" to 8". Elsewhere it may occasionally attain a height of 40' and a trunk diameter of 12". Trunk short, often inclined, and with spreading branches forming a round topped crown.

LEAVES—Alternate, compound, 16" to 24" long with 11 to 31 leaflets distributed along a stout large based petiole coated with soft pale hairs; the leaflets oblong-lanceolate, with long point and rounded base, sessile or short stalked; margins with forward pointing sharp teeth; at maturity often curving slightly downward from the depressed hairy midrib, dull dark green above; paler and often velvety white pubescent and with prominent midrib beneath; turn deep red, scarlet or crimson before falling in autumn.

BARK—On old and young trunks thin, dark brown and slightly roughened by darker horizontally elongated lenticel dots; on the very stout twigs covered for the first 2 or 3 years with dense reddish brown or very dark brown soft hair, resembles the horns of a stag when in velvet hence—staghorn sumac. When injured or punctured the bark exudes a milky sap which becomes sticky and black on exposure.

BUDS—Alternate, all axillary, rounded and rather formless, about ¼" long, composed of angular silky pubescent gray-brown scales. Before the leaves fall they are protected by the large enfolded base of the leaf petiole.

FLOWERS—In May or June in dense yellowish green panicles on the new growth, the staminate and pistillate usually on separate plants, the former 8" to 12" long and 4" to 6" broad at the base, being much larger than those of the latter which are more compact and develop later than the staminate ones.

FRUIT—August, on female plants in dense erect conical red panicles 4" to 8" long which often persist until the following spring; the single fruit, a spherical drupe with thin skin densely set with long red hairs and covering a small brownish hard stone.

WOOD—Ring-porous, light, moderately soft, brittle, with high satiny luster; heartwood greenish yellow or orange-green; sapwood rather thick, white. Weighs about 27 lbs. per cu. ft. and used in woodenware novelties and turnery. Not, however, commercially important.

RANGE AND DISTRIBUTION—New Brunswick to eastern North Dakota, southward along the Allegheny Mts. to Alabama. Probably not indigenous to the lower half of the Mississippi basin. Believed native and local only in New Castle County.

HABITAT—Prefers dry uplands and full sunlight such as along fence rows and waste places.

NOTES—The staghorn sumac is distinguished from all other sumacs by the hairy twigs and absence of a terminal bud. The tree bark and leaves are rich in tannic acid but are rarely used in this country for tanning.

Occasionally used as an ornamental and in bird food plantings. The yellowish heartwood makes attractive small woodenware articles and is often used in novelty inlay work.

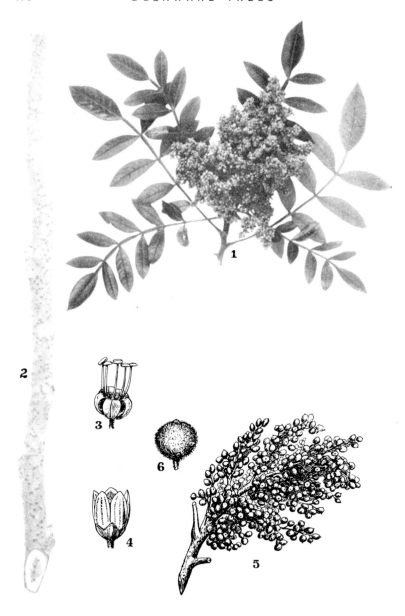

DWARF SUMAC

1. Flowering, branchlet, x ¼.
2. Winter twig, natural size.
3. Single staminate flower, enlarged.
4. Single pistillate flower, enlarged.
5. Fruit cluster, x ½.
6. Single drupe, enlarged.

DWARF SUMAC
Rhus copallina, Linnaeus

The dwarf sumac is generally a shrub but occasionally attains tree form and a height of 15' in this latitude. In the western portion of its range it may become as much as 30' tall.

LEAVES—Alternate, compound, 6" to 12" long, with slender pubescent petiole enlarged at the base and surrounding the bud, red on the upper side and equipped with leafy wings between the 9 to 21 ovate-lanceolate leaflets which are 1½" to 3" long, ¾" to 1" wide and increase in size from the base to the tip of the leaf, those at the base usually with a short stalk, graduating to sessile ones above; margins entire and turned under except the terminal leaflet which may sometimes be slightly toothed; semi-leathery, lustrous dark green above; pale green and finely pubescent with prominent midrib and veins beneath. Turn deep maroon in the fall.

BARK—On old and young trunks thin, smooth light reddish brown; on the medium stout twigs at first hairy, later light reddish or dull buff, warty and marked by numerous large orange-red lenticels and leaf scars nearly encircling the buds. Sap is fluid—not milky.

BUDS—Alternate, all axillary, small conical or stubby and thickly covered by velvety brown hairs.

FLOWERS—Opening gradually and in succession beginning about July, the male and female ones on separate plants, in compact terminal greenish yellow panicles, 4" to 6" long and 3" to 4" wide, being smaller on the female plants.

FRUIT—Matures about September in dense, nodding, pubescent, red, panicle clusters which often persist until the following spring. The single drupe is globular with thin red skin beset with short sticky hairs.

WOOD—Diffuse-porous, soft, coarse grained, weak; heartwood rich yellow streaked with red, green and black; sapwood thin white. Of little commercial importance.

RANGE AND DISTRIBUTION—Southern Maine to eastern Nebraska, south to middle Texas and Florida; Cuba. Common throughout Delaware.

HABITAT—Prefers drier soils and full sunlight. Frequents fence rows, old fields and waste places.

NOTES—The dwarf sumac is distinguished from the poison sumac, which it most closely resembles, by its winged petiole and red fruit.

The leaves are rich in tannin and were formerly much used in tanning leather and the manufacture of dyes. Foreign dye woods and extracts have largely replaced this and other native tanning materials.

Commercially the species is without value, but the rich fall coloration of its leaves and fruit make it a desirable ornamental for border and bird row planting.

POISON SUMAC

1. Branchlet with fruit, x 1/3.
2. Winter twigs with persistent fruit panicle, natural size.

POISON SUMAC
Toxicodendron vernix, (L.) Kuntze
[*Rhus vernix,* Linnaeus]

The poison sumac, sometimes called poison dogwood, poison elder, and poison oak, is generally a tall shrub but may occasionally attain a height of 25′ and a trunk diameter of 6″ to 8″. The crown is wide deep thin and rounded.

LEAVES—Alternate, compound, 7″ to 24″ long, with 7 to 13 short stalked opposite leaflets on a slender smooth petiole, usually green below, red above and deep purplish red where the leaflets are attached; leaflets ovate or obovate, 2″ to 4″ long and half as broad, usually trough like with entire abruptly revolute margins; at maturity dark green and glossy above; pale or yellow-green below. Turn shades and tints of red in the fall.

BARK—On old and young trunks, thin, comparatively smooth, light to dark reddish gray; on the stout twigs, at the end of the first year, light orange-brown and marked with orange-brown lenticels; later gray.

BUDS—Alternate, the terminal bud ⅛″ to ½″ long, conical, covered with a few purplish gray pubescent scales. The axillary buds above the large leaf scar, ovate and much smaller than the terminal one.

FLOWERS—June, staminate and pistillate on separate trees, in long loose axillary panicles, the individual flowers about ⅜″ across, yellow-green.

FRUIT—September, but often persist until the following spring, the single drupe about ¼″ in diameter, compressed oval, shiny, ivory white arranged in long arching racemes.

WOOD—Ring-porous, light, soft and brittle; heartwood golden yellow, sapwood white. The pith is large but this does not make it a good whistle wood as some school children in Dover learned to their sorrow.

RANGE AND DISTRIBUTION—Southern Maine to central Minnesota, south to Texas and western Florida. Common, in its habitat, throughout Delaware.

HABITAT—In swamps and along streams, rarely on upland.

NOTES—The poison sumac is generally regarded as the most poisonous (to human skin) tree in the flora of the Continent. Fortunately it habits swamps and inundated thickets along streams rarely visited by human beings. But those "nature fakers" who go about the country-side in the fall of the year stripping roadside trees and shrubs of their highly colored foliage and attractive fruits should, in the interest of their own health and that of their friends, learn to identify this tree. Warnings: (1) Beware of a shrub or tree growing in swampy ground bearing compound leaves with entire margined leaflets. (2) Do not collect branchlets of trees which bear grape-like clusters of small shiny white or gray-white flattish drupes. (3) Poisonous plants of this type are quite as potent in the dormant state as they are when in full foliage. (4) Avoid using salves or greasy ointments to cure poison rash. They invariably spread it.

Some people are immune to the poisonous emanation of this tree, poison ivy and other skin rash producing plants, but for those who are not so fortunate the following antidotes are recommended: (1) As soon as possible after known contact, thoroughly wash the hands and other exposed parts of the body with a thick lather made from naptha soap. Follow this with an application of grain alcohol or rubbing alcohol. (2) When contact is first discovered as a result of itching skin, bathe the parts in pure grain alcohol or rubbing alcohol and paint with iodine or potassium permanganate solution. Use a calamine-phenol lotion obtainable at most drug stores. (3) Seek the advice of your physician.

A fluid extract derived from the gum plant, *Grindelia robusta* which is indigenous to California is often administered either internally or externally in the control of poison rash. The "milk" of the common milkweed smeared on infected skin is sometimes an effective remedy.

The above warnings and recommendations are offered for what they may be worth and are not vouched for by either the Department or the author.

AMERICAN HOLLY

1. Branchlet with fruit, upper surface, x ½.
2. Cluster of male flowers, x ½
3. Cluster of female flowers, x ½.
4. Branchlet with fruit, bottom surface, x ½.
5. Fruit in cross section, x 2.
6. Seed, enlarged.

AMERICAN HOLLY
Ilex opaca, Aiton

GENUS DESCRIPTION—The genus *Ilex* is represented by about 175 species with many varieties distributed over the temperate and tropical zones of the world. Of the 13 species indigenous to the United States 6 are arborescent. In addition to the tree described below, the inkberry, *I. glabra*, a shrubby evergreen species habiting wet peaty soils and winterberry *I. verticillata*, a deciduous shrub with red berries, are common in the State. The smooth winterberry, *I. laevigata* is a shrub similar in appearance to the previous but comparatively rare here. Numerous European and Asiatic species are used ornamentally in this Country.

The American holly (c), Christmas holly, or evergreen holly, is a tree often 40' to 50' tall with a trunk 1' to 1½' in diameter but may rarely attain a height of 100' and a trunk diameter of 4'. In forest stands the crown is usually conical but on very old trees is often conical with a rounded top. Crowns of old open grown trees are usually of the latter form. Trees 300 years old are common. Adopted as the state tree of Delaware, 1939. See frontispiece.

LEAVES—Alternate, evergreen, oblong, 2" to 4" long, ½" to 2" wide with thick undulating margins equipped with few or numerous stout yellowish spines; thick, leathery, shiny and rich green above; light green beneath; petiole short and stout. Leaves persist for 2 to 3 years, and fall from the tree in spring.

BARK—On young and old trunks, thin, smooth, yellowish gray (Fig. 39); on the slender twigs at first purplish and pubescent, soon becoming buff colored and, by the end of the second year, yellowish gray.

BUDS—Alternate, the terminal one ⅛" to ¼" long, blunt conical, covered with numerous long narrow sharp tipped purplish scales; the lateral buds smaller and blunt.

FLOWERS—May and June, on the new growth in the axils of the leaves or along the lower portion of the shoot, the male and female flowers on separate trees; those on male trees in clusters of 3 to 9 on a common short stalk, appear to be perfect but ovary is rudimentary and inconspicuous; those on female plants usually solitary on a short stem or sometimes in 2's or 3's, the shiny green dome-like ovary very prominent, each about ¼" across with 4 tiny cream white petals united at the base.

FRUIT—Matures in late fall and persists during the winter, on female trees only, a globular drupe about ¼" in diameter, with dull or shiny red skin, and yellow mealy pulp enclosing 2 to 4 bony shelled corrugated nutlets.

WOOD—Diffuse-porous, medullary rays distinct but not prominent; hard, close grained and tough but not durable in contact with the soil; heartwood very slightly darker than the cream white sapwood; weighs about 36 lbs. per cu. ft., used in pianos, cabinet inlay, turnery and interior finish.

RANGE AND DISTRIBUTION—Tidewater region from Massachusetts to Florida, westward to eastern Texas and northward through the Mississippi Valley to southern Illinois, and southwestern Indiana. Common throughout Delaware but most abundant south.

HABITAT—Prefers moist to wet sandy acid peat soils and shade of other trees but is often found on drier sandy or clay Coastal Plain soils.

NOTES—There are few Americans who do not know the American holly particularly for its contribution to Yuletide decorations, the supplying of which in its heyday was an industry reputed to be worth in some years as much as $400,000.00 to the people of Delaware. Improper harvesting methods have ruined much of the potential supply of Christmas holly material, but there still remains within the State a supply which, under proper harvesting methods, is sufficient to meet demands indefinitely. Few if any evergreen trees excel the female holly in ornamental beauty, but it is extremely difficult to successfully transplant. It appears to be most successfully transplanted in August or in February at which time all or nearly all the leaves should be clipped from the branchlets. Some nurserymen prefer to move them in April as the older leaves are falling. In either case the reduction of transpiration surface through loss of foliage is the effective agent.

The European holly, *I. aquifolium* produces larger berries and has a more shiny, darker green and often more spinous leaf than the American species. It is being cultivated in warmer parts of the Continent particularly in western United States for the production of Christmas decorative material which promises to eventually replace the native species in public favor and popularity.

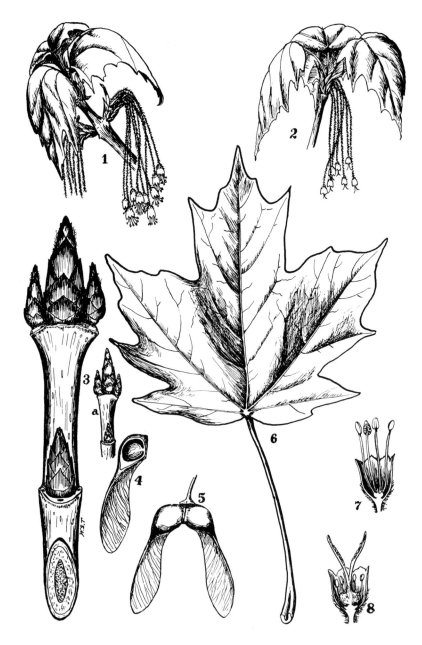

SUGAR MAPLE

1. Branchlet with staminate flowers, natural size.
2. Branchlet with pistillate flowers, natural size.
3. Terminal portion of winter twig, enlarged and (a) natural size.
4. Samara with seed cavity sectioned, natural size.
5. Fruit, natural size.
6. Leaf, x ½.
7. Staminate flower in section, enlarged.
8. Pistillate flower in section, enlarged.

SUGAR MAPLE
Acer saccharum, Marshall

GENUS DESCRIPTION—The genus *Acer* comprises about 110 species and varieties distributed over the Northern Hemisphere of the world except for a single species in Java. Of the 13 species in the United States, 3 are native to Delaware. Of the European species cultivated in this Country the Norway maple is probably the most popular. It is satisfactory as a lawn tree but has too low a head for street or highway use. Of the Asiatic species the shrubby Japanese types with attractive foliage characteristics appear to be most popular in this country.

The sugar maple, also known as hard maple (c) and rock maple (c), is a tree usually 50' to 60' tall with a trunk diameter of 1½' to 2½' but may sometimes attain a height of 100' and a trunk diameter of 4'. Trees in dense forest stands have a tall straight trunk with a few stout branches and slender branchlets forming a small rounded head. The trunk of open grown trees is clothed 8' to 10' above ground with many upright branches and slender branchlets to form a crown shaped like the flame of a candle. Reaches commercial maturity in 50 years but trees 300 years old have frequently been found in the northern part of its range.

LEAVES—Opposite, nearly circular in outline, 4" to 5" long, and 5" to 7" wide, 5 or sometimes 3 lobed with lobes further indented or toothed; bright green above, paler and prominently 3 nerved beneath; in the fall turning various brilliant shades of red and yellow often on the same leaf.

BARK—On old trunks medium thick, gray-brown and broken into long hard vertical plates which are usually free on one or both edges; on young trunks light buff and smooth or broken into narrow ridges; on the slender round twigs at first light green and smooth, by the first winter becoming lustrous reddish brown and marked by numerous oblong pale lenticels and opposite U-shaped leaf scars exhibiting 3 bundle scars.

BUDS—Opposite, narrow conical, the lateral ones appressed to the twig, about ¼" long; the terminal one about ½" long, both types covered with 8 to 16 scales, the outer ones red-brown with purplish margins and slightly pubescent on the tip.

FLOWERS—With the unfolding leaves in April from lateral and terminal buds, in clusters, on 1½" to 3" long hairy stems, the staminate and pistillate usually in different clusters on the same trees but sometimes mixed in the clusters or on separate trees.

FRUIT—September, in clusters on slender stalks, the smooth samaras (keys) in pairs with seed ends joined, diverging less than 25°, the wing about 1" long.

WOOD—Diffuse-porous, with prominent and less prominent fine medullary rays, heavy, hard, strong and close grained; heartwood reddish brown; sapwood thin nearly white; weighs about 43 lbs. per cu. ft. Used for furniture, flooring, kitchenware, turnery and fuel.

RANGE AND DISTRIBUTION—Southern Newfoundland to Manitoba, south along the mountains to northern Georgia and eastern Texas. Believed truly native only in northern New Castle County but much planted and locally naturalized elsewhere in the State.

HABITAT—Prefers rich well drained soils.

NOTES—Among native or introduced maples the sugar maple is without a peer economically or as an ornamental and street tree. This statement will no doubt provoke much contradiction on the part of many but might be further extended by adding that the species is probably the most valuable hardwood tree in North America.

The watery sap is the raw product of a large and valuable syrup and sugar industry. The birds eye, blister and curly maple of commerce are natural freaks of the grain which are rarely duplicated in any other wood. Timbermen and sugar makers are waging a silent economic war for remaining stands of the trees and present indications are that the "sugar bush" operators are losing out because of the long time factor and gambling chances they must take in manufacturing their product.

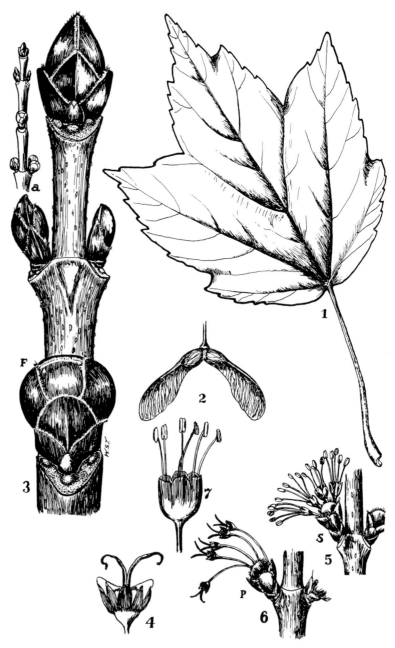

RED MAPLE

1. Leaf, natural size.
2. Fruit, natural size.
3. Terminal portion of winter twig enlarged (F) flower bud and (a) natural size.
4. Single pistillate flower, enlarged.
5. Section of twig with staminate flower cluster, natural size.
6. Section of twig with pistillate flower cluster, natural size.
7. Single staminate flower, enlarged.

RED MAPLE
Acer rubrum, Linnaeus

The red maple, also known as swamp maple, branch maple, soft maple (c), scarlet maple and white maple (c), is a tree usually 50' to 60' tall with a trunk diameter of 1' to 2' but may sometimes attain a height of 110' and a trunk diameter of 4'. In forest stands the trunk is tall and straight with a small crown composed of ascending branches. Trees in the open are clothed nearly to the ground with slender branches nearly horizontal below graduating to ascending ones above to form a dense foliaged obovoid crown.

LEAVES—Opposite, nearly circular in outline, 2" to 6" long and 2" to 4" wide, with V-shaped clefts forming 3, or sometimes 5 lobes; margins singly or doubly toothed; at maturity light or dark green and dull or shiny above; pale green or more often whitish bloom covered beneath. Petiole slender 2" to 4" long. Turn brilliant shades of red early in the fall.

BARK—On old trunks, thin, gray or reddish gray and broken by shallow fissures into narrow flat ridges; on young trunks smooth, light gray; on the slender twigs at first green or dark red, later red, glossy and marked by small white lenticels and broad U-shaped leaf scars.

BUDS—Opposite, the lateral leaf buds often short stalked, the terminal one larger and obtuse; the flower buds often clustered, usually stalked, globular or sub-globular; both types of buds covered by 6 to 8 glossy bright red scales with white wooly margins.

FLOWERS—In this latitude open sometimes as early as the middle of February, but not fully developed until March, the male and female flowers in separate clusters on the same or different trees, both deep red, scarlet, orange or yellow and on long or short stems. The stamens exserted in the staminate flowers and included in the pistillate ones, the latter apparently not functioning.

FRUIT—Matures at or before the unfolding of the leaves, borne in clusters on 2" to 4" long slender stems, the keys scarlet, red, orange or yellow, the wings usually less than 1" long and diverging at an angle of about 45°. Fall from the stem or with the stem in late spring.

WOOD—Diffuse-porous, medullary rays fine; moderately heavy, softer than sugar maple and often quite soft, rather weak, not durable in contact with the soil; heartwood pale brown or reddish; sapwood very thick, white. Weighs about 38 lbs. per cu. ft. Used for furniture, kitchenware, paper pulp and fuel.

RANGE AND DISTRIBUTION—Newfoundland to eastern Minnesota, south to eastern Texas and central Florida. Very common throughout Delaware and one of the commonest trees of the forest within its range.

HABITAT—Prefers banks of streams, swamps and wet places but may often be found on uplands and dry locations. Tolerates shade.

NOTES—In summer the red maple is easily distinguished from other maples by the small leaves with bloom covered under surface. In winter it may be confused with the silver maple but is distinguished from the latter by the red lustrous twigs which when broken do not emit the disagreeable odor characteristic of silver maple. It is one of the first if not the first of our native trees to show its abundantly produced bright crimson flowers in spring, followed promptly with the more brightly colored clusters of keys. Thus by its array of red in spring, fall and winter it is justly entitled to the "red' 'in both its common and botanical names.

Despite its ornamental beauty it is not often used as a lawn or shade tree. However, several varieties of the species, cultivated for their special foliage qualities, are growing in popularity. It is to be preferred to the much planted silver maple for both street and lawn use because of the more regular form of its crown, bright colors, smaller size and longer life. Moreover, it rarely forms the wide buttress and spreading surface root union common to silver maples when occupying confining space. Although the sap is sweet it does not contain as much sugar as that of the sugar maple and accordingly is rarely gathered and boiled down.

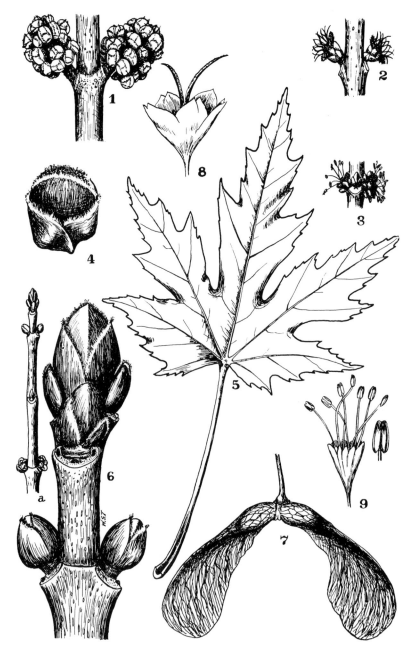

SILVER MAPLE

1. Section of twig with clusters of flower buds, natural size.
2. Section of twig with pistillate flowers, natural size.
3. Section of twig with staminate flowers, natural size.
4. Single flower bud, enlarged.
5. Leaf, x ½.
6. Terminal portion of winter twig, enlarged and (a) natural size.
7. Fruit, natural size.
8. Single pistillate flower, enlarged.
9. Single staminate flower, enlarged.

SILVER MAPLE
Acer saccharinum, Linnaeus

The silver maple, also known as white maple (c) and river maple, is a tree usually 50' to 60' tall with a trunk diameter of 1½' to 2½' but may occasionally attain a height of 120' with a trunk 4' or more in diameter. As generally observed, the trunk is short and separates 10' to 15' above the ground into several long ascending branches and generally drooping branchlets which turn up at the ends forming a broad spreading crown.

LEAVES—Opposite, 5 lobed by deep narrow sinuses which are normally rounded at the bottom, the 3 upper lobes often further lobed and sharply toothed; 4" to 7" long and nearly as broad; pale green above and, at maturity silvery white and sometimes pubescent in the axils of veins beneath; petiole 3" to 4" long, slender and often tinged with red above.

BARK—On old trunks, thick, gray, broken into vertical rows of irregularly shaped plates which are free at both ends but attached in the middle; on young trunks smooth or slightly plated and gray-brown; on the slender twigs red or tending toward brown, glossy and marked by numerous pale lenticels.

BUDS—Opposite, sessile or short stalked, leaf buds ovate, the terminal one about ⅛" long and often attended by 2 or 4 smaller compressed ones covered by shiny overlapping red scales with wooly margins; the flower buds usually in clusters, each spherical and covered with 2 outer shiny red scales and deep dull red inner ones with lighter wooly margins.

FLOWERS—Open during the first warm days of late winter, greenish yellow or pale red, the staminate and pistillate in dense clusters on the same or on different trees.

FRUIT—Matures in April and May when the leaves are nearly full grown, borne in clusters on slender drooping stems 1½" to 2" long, in paired samaras, the individual key 1" to 2" long, prominently veined with a wing sometimes ¾" broad. One samara often abortive and smaller than its mate.

WOOD—Diffuse-porous with indistinct medullary rays, moderately hard, close grained, weak and non-durable; heartwood pale brown; sapwood wide, white; weighs about 33 lbs. per cu. ft. and used for furniture, flooring, curly figured veneer, etc.

RANGE AND DISTRIBUTION—From New Brunswick and the valley of the St. Lawrence River through the Lake States to southern Minnesota, southward to eastern Oklahoma, western Florida and central Georgia. Believed originally native only in New Castle County, but having formerly been much planted as ornamental is now naturalized elsewhere in the State.

HABITAT—Prefers stream banks and borders of swamps in sandy soil, but grows very well on a wide variety of soils.

NOTES—The silver maple earns the "silver" in its name from the silvery-white under side of the distinctively shaped and deeply cut leaves. In winter it may be distinguished from the red maple by the disagreeable odor of a freshly broken or injured twig. The fruit keys are the largest produced by any species of American maple and are usually borne in great abundance. Although formerly planted in great numbers as a shade and street tree, this latter fact plus other objectionable features such as its great height and spread, the brittleness of its branches, the spreading roots, susceptibility to wood rotting fungi and comparative short life, have condemned it for such uses.

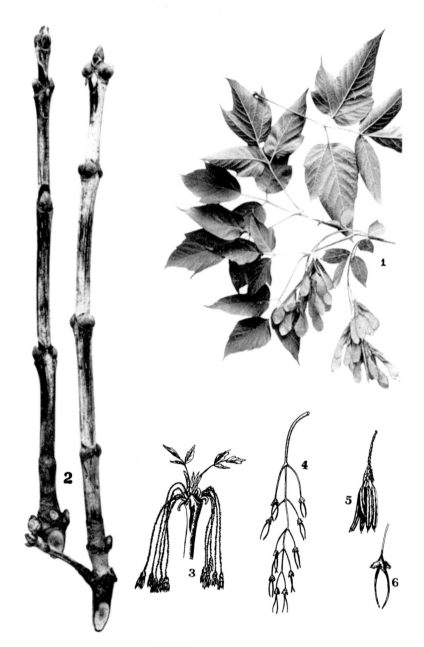

ASH-LEAVED MAPLE

1. Mature branchlet with fruit clusters, x 1/3.
2. Winter twigs, natural size.
3. Staminate flowering branchlet, natural size.
4. Raceme of pistillate flowers, natural size.
5. Single staminate flower, enlarged.
6. Single pistillate flower, enlarged.

ASH-LEAVED MAPLE
Acer negundo, Linnaeus

The ash-leaved maple or box elder is a tree usually 40' to 50' tall with a trunk diameter of 1½' to 2' but many occasionally attain a height of 70' and a trunk diameter of 4'. The trunk is often short, dividing into spreading often contorted limbs and slender branches to form a broad open crown.

LEAVES—Opposite, 3 to 5 or rarely 7 foliolate, 8" to 14" long, the individual leaflets 2" to 4" long and 2" to 3" broad, ovate or obovate with coarsely toothed or lobed margins; tomentose at first but at maturity thin, and smooth and light green above; pale green and smooth except for tufts of white hairs in the axils of the prominent midrib and veins beneath. Turn yellow in autumn. City street trees often shed some leaflets in May–June, adding to its undesirability in such locations.

BARK—On old trunks moderately thick, pale brown or gray-brown and broken by narrow fissures into narrow rounded ridges; on young trunks lighter in color and fissured; on the medium stout twigs during the first winter olive-green or purplish and splotched with white bloom, the oppositely placed, light colored, curving leaf scars joining one another at their upper ends.

BUDS—Opposite, the terminal one ovate-acute, about ¼" long, with 2 outer and 2 inner purplish red fuzz coated scales, the lateral buds globular, sub-globose or obtuse, covered by 4 scales, the two outer green or purple pair covering or nearly covering the inner pair.

FLOWERS—In March–April before or with the unfolding of the leaves, from buds of the previous season, staminate and pistillate ones on different trees, the staminate in clusters, on slender hairy drooping stems 1½" to 2½" long; the pistillate in narrow drooping racemes 4" to 5" long.

FRUIT—Fully formed by mid-summer and ripe by September, in nodding racemes 6" to 8" long, the keys joined on a 1½" to 2" long stem which persists after the keys (or samaras) often until spring, the individual samara with narrow prominently veined seed end and wing which is broadest below the middle.

WOOD—Minutely diffuse-porous, with fine colorless rays; soft, close grained, weak and not durable in contact with the soil; heartwood and sapwood cream white; weighs about 27 lbs. per cu. ft. and used for paper pulp, furniture, box boards, woodenware and fuel. Not commercially important in this state.

RANGE AND DISTRIBUTION—Vermont to Florida, westward to eastern Texas and the Plains well into Canada. Much planted and naturalized in many parts of the United States and Europe. Of questionable original nativity in Delaware but recorded in the Edward Tatnall list of plants in New Castle County (1860). Now rather common throughout the State.

HABITAT—Prefers moist rich soil but is one of the trees much used in windbreak planting in the Plains region and hence adapted to very dry soils.

NOTES—The ash-leaved maple appears to be a most descriptive common name for this species particularly since it has few characteristics similar to the elders, but does have leaflets which are similar to those of the ashes. There are many other characteristics which serve to distinguish this tree from other maples, chief among them being the olive-green twigs, the large bead-like lateral buds and the racemes of fruit maturing later in the year than other native maples.

The tree is neither important for the commercial value of its wood nor attractive as an ornamental for street or highway use because of the brittleness of its branches and the fact that it may be attacked in summer by swarms of the Box Elder Plant Bug, *Leptocoris trivittatus,* which sometimes winters in the crevices of walls of homes.

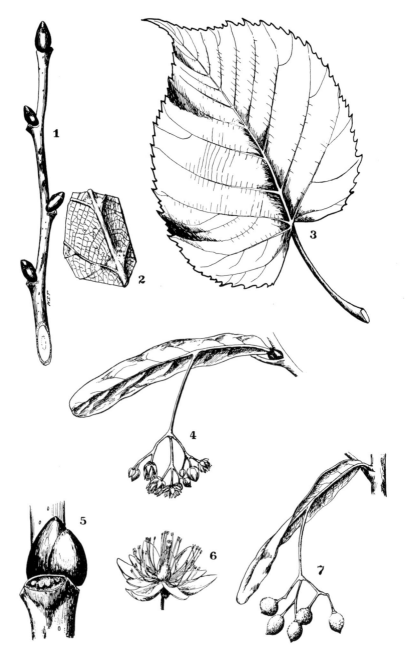

BASSWOOD

1. Winter twig, natural size.
2. Section of the lower side of a leaf, enlarged.
3. Leaf, x ½.
4. Bract with raceme of flowers, x ½.
5. Portion of winter twig enlarged to show bud and leaf scar detail.
6. Single flower, enlarged.
7. Fruit, x ½.

BASSWOOD

Tilia americana, Linnaeus

[*Tilia glabra,* Ventenat]

GENUS DESCRIPTION—The genus *Tilia* or lindens comprises some 25 to 30 species of trees distributed over the Northern Hemisphere of the world, 15 of which are native to North America and one to Delaware. Members of the genus are not only difficult to identify, because they hybridize freely and produce innumerable varieties, but there appears to be considerable confusion in the nomenclature. Several European species have been introduced into this Country as ornamentals. The great majority produce flowers rich in nectar from which bees make the finest quality honey, but the flowers of *T. tomentosa* and *T. petiolaris* are said to be poisonous to bees. The tough inner bark is manufactured into roping, mats, rough cloth, shoes, etc.

The basswood (c) also known as American basswood, American linden, linn, white wood (c) bee tree and lime tree is a large handsome tree usually 60' to 70' tall with a trunk 2' to 3' in diameter but may occasionally attain a height of 125' and a trunk diameter of 5'. Trunk tall with slender branchlets forming a dense oval head. Of rapid growth and short life, rarely exceeding 120 years of age.

LEAVES—Alternate, heart-shape with long acute tip, 4" to 8" long and nearly as broad; margins coarsely serrate with incurved often glandular teeth; at maturity thick, firm and dull dark green above, paler or yellow-green lustrous and smooth except for tufts of rusty hairs in the axils of veins, beneath; petiole slender, round and enlarged toward the base, 1½" to 2½" long.

BARK—On old trunks thick, corky, light brown, broken by deep broad furrows into narrow flat topped scaly ridges; on young trunks smooth, purplish gray, or fissured and gray-brown; on the medium stout slightly zigzag twigs finely pubescent or shiny, bright red turning green, greenish red or gray-brown the second year and marked by scattered light brown lenticels.

BUDS—Alternate, all axillary, ovoid, unsymmetrical, blunt pointed, about ⅜" long, divergent, covered by 2 outer shiny bright red or sometimes greenish scales, the outermost one making the bud unsymmetrical by its thickness and partially covering the other which enwraps the numerous light green pubescent inner ones.

FLOWERS—June, in drooping cymes attached by a 2" to 4" long stem to its 4" to 5" long linear leafy bract, flowers perfect, cream white, very fragrant and filled with nectar which the honey bees collect and make into fine flavored honey.

FRUIT—An oblong-obovoid, bony nut with rough tomentose coat, usually less than ½" long, born in cymose clusters on a long stem attached to a leafy bract which acts as a plane in disseminating the seed.

WOOD—Diffuse-porous, with colorless medullary rays; soft, light, close grained, moderately strong and tough; heartwood light brown with a tinge of red; sapwood slightly lighter and very thick; weighs 28.2 lbs. per cu. ft.; used in a great number of woodenware articles, butter tubs, candy pails, slack cooperage, berry boxes, paper pulp and formerly for butter dishes.

RANGE AND DISTRIBUTION—Confusing—In the 1953 Check List given as from New Brunswick to southern Manitoba . . . . south to eastern Neb. and Kan. . . . . and east to Mo., Ky., Tenn., and N. C. By other authors extended southward to Georgia and northeastern Texas and westward to Manitoba, the latter in most cases not recognizing some 7 species within this more inclusive range. Frequent in New Castle County, less common in Kent County and probably not native in Sussex County.

HABITAT—Prefers rich moist soil of bottomlands but is adapted to a wide range of soil and moisture.

NOTES—The American basswood is commercially important because of the straight grained soft wood it produces. Bee farmers often plant areas with the tree to afford a "pasture" from which the bees make the choicest honey. Ornamentally it is a most attractive tree of rapid growth, good form, fragrant flowers and dense foliage. It has the disadvantage of producing abundant seed and is susceptible to smoke injury, both of which often make it objectionable for city street planting. The "bass" part of the common name apparently is of European origin and refers to the use of the inner bark in making bass cloth.

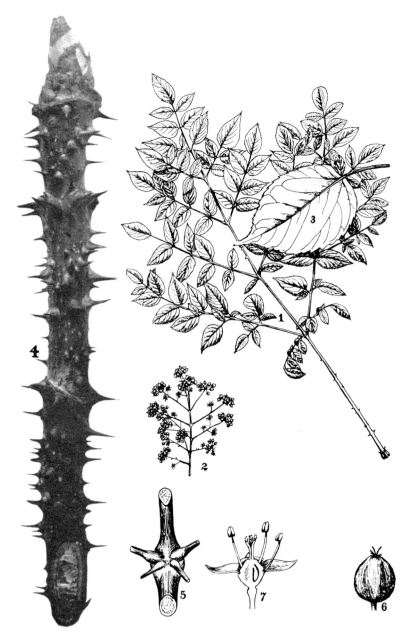

DEVIL'S CLUB

1. Leaf, x ⅛.
2. Fruit, x ⅛.
3. Leaflet, x ½.
4. Terminal portion of winter shoot, natural size.
5. Section of leaf petiole, natural size.
6. Single fruit, enlarged.
7. Single flower, enlarged.

DEVIL'S CLUB
Aralia spinosa, Linnaeus

GENUS DESCRIPTION—This genus comprises some 30 species of herbs, shrubs and small trees in North America, Asia and Malay Archipelago. Many of them possess medicinal properties. The only arborescent member native to America is described herewith.

The devil's club also known as Hercules club, devil's walking stick, angelica tree, prickly elder and spikenard tree is a small tree or large shrub, in this latitude, rarely over 15′ tall with a trunk less than 4″ in diameter. Trunk straight with rarely more than 4 forks and stout branchlets.

LEAVES—Alternate, clustered at the ends of branchlets, doubly compound, 3′ to 4′ long and nearly as wide, the smooth petiole enlarged at the base and clasping the twig or stem, armed with short sharp spines; the leaflets in opposite pairs, sessile or short stalked, ovate, 2″ to 3″ long and half as wide, sharply toothed on the margins; at maturity thin and dull green above; paler and occasionally armed on the midrib beneath.

BARK—Similar on young and old trunks, thin, light brown and divided by broad shallow fissures into broad and narrow rounded connecting ridges; inner bark bright green; on the stout ½″ to ¾″ thick shoots, light brown, armed with stout spines in a collar at the nodes and scattered between the nodes, large pale lenticels and narrow leaf scars which nearly encircle the shoot.

BUDS—Alternate, the lateral ones small (¼″) triangular, flattened, appressed to the twig at the apex of a half-dome; the terminal one, when developed, sometimes as much as 1″ long irregularly blunt conical and covered with numerous chestnut brown scales thick at the base and thin at the margin which is often split and ragged.

FLOWERS—In midsummer above the leaf on the new growth, in 3′ to 4′ long many flowered panicle-umbels, the stems pubescent and straw colored at first, later purplish and often armed with small prickles; individual flowers perfect with white or greenish white petals.

FRUIT—August, in massive panicle clusters of umbels, the single fruit an ovoid or globose berry about ⅛″ in diameter, black or deep purple, often 3 to 5 fluted, apex topped with the blackened persistent styles, the purple very juicy flesh enclosing the small seeds.

WOOD—Ring-porous with conspicuous medullary rays; light, soft, brittle; white, with a large spongy white pith.

RANGE AND DISTRIBUTION—Connecticut to southeastern Missouri, south to eastern Texas and Florida. Local throughout Delaware.

HABITAT—Prefers deep rich moist soils. Common in burned over woodlands and along fence rows.

NOTES—The spiny character of all parts of this tree distinguish it from all other species. Even so, its fruit is sometimes mistaken for and gathered as elderberries but can hardly be regarded as suitable human food. However, the bark of the roots and the berries possess stimulating and diaphoretic properties and are sometimes used as or in medicines. Commercially it is of little value but because of its tropical appearance enjoys extensive use as an ornamental especially for borders of gardens, etc.

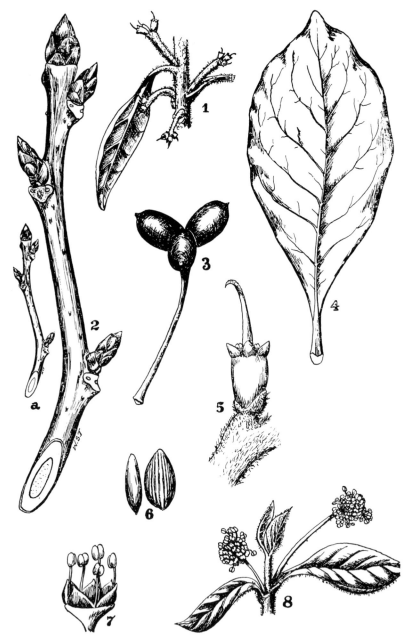

BLACK GUM

1. Section of twig with pistillate flowers, natural size.
2. Terminal portion of winter twig, enlarged and (a), natural size.
3. Fruit cluster, natural size.
4. Leaf, natural size.
5. Single pistillate flower, enlarged.
6. Two views of seed, x 2.
7. Single staminate flower, enlarged.
8. Section of spring branchlet with staminate flower clusters, natural size.

BLACK GUM
Nyssa sylvatica, Marshall

GENUS DESCRIPTION—The genus *Nyssa* is represented by 4 species in eastern North America and 2 in southern Asia, only one of which is native to Delaware.

The black gum, also known as sour gum, (c) pepperidge, white gum, (c) swamp gum and erroneously as tupelo, is usually a tree 50' to 60' tall with a trunk 1' to 2' in diameter but may occasionally attain a height of 120' with a trunk 5' in diameter. In forest stands the trunk is tall often crooked near the crown and with a few contorted limbs forming a small irregular head. In the open the trunk is rather short and clothed with many branches with spur-like branchlets to form a broad pyramidal crown.

LEAVES—Alternate, crowded toward the ends of the branchlets, obovate-oblong or oval, 2" to 5" long, 1" to 3" wide; margins entire and often thickened; at maturity thick, firm, shiny and dark green above; pale green and often pubescent beneath; turn brilliant or dark red in autumn.

BARK—On very old trunks, thick and deeply fissured into rugged ridges which have a tendency to cross fissure into rectangular blocks (Fig. 36); on young trunks less deeply fissured and ridged; on the medium stout slightly zigzag twigs at first light green or orange and often softly pubescent, becoming by the first winter lustrous, light red-gray and marked by scattered pale lenticels and raised smooth leaf scars exhibiting the ends of 3 fibro vascular bundles.

BUDS—Alternate, ovoid with acute apex, the lateral ones about ⅛" long divergent; the terminal one broadly triangular and about ¼" long, both covered by imbricated, triangular, shiny, light brown or dark purplish brown scales.

FLOWERS—In May or June when the leaves are partly developed, male and female flowers on the same or on separate trees, the male ones in dense many flowered irregular heads ½" to 1" across, on slender slightly pubescent stalks 1" to 1½" long in the axils of leaves; the female ones in pairs or few flowered clusters on a long or short stout pubescent stalk; both types greenish white in color.

FRUIT—October, singly in pairs or clusters on 1" to 2" long slender stalks each an ovoid dark blue shiny drupe ⅜" to ⅝" long, with thin flesh enclosing a single ovoid, compressed, pale brown seed marked with numerous longitudinal grooves and ribs.

WOOD—Diffuse-porous, with indistinct medullary rays and rather indistinct growth rings; moderately heavy, soft, extremely tough and cross grained: heartwood light yellow; sapwood thick white; weighs about 36 lbs. per cu. ft. Difficult to season but used for flooring, wheel hubs, rollers, heels of women's shoes, wooden shoes, chopping bowls, maul plugs, veneer for baskets and for fuel.

RANGE AND DISTRIBUTION—Maine to southern Ontario, southwestward to eastern Texas and Florida. Common throughout the State.

HABITAT—Prefers wet or moist soils and reaches its best development on such sites, but is found scattered throughout its range on most any type of soil. Generally develops a deep central tap root.

NOTES—The black gum appears to be one of the less desirable trees indigenous to the region because its wood is difficult to season, is not durable in contact with the soil and is difficult to work. Although occasionally used as an ornamental, chiefly for the bright autumnal coloration of its foliage, it is difficult to transplant except when very young. It is one of the first, if not the first, of our native trees to show the rare bright red to purple autumnal coloration which is confined to the upper surface of the leaves.

FLOWERING DOGWOOD

1. Leaf, x ½.
2. Flowering branchlet, x ½.
3. Single flower, enlarged.
4. Terminal portion of winter twig with leaf bud, enlarged.
5. Terminal portion of winter twig with leaf bud, natural size.
6. Fruit cluster, slightly enlarged.
7. Seed, slightly enlarged.
8. Terminal portion of winter twig with flower bud, x 2.

FLOWERING DOGWOOD
Cornus florida, Linnaeus

GENUS DESCRIPTION—The genus *Cornus* or dogwood comprises some 40 species of trees and shrubs or rarely herbs in the Northern Hemisphere of the world, with a single species in Peru. Of the 15 credited as native to North America 4 are found in Delaware, 2 of which attain tree size. Nearly all native and exotic species are used more or less in ornamental planting. Of the exotic species the cornelian cherry, *C. mas,* L. and its varieties is probably the most popular in this country.

The flowering dogwood, white dogwood or cornel is a small tree sometimes attaining a height of 40' and a trunk diameter of 18". Trunk short with low broad rounded crown.

LEAVES—Opposite, mostly clustered on the ends of the twigs, ovate to elliptical, usually with an abrupt apex and broad tapering base; 3" to 5" long and 1" to 3" wide; margins entire and wavy; at maturity bright green minutely hairy and roughened by sunken veins above; pale green or often nearly white and more or less pubescent beneath; petiole rather short and grooved above.

BARK—On old trunks rather thick, red-brown or weathered to reddish gray and broken into irregular squarish thick plates; on young trunks similarly roughened; on the slender upward curving twigs smooth and glossy or grainy to the touch, dark red or greenish and sometimes covered with a glaucous bloom, roughened by the enlarged opposite leaf shoulders.

BUDS—The terminal leaf buds about ¼" long, long pear-shaped and flattened at right angles to the twig node and inserted on the end of the twig, covered by 2 red outer scales which are united below the middle; the lateral leaf buds minute; the flower buds terminal, flattish-globular ¼" to ⅜" across, covered by 4 involucral scales covered, like its club-like stalk, with white pubescence.

FLOWERS—In April, from flower buds formed the previous summer, clustered and surrounded by the involucral scales which, as they unfold and enlarge, change from green to pure white, delicate cream or pink, becoming at maturity 1" to 1½" long and often purplish and notches at the tip; the true flowers, perfect, with 4 yellow strap-like corolla lobes in a tubular acutely lobed yellow-green calyx. The opposite white bracts which are sometimes mistaken for the corolla, may measure 3" to 5" from tip to tip.

FRUIT—October, borne in clusters on a moderately stout stalk, the individual drupe ½" to ⅝" long, ovoid or oblong with a shiny bright red coat and mealy yellow flesh surrounding 1 or 2 pear-shaped, grooved, bony seed.

WOOD—Diffuse-porous, with distinct rays, very hard, very strong, very tough and close grained; heartwood pale reddish brown; sapwood thick, white; weighs 50.4 lbs. per cu. ft.; used for mallets, tool handles, shaft and wheel bearings, wheel hubs, shuttles or anywhere that a hard tough close grained wood is required.

RANGE AND DISTRIBUTION—Southern Maine to eastern Kansas, southward to central Florida and eastern Texas to the mountains of northern Mexico. Common throughout the State.

HABITAT—Prefers fertile moist soils and the shade of other trees, but adapted to most any soil or exposure where ample moisture prevails.

NOTES—The merits of the flowering dogwood for ornamentation are well known and numerous varieties accentuating one or more of the attractive features have been developed. Early settlers learned from the Indians many of the medicinal properties it possesses. For instance the bark contains the same property as that of cinchona, from which quinine is derived. The simple process of chewing the twigs is reputed to be adequate to ward off fever. The powdered inner bark and pith of twigs makes a satisfactory tooth powder. Extract of the twig bark when mixed with iron sulphate is reputed to make a good black ink and the bark of the roots may be made to yield a red dye. The common name dogwood is said to owe its origin to the fact that a decoction of the bark of the European species *C. sanguinea* was at one time used to wash mangy dogs.

BLUE DOGWOOD

1. Autumn branchlet with fruit, natural size.
2. Seed, natural size.
3. Winter twig, natural size.
4. Single flower, enlarged.
5. Flowering branchlet, natural size.

BLUE DOGWOOD
Cornus alternifolia, Linnaeus

The blue fruited or alternate leaved dogwood is generally a large many stemmed shrub or occasionally small tree rarely exceeding a height of 25' and a diameter of 6". The ascending branches are clothed with numerous ascending twigs spread along the top of the branch.

LEAVES—Alternate, but like the flowering dogwood, clustered at the ends of the branchlets so that they occasionally appear opposite, 3" to 5" long and 2½" to 3½" broad, oval, broadest at or slightly below the middle tapering to a long slender point at the apex and gradually to the base; margins entire slightly wavy and abruptly curved downward; at maturity thin and, on plants in full sunlight, dull dark green, sparsely pubescent and corrugated by the depressed veins above, but on shaded plants bright green; very pale, usually nearly white and downy beneath, with prominent raised midrib and veins; petiole 1½" to 2" long, slightly grooved above, the enlarged base clasping the twig.

BARK—On old trunks similar to flowering dogwood but darker; on young trunks and large branches thin, dark red-brown and smooth or slightly fissured; on the long-jointed diverging slender twigs, glossy reddish green at first, turning darker and often mottled with white, the leaf scars narrowly lunate and partially encircling the twig.

BUDS—Alternate or rarely opposite, mostly terminal, long-oval, covered by a few loose fitting shiny red-brown scales.

FLOWERS—May and June, in oval to flat cymes 1½" to 2½" across, terminal on the new growth of lateral branchlets, the individual flowers perfect, ¼" across with 4 cream colored narrow petals.

FRUIT—October, in loose spreading clusters on red stalks, a subglobse dark blue bloom covered drupe about 1/3" in diameter, depressed at the apex with thin bitter flesh surrounding an obovoid thick shelled and grooved nutlet containing one or two seeds.

WOOD—Similar to flowering dogwood. Not commercially important.

RANGE AND DISTRIBUTION—Nova Scotia to Minnesota, south to northern Georgia and eastern Florida. Frequent in the northern part of New Castle County, but rare elsewhere in that county and believed not native in other counties of the State.

HABITAT—Prefers moist soil of stream banks and edges of swamps, but is common along fence rows, the edges of forests and waste places.

NOTES—The blue fruited dogwood is sometimes planted as an ornamental but otherwise is commercially unimportant. It may be distinguished at a distance by the tiers of foliage masses apparently caused by the more or less whorled arrangements of the branches.

Other species of *Cornus* recorded as native to Delaware but of shrubby growth are: red osier dogwood, *C. stolonifera*, Michx.; rough leaf dogwood *C. asperifolia*, Michx.; panicle dogwood *C. paniculata* L'Her. and purple dogwood *C. amomum*, Mill.

MOUNTAIN LAUREL

1. Flowering branchlet, x ½.
2. Fruiting branchlet, x ½.

MOUNTAIN LAUREL
Kalmia latifolia, Linnaeus

GENUS DESCRIPTION—The genus *Kalmia* named after Peter Kalm, a Swedish botanist, comprises 7 species of shrubs, only one of which occasionally attains tree size. All are native to eastern North America with one in Cuba. Two are native to Delaware. The sheep laurel, *K. angustifolia* rarely exceeds 2½' in height.

The mountain laurel or calico bush is a shrub which occasionally attains tree form and a height of 30'. At such times the trunk is inclined, gnarled and crooked with a rounded crown composed of contorted branches and slender forked branchlets.

LEAVES—Alternate, or in 2's or 3's, clustered on the ends of branchlets, evergreen, oblong and tapering to an acute, often callous tip and gradually to the base, 2" to 4" long and 1" to 1½" wide; margins entire; at maturity thick, leathery, glossy and dark green except for the yellow midrib above, light green and smooth except for the prominent midrib beneath; deciduous by the end of the second year.

BARK—On old trunks very thin, rich dark red-brown and longitudinally fissured into flat ridges which will shred into long strips; on the slender straight twigs at first reddish green and covered with sticky hairs, later becoming bright green and, by the second year, red-brown.

BUDS—Alternate, the leaf buds formed early in the year in the axils of leaves below the flower buds, covered by numerous overlapping pubescent green scales coated with sticky white hairs; the flower buds are actually the undeveloped flowers and occur in tight clusters above the leaf buds.

FLOWERS—May or June from the flower buds which began to develop with the beginning of spring growth and form many flowered corymbs 3" to 5" across; the single flower on a slender hairy and sticky stem, the corolla nearly 1" across, pink, 5 sided with the numerous anthers held under tension in depressions until released when they spring up to catapult the pollen onto the stigma.

FRUIT—September, in clusters on long slender pubescent stalks persisting until the following year, each fruit a globular, 5 lobed, light brown seed filled capsule, about ¼" in diameter, rusty pubescent coated and surmounted by the persistent style.

WOOD—Diffuse-porous, hard, close grained, strong; heartwood light reddish brown; sapwood lighter; weighs about 44 lbs. per cu. ft. and used in turnery, for novelty wooden articles; rustic furniture, tobacco pipes and fuel.

RANGE AND DISTRIBUTION—From New Brunswick, southward along the mountains and Coastal Plain to Florida and Arkansas. Common and local throughout the State.

HABITAT—Requires rich moist soils with a high humus content. Usually prefers the shade of other trees but often forms impenetrable thickets on mountain tops and slopes below 3,000' in elevation.

NOTES—Although the mountain laurel rarely attains tree size in this State, failure to include a description of it in this publication might be construed as unjust treatment of the most attractive shrub of our forest flora. Its just popularity as a plant for ornamental use is greatly curtailed by the fact that it will not thrive on lime bearing soils. It has been adopted as the state flower of Connecticut. Numerous varieties, cultivated for ornamental use are recognized in the nursery trade.

Roping made from the shoots was a sizeable item in the Christmas greens industry of Delaware. Elsewhere, the wood is commercially important and when harvested for the manufacture of tobacco pipes is sold by the pound.

The foliage is generally regarded as poisonous to browsing animals, but deer appear to be able to feed on it to a limited extent without succumbing. The poisonous effect of *K. angustifolia* on such animals is definitely established and honey made from the blossoms appears to be poisonous to some people.

PERSIMMON

1. Fruiting branchlet, x 2/3.
2. Section of branchlet with pistillate flower, natural size.
3. Section of twig, enlarged.
4. Terminal portion of winter twig, natural size.
5. Section of branchlet with staminate flowers, natural size.
6. Ripened fruit, x 2/3.
7 Seed, natural size.

PERSIMMON
Diospyros virginiana, Linnaeus

GENUS DESCRIPTION—The genus *Diospyros* is represented by more than 200 species, mostly tropical. Of these only two, both arborescent, occur in North America. Several of the tropical species furnish the ebony wood of commerce and several Asiatic species or varieties are cultivated for their large fruits.

The persimmon, also known as simmon, dog berry, date plum and possum wood, is a tree usually 40' to 60' tall with a trunk diameter of 16" to 24". Trunk usually straight with little taper into the broad spreading crown where it breaks into stout contorted limbs with drooping branchlets.

LEAVES—Alternate, elliptical with acute apex and wedge-shaped or rounded base 4" to 6" long, 2" to 3" wide; margin entire and wavy; thick leathery dark green and shiny except for the broad yellowish midrib above; pale green and often with minute black spots and prominent midrib beneath; petiole ½" to 1" long, stout.

BARK—On old trunks thick, dark red-brown or weathered dark gray and broken into thick rectangular blocks; on the moderately stout twigs, light brown or grayish and roughened by enlarged leaf bases exhibiting a broadly lunate depressed leaf scar. Pith sometimes chambered.

BUDS—Alternate, all axillary, broadly ovoid, slightly flattened about ⅛" long, covered by 2 dull dark brown or purplish scales.

FLOWERS—May and June on the new growth when the leaves are nearly full grown, staminate and pistillate flowers on different trees, the staminate in 2 to 3 flowered axillary stalked clusters, corolla cream white, about ½" long, tubular and constricted below the 4 short lobes, enclosing the 16 stamens; the pistillate solitary on a very short hairy stalk with large 4 lobed hairy bract clasping the cream-white corolla, ¾" long and broader than the staminate ones, the stamens rudimentary and 8 in number.

FRUIT—October, borne on female trees only, a spherical berry ¾" to 2" in diameter, on a very short stout stem; when mature but still green, bloom coated, firm and very astringent but when ripened, generally by one or more severe frosts, is dark orange, shriveled, and of rare sweet flavor. Seed 8 or less in each berry arranged radially from the center, about ½" long, oblong, flattish, with thick hard shiny chestnut brown coat.

WOOD—Ring-porous, medullary rays inconspicuous, heavy, hard, tough, close grained, strong, difficult to season but takes a high polish; heartwood dark brown or black but rarely present in trees less than a century old; sapwood yellowish white; weighs about 49 lbs. per cu. ft.; used for shuttles, shoe lasts, golf clubs, imitation ebony and fuel.

RANGE AND DISTRIBUTION—Connecticut to Florida, westward through southern Pennsylvania to eastern Kansas and eastern Texas. Common throughout the State.

HABITAT—Not choosy as to soil fertility or moisture, but prefers sunlight.

NOTES—Most people know the female persimmon tree by its fruits which are eaten by humans, dogs, and forest creatures such as the raccoon, possum and fox. The wood is not commercially important in this region.

SWEET LEAF

1. Autumn branchlet with leaves and fruit, x ⅓.
2. Winter twig with flower buds, natural size.
3. Winter twig with leaf buds, natural size.

SWEET LEAF
Symplocos tinctoria, L'Heritier

GENUS DESCRIPTION—This genus with some 285 species, mostly tropical, is represented in eastern North America by the single species described herein.

The sweet leaf or horse sugar is a small tree 20' to 30' tall with a trunk rarely more than 10" in diameter. Trunk 10' to 15' tall with slender upright branches above and horizontal ones below forming a pyramidal open head.

LEAVES—Alternate, oblong or obovate, 4" to 6" long, 1" to 2" wide: margin obscurely round toothed from the center to the acute apex, but often entire below the middle; at maturity, leathery glossy and dark green with large convex midrib above, pale green, pubescent and with stout yellowish midrib beneath; petiole short, stout. Leaves often persist partly through winter in this State.

BARK—On old trunks thin, close fitting, smooth, ashy gray or splotched with purplish areas, broken by scattered non-continuous fissures with callous edges; on young trunks smooth ashy gray or purplish gray; on the slender upcurving twigs at first pale green and fuzz coated, becoming smooth and dull gray or reddish gray and marked by semicircular leaf scars exhibiting a central bundle scar. Pith is chambered.

BUDS—Alternate, the lateral leaf buds, obtuse, very small and stand out from the twig; the terminal leaf bud about ¼" long, angular, covered with 3 deep dull red to greenish red scales, the two opposite scales overlapping the third; the flower buds globular, divergent, about ¼" in diameter, covered by several round tipped scales, usually reddish green in color but with a red marginal band.

FLOWERS—March–April, from buds formed the previous season in the axils of the leaves, sessile, usually in whorls, each perfect, with a 5 lobed, bell-shaped, fuzzy, creamy-white corolla ½" across; delicately fragrant.

FRUIT—September, a ½" long tubular drupe with thin bloom covered orange-brown skin covering a bony seed.

WOOD—Diffuse-porous with inconspicuous rays and poorly defined annual rings, light, soft, close grained; heartwood reddish; sapwood thick, nearly white. Not commercially important.

RANGE AND DISTRIBUTION—Coast region from Delaware to Texas and inland to the Blue Ridge Mts. Common in the Cedar Swamp region of Sussex County. Most northern location in State so far reported is near Redden.

HABITAT—Particular in its requirements and demands rich moist soils in this latitude but further south in its range ascends to altitudes of over 3,000'. Prefers deep shade.

NOTES—The common names applied to this tree are derived from the fact that the leaves are rather sweet in taste and are devoured by browsing animals, particularly horses. The leaves, bark and fruit contain a yellow sap which is occasionally used as a dye.

The sweet leaf is perhaps the oddest tree of Delaware's flora in that it is rarely seen by the roadside and thrives under the densest shade seeming to waste its beauty in the darkness of the hummocks of peat swamps. When observed in its native haunts one is so struck by its singular beauty that it is not soon forgotten. It is not known in cultivation and is probably not hardy out of its natural range and habitat.

Family: OLEACEAE

Genus: FRAXINUS

THE ASHES

The genus *Fraxinus* with about 50 species in the temperate portions of the Northern Hemisphere of the world and Cuba, is represented by 16 species in North America. Four or five of these are found in Delaware.

The ashes for the most part are important timber trees producing wood which, for special uses, is superior to hickory. There is so little difference in the strength and shock resistance qualities of the species indigenous to eastern United States that the wood, with the exception of that of the black ash, is generally sold as white ash. Because the ashes are quite exacting in their preference for rich moist or wet soil, they are rarely used successfully in reforestation planting in this region.

Although the ashes, as a group, are easily recognized by their compound **leaves** which occur oppositely on the branch and are composed of an odd number of leaflets also opposite on the petiole, the leaf characteristics of the individual species does not necessarily readily identify it.

The trunk **bark** is distinctive and aids in identifying the various species. Generally speaking those producing the best wood have more or less diamond-shaped and narrow ridges. The black ash alone has a corky scaly bark.

The **buds** are opposite and terminal and range from reddish to black in color.

The **flowers** are borne in dense clusters in early spring usually preceding the leaves, the male and female usually on separate trees but occasionally on the same tree.

The **fruit** is a winged samara usually with a single elongated seed cavity on the stem end. They are borne in large clusters and ripen in the fall.

The **wood** is ring-porous, generally straight grained, tough, and with high resistance to shock. It is manufactured into tool handles, sporting goods, wagon wheels and furniture.

In some sections the ashes are popular as shade, street and ornamental trees and in the Plains States, the green ash is much used in windbreak and protection plantings.

The southern European species *F. ornus,* L., produces manna as an exudation from the trunk and some of the Chinese species notably *F. chinesis,* Roxbg., and *F. mariesi,* Hook., produce the Chinese white wax of commerce.

With only the winter characteristics present, it is difficult for the trained dendrologist to distinguish between the red, white and green ashes in Delaware. The layman should therefore be content to identify them when most of the distinguishing characteristics are present.

WHITE ASH

1. Autumn branchlet with leaves and fruit. x ¼.
2. Winter twig, x ½.

WHITE ASH
Fraxinus americana, Linnaeus

The white ash (c) is a tree usually 60' to 75' tall with a trunk diameter of 1½" to 2½", but may occasionally attain a height of 120' and a trunk diameter of 6'. In forest stands the trunk is tall, straight and clear of limbs for the greater portion of its length ending in a narrow oval head. In the open, the trunk is usually short and the crown broad and rounded.

LEAVES—Opposite, compound, 8" to 14" long, with 5 to 9 but usually 7 leaflets on a stout grooved petiole. Leaflets short stalked, 3" to 5" long about 1½" wide, acute at the apex, tapering or rounded at the base; margins entire, wavy or obscurely toothed toward the apex; at maturity usually smooth and dark green above, pale green or slightly pale pubescent and with prominent midrib and veins beneath; turn bright yellow before falling in the fall.

BARK—On old trunks 1" to 1½" thick, gray-brown, divided by deep diamond-shaped fissures and interlacing flat-topped ridges of closely appressed scales; on young trunks lighter brown and irregularly narrow and deep fissured; on the stout twigs at first green and often bloom covered, flattened and enlarged laterally at the nodes, becoming grayish brown and lustrous by the end of the first winter, marked by scattered large pale lenticels and opposite semicircular light brown leaf scars notched at the top and exhibiting a line of darker bundle scars.

BUDS—Opposite and terminal; the terminal one obtuse or broadly ovoid with 4 pairs of scales, the exposed ones granular brown, the outermost pair thick, ovate with acute keeled tip, covering the joining margins of the second and third pairs at the base. The lateral buds small, obtuse or sub-globular, inserted in the top of the leaf scar, the first pair at the same level as the terminal one.

FLOWERS—May before the leaves, staminate and pistillate on different trees, the staminate in dense purplish brown clusters often more than 1" across; the pistillate in upright open panicles 2" to 4" long.

FRUIT—October and often persists into the winter, samaras borne in dense drooping panicles about 7" long, the individual samara about 1½" long and consist of cigar-shaped seed end from the bottom end of which extends a flat linear wing which is occasionally notched at the bottom. The wing aids in wind and water dissemination of the seed.

WOOD—Ring-porous, with large pores in spring wood and smaller ones in wavy rows in the summer wood; medullary rays fine and inconspicuous; hard, flexible, strong and tough; heartwood light brown; sapwood thick, lighter; weighs 40.7 lbs. per cu. ft. and used for tool handles, wagon wheels, sporting goods, furniture, oars and canoes.

RANGE AND DISTRIBUTION—Nova Scotia to Minnesota, southward to northeastern Texas and northern Florida. Common throughout Delaware, but not as common as red ash.

HABITAT—Prefers rich moist but well drained soils usually adjacent streams and bodies of water.

NOTES—The white ash may be distinguished from the red ash by the absence of velvet on the twigs which is characteristic of the latter. The leaf scars of white ash are semicircular or lunate convex and notched by the bud, while those of red ash are often semielliptical, only slightly or not notched by the bud, and are mostly concave. By scraping the bark of the twig of white ash the color of the shaving will be observed as pale brown, while the same act on a red ash twig will show a deep orange-red shaving. The leaflets of the white and red ash are short stalked, the former more so, while those of the black ash except for the terminal one are sessile and sharply toothed on the margin. The first pair of lateral buds of the white ash generally occur beside and at the same level as the terminal one.

RED ASH

1. Autumn branchlet with leaves and fruit, x ¼.
2. Winter twig, natural size.
3. Branchlet with staminate flower clusters, x ½.

RED ASH
Fraxinus pennsylvanica, Marshall

The red ash is a medium sized tree usually 50' to 60' tall with a trunk 1' to 1½' in diameter, but may occasionally reach a height of 70' and a trunk diameter of 5'. In forest stands the trunk is moderately tall and straight with stout upright branches and branchlets forming a thin irregularly shaped crown.

LEAVES—Opposite, compound with 5 to 9 (usually 7) short stalked leaflets on a 10" to 12" long slightly grooved finely pubescent petiole; leaflets 3" to 6" long and 1" to 1½" wide with long pointed apex and usually unequal wedge-shaped base; margins obscurely toothed, but sometimes entire and wavy below the middle; at maturity thin, firm, smooth and light green above, pale and softly pubescent with prominent yellowish midrib beneath.

BARK—On old trunks ½" to ¾" thick, light reddish brown and broken by short narrow fissures into flat finely scaled ridges, sometimes diamond-shaped but the diamonds shallower and narrower than white ash and the ridge more often broken by cross fissures; on young trunks buff colored and more finely fissured; on the moderately slender twigs at first coated with pale pubescence which may persist until the second season or disappear by the end of the year leaving a dull or shiny greenish gray minutely fissured surface marked by large elongated pale lenticels and semi-orbicular leaf scars exhibiting a fine central row of fibro-vascular bundle scars shaped into a "c". The shaving of a twig, when scraped, is orange-red and the inner bark of the branches is of similar color.

BUDS—Opposite and terminal; the terminal one about ¼" long, usually slightly inclined, acute, truncate, with 3 pairs of scales, the outer pair granular red-brown or rufous tomentose, not sharply keeled but abruptly truncate at the apex and shorter than the other pairs; the lateral buds obtuse or subglobose, not or slightly inserted in the top of the leaf scar, the first pair usually below the plane of the terminal bud.

FLOWERS—May, with the leaves, male and female flowers on separate trees, the male ones in dense purplish red clusters, the female ones in open pubescent panicles.

FRUIT—September in open panicle clusters, each a samara 1" to 2" long, the thin cigar-shaped many ribbed seed end attached to a lance-shaped wing beginning at about the middle of the narrow seed cavity.

WOOD—Similar to and used for the same purposes as white ash, but somewhat inferior to it in strength.

RANGE AND DISTRIBUTION—New Brunswick to South Dakota, south to eastern Kansas, Missouri, northern Alabama and northern Florida. Common, in its habitat, throughout Delaware.

HABITAT—Observed in this State in moist rich soils along streams and in swamps, but ascends to higher altitudes where there is sufficient moisture.

NOTES—The red ash resembles white ash in many of its characteristics but may be distinguished from it by the absence of prominent diamonds in the trunk bark, by the fruit with wing extending along the seed cavity and by the orange-red color of the shaving when a twig is scraped. The presence of fine pubescence on the winter twigs usually suffices to identify the true red ash from the variety or species known as green ash. In eastern United States the green ash may be identified from the red ash by the brighter green leaflets with sharply toothed margins and in winter by the smooth gray twigs.

GREEN ASH

1. Autumn branchlet with fruit. x ½.
2. Winter twig, natural size.

GREEN ASH

Fraxinus pennsylvanica lanceolata, Sargent

[*Fraxinus lanceolata,* Borkhausen]

[*Fraxinus viridis,* Michaux]

The green ash is considered by some authors as a distinct species but by others as a variety of red ash which it most closely resembles. Although in the eastern part of its range its characteristics vary slightly from red ash, trees east of the Mississippi River exhibit more pronounced differences. The main differences between it and the red ash are:

(1) Narrower shorter and more sharply serrate leaflets which are bright green on both sides.

(2) Pubescence usually absent on the leaf stalk, underside of leaflets and twigs, i.e. resembling white ash.

(3) Terminal bud often overhanging its supporting stalk, alone and usually well above the first pair of lateral ones.

(4) Diamonds of bark of old trees not as broad as white ash and broader than red ash.

RANGE AND DISTRIBUTION—Because of its resemblance to red and white ash probably is imperfectly known, but usually recorded from Maine to western Florida westward to Texas, Arizona, Alberta and Saskatchewan. Imperfectly known in Delaware but believed mixed with both white and red ash wherever these occur.

BLACK ASH

1. Autumn branchlet with leaves and fruit, x ¼.
2. Winter twig, natural size.

BLACK ASH
Fraxinus nigra, Marshall

The black ash, also known as hoop ash, basket ash, swamp ash, water ash and cork bark ash, is a tree usually 50' to 60' tall with a trunk diameter of less than 1' but may rarely attain a height of 90' and a trunk diameter of 3' to 4'.

LEAVES—Opposite, compound, 12" to 16" long with 7 to 11 sessile (except the terminal) leaflets on a stout petiole; leaflets lanceolate with long acute apex and tapering or rounded and usually uneven base; 4" to 7" long, 1" to 2" wide; margins with small incurved teeth; at maturity dark green with sunken midrib above, slightly paler and with yellowish red hairs along the midrib beneath.

BARK—On young and old trunks thin, gray and divided by shallow fissures into irregular corky scaly ridges; on the medium stout twigs, at first slightly hairy but soon smooth ashy gray or light red-brown, becoming during the winter darker and marked by numerous large pale lenticels and large pale leaf scars with bundle scars often in the shape of a "D".

BUDS—Opposite and terminal, similar to other ashes but dark brown or black.

FLOWERS—In May, before the leaves, the male and female flowers on the same or on different trees, the male ones in dense purplish clusters, the female ones in open panicles 2" to 5" long.

FRUIT—September and often persisting into winter, borne in horizontal drooping panicles 8" to 10" long, the individual samara 1" to 1½" long, oblong, with flattish comparatively broad wing usually notched on the outer end and completely surrounding the seed cavity.

WOOD—Ring-porous, with pores taking up about half the width of the annual ring and few pores in late wood; medullary rays fine, inconspicuous; weak, soft, tough, coarse grained and readily separable along the rings; heartwood dark brown, sapwood white; weighs about 39 lbs. per cu. ft. and used for interior finish, basket and chair splints, and formerly for barrel hoops and furniture.

RANGE AND DISTRIBUTION—Quebec to Manitoba, south to New Castle County Delaware, Virginia, West Virginia and Indiana. Not common in New Castle County and not observed by the author in either Kent or Sussex County.

HABITAT—Prefers wet and swampy sites along streams and in swamps. Reaches its maximum development in the north central portion of its range.

NOTES—The black ash may be distinguished from all other native ashes in summer by the sessile dark green leaflets which are decidedly toothed on the margins, and in winter by the black buds and corky scaly grayish bark of the trunk. In autumn the broad samaras with wings extending from the apex of the flattish seed cavity are characteristic. In all other native ashes the wing does not start higher than the center of the seed cavity which generally is cigar-shaped—not flattened as in the black ash.

The tree is of little commercial importance at the present time and because of its love for water is unsuited to ornamental use.

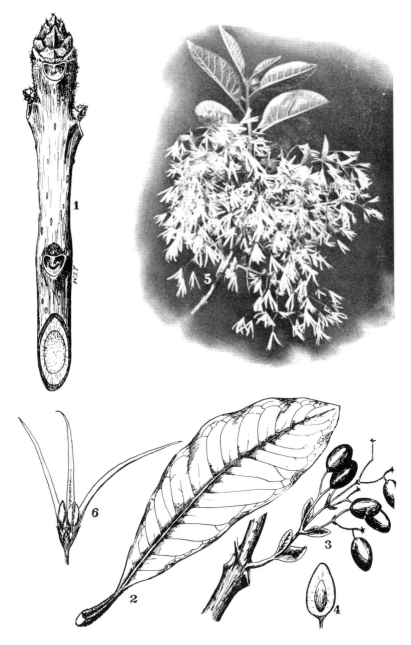

FRINGE TREE

1. Portion of thrifty winter twig, x 2.
2. Leaf, x ½.
3. Section of branchlet with fruit, x ½.
4. Section of berry, natural size.
5. Flowering branchlet, x ¼.
6. An apparently staminate flower, enlarged.

FRINGE TREE
Chionanthus virginica, Linnaeus

GENUS DESCRIPTION—The genus *Chionanthus* is represented by only one other species in the world, the *C. retusa,* Lindley, indigenous to eastern Asia.

The fringe tree, also known as white fringe, old man's beard, gray beard and flowering ash, is more often a shrub than a tree. When it attains tree size it rarely exceeds a height of 25' and a diameter of 10". Trunk short and usually inclined, with stout ascending branches, in the open, forming a broad dense globose head.

LEAVES—Opposite or nearly so, simple, clustered at the ends of the branchlets, ovate, 4" to 8" long, 1" to 3" wide, widest at or above the middle with short apex and wedge-shaped base; margins entire or turned under; rusty pubescent beneath at first but at maturity thick, leathery, shiny and deep green above, pale and smooth beneath except on the broad and conspicuous midrib and veins which often retain the pubescence; petiole short, stout and grooved above. The leaves bear a resemblance to those of tropical evergreens but are early deciduous.

BARK—On old trunks, thin, reddish brown and broken by irregular short fissures; on the stout twigs light green and pubescent at first, becoming at length slightly or strongly 4 angled yellowish gray, often retaining some pubescence and marked by opposite semi-circular deeply concave leaf scars and scattered large raised orange tinged lenticels.

BUDS—Opposite or nearly so and terminal, the terminal one broadly pyramidal, sharply 4 angled, about ¼" long covered with keeled, sharp pointed, oppositely set scales which are light brown at the base, grayish white toward the tip and are hairy on the margins.

FLOWERS—Borne in loose mildly fragrant drooping pubescent panicles 4" to 6" long in May or June when the leaves are about half grown, male and female flowers on the same or different plants or perfect with 3 to 5 white linear petals ¾" to 1" long. The main stem of the panicle often equipped with oppositely placed sessile leafy bracts.

FRUIT—September, in few fruited panicles with opposite leafy bracts often 2" long scattered along the central stem; the individual drupe egg-shaped or oblong, ½" to ¾" long, with thick dark blue shiny or bloom covered skin and yellowish pulp inclosing an ovoid flattish thin-shelled seed.

WOOD—Ring-porous with inconspicuous rays, close grained, hard; heartwood light brown; sapwood lighter; weighs 39.7 lbs. per cu. ft. Not commercially important.

RANGE AND DISTRIBUTION—Southern Pennsylvania and Delaware, south to southern Arkansas, eastern Texas and western Florida. Comparatively rare and local but present in many localities throughout the State.

HABITAT—Prefers rich moist soil of stream banks and edges of swamps but ascends to elevations of 4,000' in the southern Appalachian Mts.

NOTES—The fringe tree gets its common name from its white lacy inflorescence which literally covers the tree with whiteness in late spring. It enjoys considerable use as an ornamental lawn shrub or tree, but is not as extensively used in this State as many flowering trees of foreign origin. Because of its preference for wet places which make it difficult to establish on drier sites, the nursery trade has adopted the practice of grafting it on the white or green ash which will thrive on drier soils. The bark is said to contain medical properties useful in the treatment of fevers, as a tonic and diuretic.

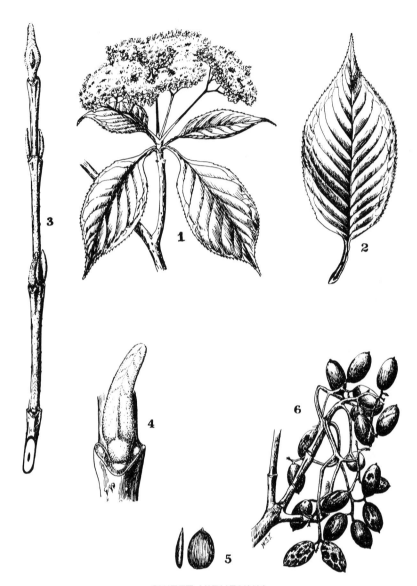

SWEET VIBURNUM

1. Flowering branchlet, x ½.
2. Leaf, x ½.
3. Winter twig, natural size.
4. Portion of winter twig, enlarged to show bud and leaf scar.
5. Seed, natural size.
6. Fruiting branchlet, natural size.

SWEET VIBURNUM
Viburnum lentago, Linnaeus

GENUS DESCRIPTION—The Viburnums are shrubs or small trees, numbering about 120 species, widely scattered throughout the temperate regions of both the Northern and Southern Hemispheres. Of the 15 species indigenous to North America, 4 are arborescent. Two of these are native to Delaware. The native and introduced species and their varieties are among the most attractive ornamental shrubs and enjoy wide use for such. Besides exhibiting showy flowers, fruits and foliage—which is sometimes evergreen as in *V. rhytidophyllum*—the leaves of deciduous species generally turn bright colors in autumn. The flowers of *V. carlesii,* which are borne in large globose cymes, are among the most fragrant flowers produced on any shrub.

Sweet viburnum, also known as nannyberry, sheepberry, wild raisin and stinking viburnum, is a shrub or small tree usually 10' to 15' tall but may occasionally attain a height of 30' with a trunk 10" in diameter. Trunk short, often in clusters, with outward arching branches and pendulous branchlets forming a rounded or globose head.

LEAVES—Opposite, clustered at the ends of the branchlets, ovate or oval with an abruptly acute long apex and gradually narrowing or rounded base, 2½" to 5" long, 1" to 1¾" wide; margins sharply toothed with incurved callous teeth; at maturity bright green and shiny above, yellowish green and marked by small black dots and a conspicuous midrib beneath; petiole broad, grooved above, those of the lower pairs of leaves rusty pubescent and with intermittent narrow wings.

BARK—On old trunks reddish brown, divided into small thick rectangular scaly surfaced plates; on the slender twigs at first greenish and covered with rusty pubescence, later becoming light red, rough to the touch and marked by pale orange colored raised lenticels and a V-like leaf scar marked by 3 large bundle scars: Bark of twigs emits a disagreeable unmistakable odor.

BUDS—Opposite and terminal, reddish brown, naked and rough to the touch; the leaf buds long, slender, flattened toward the apex and often curved; those ultimately developing into flower bearing branchlets are about ¾" long, globular near the base and abruptly constricted into a long conical or compressed point.

FLOWERS—April to June after the leaves, in convex cymes 3" to 5" across, the single flower about ¼" across, perfect, with 4 lobed cream colored corolla.

FRUIT—September, in slender red stemmed drooping clusters, each an oval, dark blue or black sometimes bloom covered drupe, about ½" long, with thick skin and juicy sweet flesh surrounding a flat oval stone having a pointed base.

WOOD—Diffuse-porous, heavy, hard, close grained; heartwood yellowish brown and with the same very disagreeable persistent "stinking feet" odor common to other parts of the plant. Not commercially important.

RANGE AND DISTRIBUTiON—Quebec to Saskatchewan; in the east, southward in the Coastal Plain to northern Virginia and along the Appalachian Mts. to Georgia and, in the west, through Ohio to eastern Nebraska, Wyoming and Colorado. Frequent in New Castle County but rare in Kent and Sussex Counties.

HABITAT—Prefers moist soils and the banks of streams, borders of swamps and moist places on rocky hillsides.

NOTES—The chief identifying characteristic of the sweet viburnum is the very disagreeable and strong odor not unlike that of dirty sheep or goats, (hence sheepberry and nannyberry) which emanates from the plant. The "sweet" and "raisin" parts of binomial common names applied to this viburnum no doubt refer to the sweet taste of the fruit and the fact that it may often be found on the tree in a shriveled and dry form late in the fall.

BLACK HAW

1. Winter twig, natural size.
2. Portion of branchlet with cyme of flowers, x ½.
3. Leafy branchlet, x ½.
4. A terminal flower bud, natural size.
5. Single flower, enlarged.
6. Fruit in section, enlarged.
7. Fruiting branchlet, x ½.
8. Leaf scar, enlarged.
9. Seed stone, x 2.

BLACK HAW
Viburnum prunifolium, Linnaeus

The black haw or stag bush is generally a small bushy tree which occasionally attains a height of 25' and a trunk diameter of 8". The trunk, in this latitude, is usually straight and clothed nearly to the base with many stiff horizontal branches beset with slender rigid spine-like horizontal branchlets.

LEAVES—Opposite, ovate with short or acute pointed apex and usually tapering base, 1" to 3" long and ½" to 2" wide; margins finely toothed with incurved callous tipped teeth; at maturity thick, often leathery, dark green and smooth above; pale green beneath; petiole short, often grooved above and on vigorous shoots, often with a narrow winged margin.

BARK—On old trunks thin, reddish brown, broken into thick irregular plate-like scales; on the slender, stiff, spine-like opposite spreading twigs at first red or pinkish and smooth, soon becoming green and later reddish, splotched with film-like gray bloom and marked by raised orange colored lenticels and enlarged nodes bearing opposite U or V-shaped leaf scars marked with 3 button-like fibro-vascular bundle scars.

BUDS—Opposite, the leaf buds about ¼" long, covered by 2 opposite grayish red grainy surfaced scales; the buds containing flower bearing branchlets of similar color and surface but ½" to ¾" long, with a bulbous expansion near the base abruptly constricted into a long apex.

FLOWERS—May, in dense terminal flat or slightly concave cymes 2" to 4" across, the single flower perfect, about ¼" across, with a corolla having 5 broad white lobes.

FRUIT—October, in upright red stalked clusters, each an ovoid, dark blue heavily bloom coated, sweet, juicy drupe containing a flat, rather rectangular stone.

WOOD—Similar to sweet viburnum but without the disagreeable odor.

RANGE AND DISTRIBUTION—Connecticut to Iowa, southward to eastern Kansas and northern Georgia. Local throughout the State and quite common in some localities.

HABITAT—Prefers dry uplands along fence rows, roadsides and margins of forests, where it often forms dense thickets.

NOTES—The black haw is most easily distinguished from the sweet viburnum by the dense spur-like branching and the absence of the disagreeable odor characteristic of the latter. The flower clusters of the black haw are usually flat topped while those of the other arborescent species are convex. Both may be distinguished from the shrubby maple leaved viburnum, *V. acerifolium* which has maple-like leaves and from the arrowwood, *V. dentatum* which has coarsely dentate leaves.

The fruit of the black haw is edible and the bark, especially that of the roots, contains medicinal properties valuable as an ingredient of tonics and diuretics.

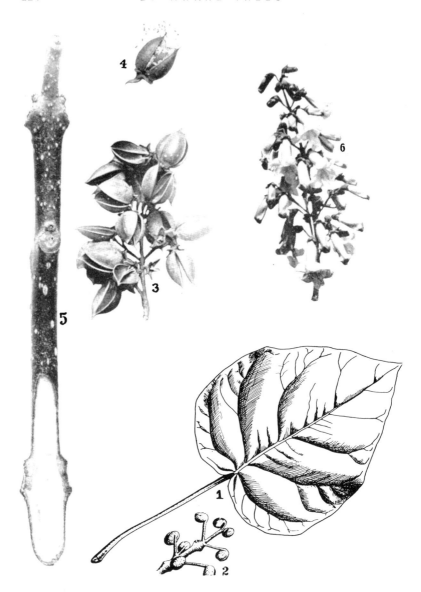

EMPRESS TREE

1. Leaf, x about ¼.
2. Portion of dormant flower panicle. x ¼.
3. Fruit stalk with empty capsules. x ½.
4. Single fruit with seed. x ⅕.
5. Winter twig, natural size.
6. Panicle of flowers, x ¼.

EMPRESS TREE
Paulownia tomentosa (Thunberg) Steudel

The empress tree, also known as princess tree, paulownia and blue catalpa, is a native of the Orient but has been much planted as an ornamental in eastern United States. It attains heights of 60' to 80' and a trunk diameter of 2' to 4'. Trunk usually short, dividing into large branches with stout laterals to form a wide spreading, uneven, rather flat topped crown.

LEAVES—Opposite, broadly heart-shaped, 5" to 8" long and nearly as broad but longer and broader (sometimes 4' long), on young vigorous shoots; margins entire; at maturity pubescent and dark green above, light green and tomentose beneath; petiole often 3" to 4" long, stout and tomentose.

BARK—On old trunks thin, marked by very shallow dark brown often diamond like fissures and broad flat light reddish brown interlacing ridges; on the stout twigs at first green, soon becoming reddish brown and marked by numerous large elongated nearly white lenticels and nearly circular raised opposite or whorled leaf scars. Pith large, hollow or filled, white.

BUDS—All leaf buds axillary, located over the top of the leaf scars, globular, covered by broad prickle tipped light brown or purplish colored scales; the naked flower buds born in terminal, upright, velvety tomentose, light reddish brown panicles, often 1' long, reminding one of clusters of musical symbols.

FLOWERS—Developing in April–May with the unfolding of the leaves, from terminal panicle clusters formed the previous year, each flower perfect, with lavender colored pubescent tubular corolla 1½" to 2" in length extending from the rusty tomentose blunt lobed persistent calyx.

FRUIT—November, borne in clusters on a stout woody stalk about 1' long, each an ovoid sharp-pointed woody capsules about 1" long which, upon the separation of the 2 valves, often as late as December and January, releases large quantities of small brown seeds which may be carried great distances in the wind by their film-like ragged edged wings. Fortunately, of all the seed produced, only an infinitesimal percentage fall on sites where conditions are favorable for germination and growth. Apparently the cracks in masonry, such as those in sidewalks and walls, offer ideal conditions because it may often be found growing from such niches and crevasses. The clusters of empty pods persist on the branchlets to rattle throughout the winter and longer.

WOOD—Ring-porous, light, soft, seasons well, works well and exhibits a satiny luster; heartwood purplish brown; sapwood thin nearly white. Not commercially important in this Country but highly valued in the Orient.

RANGE AND DISTRIBUTION—Native of the Orient and since its introduction into this Country as an ornamental has become widely naturalized in many localities from New York to Florida and in the Gulf States to Texas. Naturalized locally in all counties in the State, but more common in New Castle.

HABITAT—Appears to prefer rich, well drained, light but moist soils and is quite intolerant of shade.

NOTES—The names empress tree and paulownia applied to this tree honors Anna Paulowna, a princess of the Netherlands. The tree is unique in many ways such as the large leaves produced on vigorous shoots and the fact that it is one of the few trees that produce conspicuous lavender colored flowers. However, much of its ornamental value is to be discounted when one realizes that the fragrant blossoms last but a few days and that the fruit pods persist to rattle in the wind from year to year.

PART III

Supplemental Notes

on

Trees and Shrubs

TREES NOT NATIVE TO, BUT OFTEN SEEN IN DELAWARE

CONIFEROUS TREES:

AMERICAN RED PINE
Pinus resinosa, Solander

This tree, although sometimes erroneously called Norway pine, is strictly an American species being indigenous to eastern Canada and the United States east of Minnesota, with a southern range that does not extend as far south as Delaware. In the Great Lakes region, where it attains its maximum development, it sometimes attains a height of 100' or more. Its rapid growth and adaptability to planting on a variety of soils recommended it for reforestation in this and neighboring states but its failure to develop satisfactorily when used for forestation in areas southeasterly of the Allegheny Mts. nullifies the recommendation. Leaves in clusters of 2 with persistent sheaths, straight, slender, flexible, dark green, 4" to 6" long. Cones 1¾" to 2½" long. Cone scales with diamond-shaped umbo not equipped with a prickle or spine; bark reddish.

SCOTCH PINE. SCOTS PINE
Pinus sylvestris, Linnaeus

In Europe, this tree is regarded as one of the best timber and reforestation trees because of its rapid growth, liberal soil demands and the good quality lumber it yields. This reputation probably accounts for its introduction into this Country for the same purposes. In fact, it was formerly recommended by the State Forestry Department but was soon found to be inferior in nearly all respects to native pine species. The leaves are in clusters of 2, stiff, twisted, blue-green and 2" to 3" long. Delaware's oldest planting of the species was established in 1910 on P. R. R. property near St. Anne's Church south of Middletown.

NORWAY SPRUCE
Picea excelsa, Link

This tree is a native of Europe where for several centuries it has been cultured as one of the most valuable timber species. In eastern United States it has been a popular ornamental and is recommended as a reforestation, windbreak and Christmas tree plantation tree in this and neighboring states. The shiny dark green leaves arranged spirally along the twig are ¾" to 1" long, sharp pointed, rigid, curved and 4 angled. Cones develop from wine-red pistillate flowers and mature in one year. They are 3" to 7" long and 1" to 1½" in diameter at maturity. Cone scales unarmed and with finely toothed outer margin.

BLUE COLORADO SPRUCE
Picea pungens var. *glauca,* Beissner

The silver-blue foliaged spruce commonly seen in a predominating position in many front yards. It is strictly formal and individualistic in character, drawing first attention to itself. Leaves 1" to 1½" long, rigid, needle pointed, 4 angled, blue-green to grayish green.

AMERICAN ARBORVITAE. NORTHERN WHITE CEDAR
Thuja occidentalis, Linnaeus

A swamp inhabiting tree which sometimes attains a height of 80'. Native to eastern Canada and northeastern United States. Leaves scale-like, 4 ranked, green, in flat sprays. Cones mature in autumn of the first year, ½" long; scales unarmed. Seed 1/3" long with encircling wing. Often used as an ornamental, and as a result of which, numerous varieties have been developed.

ORIENTAL ARBORVITAE. BIOTA
Thuja (or *Biota*) *orientalis,* Linnaeus

Native to Persia and eastern Asia. Cones ½" to 1" long, globose, with horn-like processes on the 6 scales. Seed oblong purplish brown, without wings. Leaves similar to American arborvitae but sprays mostly arranged in vertical alignment. Ornamental with numerous varieties.

RETINOSPORA SPECIES

All retinosporas are juvenile foliaged forms of *Chamaecyparis* and *Thuja* which have been propagated from cuttings for their respective ornamental values. For instance, Retinispora filifera is botanically *Chamaecyparis pisifera* var. *filifera;* Retinispora plumosa is botanically *Chamaecyparis pisifera* var. *plumosa* and Retinispora squarrosa is *Thuja orientalis* var. *decussata.*

EUROPEAN LARCH
Larix decidua, Miller

A tall pyramidal deciduous conifer, native to Europe. Early introduced into this Country as an ornamental and reforestation tree. Grows rapidly under favorable conditions and bears soft, light green, linear leaves, ¾" to 1¼" long, scattered along the twig on the new growth but on the old growth arranged in rosettes about buttons scattered along the slender yellowish twigs. Formerly distributed by the State Forestry Department for reforestation purposes but discontinued because of lack of demand and unsatisfactory results when not cultivated for a year after planting.

JAPANESE LARCH
Larix leptolepis, Murray

Similar to European larch but with reddish purple twigs and blue-green leaves. Also formerly but not now recommended for reforestation purposes in the State.

DOUGLAS FIR
Pseudotsuga taxifolia, Britton

A large and important timber tree of western United States, used as an ornamental in the East and recommended by the State Forestry Department for Christmas tree planatations. The largest tree of this species so far found, in its natural range, is reported to be 324' tall and 12' in diameter. (Amer. Lumberman, Jan. 2, 1937, p. 47.)

BROADLEAVED TREES:

GINKGO. MAIDENHAIR TREE
Ginkgo biloba, Linnaeus

This tree, a native of the Orient, was introduced into the United States about a century ago and because of its tall pyramidal habit, freedom from insect pests and resistance to smoke, gas and dust injury, is becoming a popular city street tree in eastern United States. It is classified under the sub-division *Gymnospermae* but is generally regarded as intermediate between the cycads (palms) and conifers (cone bearing trees). It is the sole survivor of a more numerous group in geologic time and probably owes its present day existence to Oriental reverence, protection and propagation in temple gardens. The leaves are light green, 3" to 5" long, fanshaped, with or without a central cleft and are scattered along and clustered at the terminus of the new twigs or arise from buttons arranged alternately along the older wood. The male and female flowers are borne on separate trees. Despite the fact that the plumlike fruit, which is about 1" long with fleshy foul smelling yellowish pulp surrounding a smooth thin shelled seed, is much esteemed as a food delicacy by the Orientals, the planting of female trees is to be strongly discouraged. To step on the mushy pulp of dropped fruit invariably means that its strong butyric odor will be taken into the home to contaminate the air for days.

WEEPING WILLOW
Salix babylonica, Linnaeus

Introduced from Europe. Ornamental willow trees with long descending (weeping) branchlets. Prefers moist soils. Easily propagated from cuttings. Numerous ornamental varieties have been developed.

KENTUCKY COFFEE TREE. AMERICAN MAHOGANY
Gymnocladus dioica (Linnaeus), Koch

Large tree with alternate, unequally twice-pinnate leaves and stout branchlets. Female trees bear purplish brown, thick bean-like fruit 3" to 8" long and 1" to 1½" wide, containing several ½" round, slightly compressed, hard coated seeds imbedded in the mucilaginous pulp. Pith large reddish. Pruning or other repair work should not be done on this species when it is in foliage.

HONEY LOCUST
Gleditsia triacanthos, Linnaeus

Large rapid growing tree equipped with stout often compoundly branched sharp thorns in early life. Common in the Mississippi River basin and introduced in other parts of the United States. Leaves alternate doubly compound, 7″ to 10″ long with numerous small oblong-lanceolate short stalked leaflets. Fruit pods shiny purplish brown, 10″ to 18″ long, 1″ to 1½″ wide, thin, twisted or contorted and containing numerous small, hard, ovoid, compressed, brown seeds surrounded by the sweet mucilaginous inner pulp of the pod. Thornless varieties have been developed.

EVERGREEN MAGNOLIA
Magnolia grandiflora, Linnaeus

A large tree in its natural range which is along the Coastal Plain from North Carolina to eastern Texas and inland to Arkansas. Much planted as an ornamental and precariously hardy in protected locations as far north as northeastern New Jersey. As the common name indicates the alternate leaves are evergreen, leathery rich dark green and very shiny above, paler and rusty tomentose beneath, deciduous in spring at the end of their second year. The fragrant white flowers open from May to August and may measure as much as 8″ across. Fruit, an ovoid rusty pubescent cone 3″ to 4″ long which on ripening releases bright red flattish seeds about ½″ long. One of the most beautiful of magnolias.

PURPLE MAGNOLIA
Magnolia soulangeana, Soulander

Native of the Orient. Much planted shrub or ornamental magnolia with large early spring flowers, the petals of which are of pink or purple hue on the outside. Differentiation of the numerous varieties is largely based on the depth of the purple color of the petals. Generally speaking they are hardier than many other magnolias but are precariously hardy in this State when planted in exposed situations.

EUROPEAN SMALL LEAVED LINDEN
Tilia cordata, Miller

A tree much planted in eastern United States for shade and ornamentation. Identified by inverse heart-shaped alternate leaves 1½″ to 2″ long, often broader than long; margins with short teeth; dark green and moderately shiny above, bloom coated and with brown axillary tufts of hair beneath. Fruit has a thin fragile shell.

EUROPEAN LARGE LEAVED LINDEN
Tilia platyphyllos, Scopoli

Similar to *T. cordata* in form. Identified by inverse heart-shaped alternate leaves 3″ to 4″ long, with abruptly acute tip and regularly serrate margins. Dull green above, lighter and pubescent beneath; petiole stout, hairy. Flowers in 3 flowered cymes in June, the earliest of the group. Fruit about ⅛″ long, sharply 3 to 5 ribbed and thick shelled. Has numerous varieties.

COMMON CATALPA. INDIAN CIGAR TREE
Catalpa bignonioides, Walter

A small tree native to the Gulf States which because of its conspicuous upright pyramidal panicles of white or purple marked flowers in June has been much planted as an ornamental beyond its range in this country and in Europe. The leaves are 6″ to 12″ long, heart-shaped with entire margins, dull light green above, pubescent and with dark glands in the axils of the veins beneath, arranged oppositely or in whorls of 3 about the twig. The fruit is a cylindrical capsule, 10″ to 20″ long, ¼″ to ½″ in diameter containing many flattened seeds fringed at both ends.

HARDY CATALPA
Catalpa speciosa, Warder

A medium to large sized tree of better form than *C. bignonioides* and much planted in some regions for the production of fence post and R. R. ties. Its flower clusters are shorter than those of its southern relative but are, however, much larger. Demands full sunlight and deep fertile soil for satisfactory development. The catalpas are often attacked and completely defoliated in summer by attacks of the sphinx moth larvae.

COMMON HORSE CHESTNUT, EUROPEAN BUCKEYE
Aesculus hippocastanum, Linnaeus

Tree, native to southern Asia, introduced into this Country about 1850 as a shade and ornamental tree. Leaves opposite, with usually 7 leaflets radiating from the top of the petiole. The 8″ to 12″ long terminal panicles of purple marked white flowers are very showy. Fruit subglobose, light green 1½″ to 2½″ in diameter, the outer husk spinose which upon breaking apart or falling from the tree, releases 1 to rarely 3, 1″ to 1½″ diameter shiny chestnut brown seeds, each having a large white bloom coated hilum area. In Delaware climate is subject to heat and drought injury and is commonly attacked by the buckeye leaf blotch disease which in advanced stages makes the tree appear as if it had been seared by fires and may sometimes nearly defoliate it.

ALBIZZIA. POWDER PUFF TREE. Erroneously called MIMOSA
Albizzia julibrissin, Durazz.

A tree usually not over 25′ tall in this region. Native of Asia and the Orient. Introduced as an ornamental and formerly much used in burial grounds. Leaves alternate bipinnate with feathery foliage; leaflets about ½″ long, opposite; quite sensitive to injury or sudden temperature changes, showing such by folding together. Flowers in June, July and August, in dense yellowish or pinkish "powder puff" heads on slender stems crowded on upper ends of the branchlets. Not very hardy north of Dover.

CHINA-BERRY. CHINA TREE. PRIDE OF INDIA. TEXAS UMBRELLA or BREAD TREE
Melia azedarach, Linnaeus

A tree of umbrella-like form sometimes planted as an ornamental in the southern part of the State. Native of Asia but now naturalized in many parts of the South where it makes an ideal shade tree. Not hardy in Delaware but will survive unless the temperature drops below 6° F. A temperature of 0° F. or below is usually fatal to it. Leaves doubly compound 2′ to 3′ long, with many ovate dark green leaflets having broadly toothed margins. The fruit is a yellow berry drupe, about ½″ in diameter borne in long panicle clusters.

KOELREU TREE
Koelreuteria paniculata, Laxm.

An introduction from the Orient, of late, being planted for ornamentation in this region. Recognized by its bipinnate alternate leaves, sharply toothed leaflets and large panicles of bright yellow flowers in midsummer, followed by the clusters of large light brown bladder-like 3 angled capsules, 1½″ to 2″ long, containing 3 small dark gray globose seeds.

CRAPE MYRTLE
Lagerstroemia indica, Linnaeus

Shrub or rarely a small tree introduced from India but probably of Chinese origin. Well known by its profusely produced large panicles of pink, carmine or white flowers in July and August. Hardy in protected location throughout the State, but is generally killed by temperatures at or near 0° F. if exposed to such for a period of 24 hours or more.

BLADDER NUT
Staphylea trifolia, Linnaeus

A shrub or rarely a small tree common along streams in New Castle County. Leaves opposite with 3 ovate, pointed leaflets on short stalks, finely serrate on the margins, light green above, pubescent beneath. Flowers bell-like, about 1/3″ long in nodding clusters with greenish sepals and white petals. Fruit a bladder-like 3 lobed capsule about 1½″ long, brown when ripe. Occasionally used as an ornamental. Interesting in flower and fruit but hardly showy.

A CATALOGUE OF FOREST SHRUBS OF RATHER COMMON OCCURRENCE IN THE STATE

WINTERBERRY. BLACK ALDER. COONBERRY
Ilex verticillata, Linnaeus

Common to low ground and swampy places. Distinguished in summer by wedge-lanceolate sharply serrate alternate leaves 1½″ to 3″ long, with acute apex and long-acute base dark dull green and roughened by sunken veins above, paler and smooth except the midrib beneath; and in winter by the persistent, red, holly-like fruit. Flowers in short panicle clusters in June.

INKBERRY. GALLBERRY
Ilex glabra, Linnaeus

Much branched evergreen shrub 2′ to 6′ tall. The thick, shiny evergreen alternate leaves are ¾″ to 1½″ long, oval, entire or toothed toward the apex. Fruit about ¼″ in diameter, shiny black. Common to peaty swamps and low ground.

STRAWBERRY BUSH. EVONYMUS
Evonymus americanus, Linnaeus

Distinguished by oblong-lanceolate serrate opposite leaves, 2″ to 3″ long, green 4 angled stems and rough warty or weak prickled 4 lobed fruit pods which are orange to deep crimson when ripe. Seed shiny, bright crimson or orange.

RED OSIER DOGWOOD. RED CORNEL
Cornus stolonifera, Michaux

Many stalked shrub to 8′, identified by purplish red bark of stalks and twigs. Flowers white, in flat cymes, 1″ to 2″ across. Fruit globose, white or slate colored.

PANICLE DOGWOOD
Cornus paniculata, L'Her.
[*Cornus racemosa*, Lamarch]

Shrub to 15′; identified by smooth gray or yellowish tinged stalks, ovate-lanceolate leaves which are whitish beneath and by white or cream colored flowers in convex panicle-like cymes. Fruit, white, on red pedicels.

SWEET PEPPERBUSH
Clethra alnifolia, Linnaeus

Branched or single stalked shrub to 8′ forming dense thickets in low ground in forests, especially following forest fire. Leaves obovate, narrowing to the very short petiole, green both sides, 1″ to 3″ long. Flowers, July to September, in elongated slender terminal racemes, very fragrant.

DEERBERRY. SQUAW HUCKLEBERRY
Vaccinium stamineum, Linnaeus

Low shrub rarely to 5′, with pubescent twigs not speckled with white. Flowers white or purple tinged. Identified by large bloom covered greenish or yellowish globular or pear-shaped sour tasting berries.

LOW SWEET OR EARLY BLUEBERRY
Vaccinium pennsylvanicum, Lamarch

A low shrubby sort with green branchlets; lanceolate leaves green and smooth both sides and bloom coated blue delicious fruit.

HIGH BUSH OR SWAMP BLUEBERRY
Vaccinium corymbosum, Linnaeus

Tall shrub with larger elliptical-lanceolate leaves; with generally larger delicious blue-black berries.

BLACK HIGH BUSH BLUEBERRY
Vaccinium atrococcum, Gray
Tall shrub with leaves wooly beneath and shiny black fruit.

BLUE HUCKLEBERRY. BLUE TANGLE. DANGLE BERRY
Gaylussacia frondosa, Torrey and Gray
Shrub sometimes 6' tall. Leaves ovate, entire, pale green above, whitish beneath. Flowers in loose racemes, corolla broad bell-shaped, greenish purple. Fruit ripens in July, blue with glaucous bloom, sweet and edible. Distinguished from blueberries by fruit with 10 nutlets, one to a cell.

BLACK HUCKLEBERRY
Gaylussacia baccata, Koch
Shrub to 3', with branchlets slightly pubescent, resinous and clammy when young. Leaves oval or oblong-lanceolate, 1" to 1½" long, light green above, pale beneath. Flowers May and June. Fruit July and August, black, sometimes roughened by resin globules.

Author's Note—In some sections of the Country the word "huckleberry" is applied indiscriminately to berries of both *Vaccinium* and *Gaylussacia*, but in other sections the name "blueberry" is reserved as descriptive of the marketable and deliciously flavored fruits of the low and high bush *Vacciniums*, while the name "huckleberry" is applied to the black or sometimes blue and coarser fruits of *Gaylussacia*. This latter differentiation appears most descriptive.

MARSH ELDER. HIGH WATER SHRUB. SALT BUSH. MYRTLE BUSH
Iva frutescens, Linnaeus
[*Iva oraria*, Bartlett]
The tall, shrub-like, somewhat fleshy or herbaceous perenial common to salt marshes and mud flats along the Delaware Bay and Atlantic Ocean. Leaves mostly oblong-lanceolate, the lower ones opposite, short petioled, 3 nerved; coarsely toothed especially toward the apex; fleshy gray-green, 4" to 6" long. Flowers July to September from the axils of which develop the panicled racemes of small flowers not unlike those of ragweed. It may be distinguished from the following species at a distance by the branching which is sparse and quite upright in contrast to the spreading form of *Baccharis*.

BACCHARIS. GROUNDSEL TREE OR BUSH. PENCIL TREE. SALT BUSH. COTTON-SEED TREE. MYRTLE BUSH
Baccharis halimifolia, Linnaeus
A shrub 3' to 10' high, with numerous spreading and angled smooth (or sometimes minutely scurfy) branchlets. Common along salt marshes and on saline soils of the Delaware Bay and Atlantic Ocean. Leaves of varying shapes and forms, but on larger branches petioled, wedge-shaped at the base, broadly and irregularly toothed or lobed toward the apex or on branchlets short petioled or sessile and entire; thick and fleshy, blue-green, 1" to 2½" long. Flowers, in midsummer in heads scattered at the ends of branchlets to form pyramidal panicles. The fertile plants conspicuous in autumn by reason of the dense white cotton-like clusters of pappus.

SPICE BUSH
Lindera benzoin (L.) Blume
[*Benzoin aestivale*, Nees]
Shrub to 10' or more, common along streams and wet places. Said never to occur naturally where the water table is more than 5' below the surface. Much branched with slender twigs. Bark lustrous deep yellow-green and very spicy. Leaves oblong-obovate, entire, bright green above, paler beneath, 3" to 5" long. Flowers in April, before the leaves, yellow. Fruit in early fall, cylindrical oval, shiny bright red, rarely persisting long after the leaves turn bright yellow. Extracts of the bark and fruit used medicinally as a tonic.

MOUNTAIN HONEYSUCKLE. PINK AZALEA. WILD PINK AZALEA
Rhododendron nudiflorum, Torrey
Shrub 2' to 6' tall, sparingly branched with pubescent and often bristly hairy branchlets. Flowers in April and May before or with the leaves from terminal buds formed the previous year, pink, 1½" broad, faintly fragrant. *R. canescens,* Don, which resembles the previous species, is rarely more than 3' tall but has smaller leaves which are pubescent beneath. The flowers are similar in color but larger, very sticky outside and very fragrant.

SWAMP HONEYSUCKLE. WHITE SWAMP AZALEA
Rhododendron viscosum, Torrey

Shrub common to wet places, 4' to 6' tall; branchlets set with hairs. Leaves shiny dark green above, paler and with bristly hairs on the midrib and veins beneath. Flowers in June and July, white, sticky outside, 1½" to 2" across, very fragrant.

MAPLE LEAVED VIBURNUM
Viburnum acerifolium, Linnaeus

In addition to the mention made of viburnums in this text on pages 221–223 further description is here included. The maple-leaved species is distinguished by the leaves which, because of their 3 lobes, resemble those of the maples and turn deep crimson in autumn. It is a shrub sometimes attaining a height of 6'. Flowers in May and June, yellowish white, in long stemmed terminal cymes, 1½" to 3" across. Fruit October ovoid, blue-black.

ARROW-WOOD. DENTATE LEAVED VIBURNUM
Viburnum dentatum, Linnaeus

Strong growing shrub sometimes 15' tall with smooth branchlets and ovate-oblong leaves which are dentate on the margins, dark green strongly veined and often shiny above, paler and with silky hairs on the veins beneath. Flowers cream-white in semi-globose cymes, 2" to 3" across in May and June. Fruit, October, subglobose, bluish black and bloom coated. Habits stream banks and wet locations.

RED CHOKEBERRY
Aronia arbutifolia, Spach

Shrub to 10' with oval serrate leaves, green and smooth except for glands in the midrib above, grayish green and tomentose beneath, 1½" to 3" long. Flowers April and May in corymbs 1" to 1½" across, white or tinged with red. Fruit, October, subglobose or pear-shaped, about ¼" across, bright or dull red, remain plump and bright often until midwinter and consequently sometimes mistaken for winterberry or coonberry, *Ilex verticillata.*

PURPLE CHOKEBERRY
Aronia atropurpurea, Britton

Shrub to 12', closely resembling *A. arbutifolia,* but with leaves grayish pubescent beneath. Flower corymbs tomentose. Fruit ovoid to subglobose, purplish black, 1/3" in diameter, usually dried and shriveled by the beginning of winter.

BLACK CHOKEBERRY
Aronia melanocarpa, Spach

A low shrub in this latitude rarely more than 3' with leaves resembling the two previous species in shape, but pale green and smooth beneath. Flowers in April–May, white tinged with red. Fruit shiny black and produced in great abundance but not persistent.

NEW JERSEY TEA
Ceanothus americanus, Linnaeus

A low shrub with many stems ascending from a deep reddish root. Leaves alternate, 3 nerved, oblong-ovate with long acute apex, 1" to 3" long; margins finely toothed; dark green above, lighter and very pubescent beneath. Flowers, May to July in conspicuous terminal or axillary-terminal panicles.

BUTTON BUSH. BUTTON BALL
Cephalanthus occidentalis, Linnaeus

Shrub or rarely a small tree habiting borders of streams, swamps and estuaries throughout its range which is continent wide. Leaves oval, 4" to 7" long, margins entire, dark green above, paler and with yellowish midrib and veins beneath. Flowers in yellowish white globular heads, 1" to 1½" in diameter on long stalks. Fruit in globular heads about ¾" in diameter on stiff upright stalks; resemble the fruit of the sycamore or "buttonwood" tree.

BEACH PLUM
Prunus maritima, Marshall

Bushy shrub to 6', common on sandy areas mostly along the Atlantic Coast. Leaves oval with short angled apex and base, margins sharply serrate, blue-green above, paler and somewhat pubescent beneath. Flowers profusely produced in early spring before the leaves, small, white, in few flowered umbels. Fruit about ½" in diameter, globular, depressed at the stem end, bloom coated, dull purple when ripe, with firm sweet and edible flesh enclosing a free cherry-like stone.

COMMON ELDERBERRY
Sambucus canadensis, Linnaeus

Shrub to 5', with pinnate leaves, white flowers in broad flat compound cymes in June. Fruit purplish, sweet, edible, and locally gathered for the making of pie, jelly and wine.

AMERICAN HAZELNUT. AMERICAN FILBERT
Corylus americana, Walter

A forest shrub abundant in some localities principally in New Castle County of this State. Attain a height of 6' to 8'. Branchlets pubescent and densely set with hair-like red bristles. Leaves 3" to 6" long, broadly ovate or oval with irregularly toothed margins and tomentose beneath. The ½" long hard shelled nut is inclosed by 2 cockscomb-like margined involucres. Kernel sweet and edible.

HOW A TREE GROWS

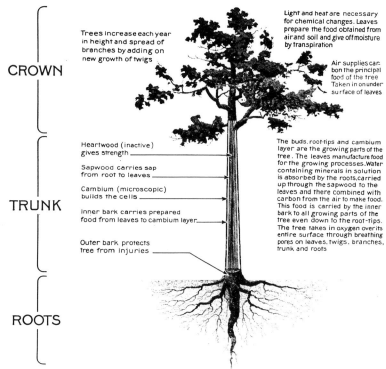

CROWN

Trees increase each year
in height and spread of
branches by adding on
new growth of twigs

Light and heat are necessary
for chemical changes. Leaves
prepare the food obtained from
air and soil and give off moisture
by transpiration

Air supplies car-
bon the principal
food of the tree.
Taken in on under
surface of leaves

TRUNK

Heartwood (inactive)
gives strength

Sapwood carries sap
from root to leaves

Cambium (microscopic)
builds the cells

Inner bark carries prepared
food from leaves to cambium layer.

Outer bark protects
tree from injuries

The buds, root-tips and cambium
layer are the growing parts of the
tree. The leaves manufacture food
for the growing processes. Water
containing minerals in solution
is absorbed by the roots, carried
up through the sapwood to the
leaves and there combined with
carbon from the air to make food.
This food is carried by the inner
bark to all growing parts of the
tree even down to the root-tips.
The tree takes in oxygen over its
entire surface through breathing
pores on leaves, twigs, branches,
trunk and roots

ROOTS

From U. S. Forest Service Chart

AGE AND SIZE ATTAINED BY TREES

Of the many questions asked about trees, perhaps the two most difficult to answer are—"How old do trees become" and—"How large do trees become?" The answer to both is indefinite in its most literal interpretation, in that under ideal conditions a tree might truly live forever and attain tremendous size because the living parts are confined to the outer portion of the plant; the heart or innermost part, being lifeless, serves only as the structure united with, and upon which, the living portion is supported.

Beyond certain established and proven age limits there exists fertile fields of speculation on tree age. Hence designation of the most aged is largely a matter of individual opinion. However, the dragon tree (*Dracaena draco*), of the Canary Islands is generally conceded this honor on an estimated age of 6,000 or more years. Other authorities hold that the largest and oldest living thing in the world is the "Big Tree of Tule," a montezuma cypress (*Taxodium mucronatum*, Ten.) which stands in the Indian village of Santa Maria del Tule near Oaxaca, Mexico. A United States Dept. of Agriculture record of measurements taken of this tree in 1936 give the circumference as 113'-4" and the height as 118'-7". Its age is estimated at approximately 4,000 years. Title to the "Oldest Living Thing" in the U. S. A. currently (1950) is vested in an ancient but gnarled bristlecone pine (*P. aristata*) growing on a high peak within the Inyo National Forest of California.

LARGE, OLD AND UNUSUAL TREES OF DELAWARE

Space and funds will not permit a detailed presentation of that which might be included here; moreover, it is a moot question whether such is warranted when it might soon become obsolete, controversial or incorrect. Because lands may be sold and trees felled some of the following data may, even at this printing, be obsolete. Accordingly only a small portion of the data which has been gathered by the State Forestry Department or contributed by interested persons within the last 20 years is here offered with grateful acknowledgment to all who have contributed thereto.

HISTORIC TREES 1995

The following unusual trees that were noted in the 1939 edition of *The Delaware Tree Book* are still standing today.

KENT WHIPPING POST WALNUT—This tree is located in the northeast corner of The Green in Dover. Over the last 55 years, it has grown an additional seven inches in circumference.

THE ELMS ON DOVER GREEN—Unfortunately, some of the elms on The Green have succumbed to Dutch elm disease and had to be removed. Today, the largest American elm in Delaware can be seen on the southwest corner of The Green. This tree is the sole survivor of the original plantings of American elms on The Green in 1849.

DOVER'S GINKGO—This tree is situated in the backyard of a property on the northwest corner of The Green. This tree has grown 49 inches in circumference since it was first measured in 1938.

ST. ANNE'S CHURCH WHITE OAK—This tree is located in the church cemetery in Middletown along Route 896. It has grown 23 inches in circumference since it was measured in 1938.

DOVER'S COFFEE TREES—These trees, located behind The Green in Dover, have grown considerably since 1938 when William Taber reported their measurement of eight inches in circumference. Today, these three trees measure from 106 to 151 inches in circumference.

HISTORIC TREES

THE COUNCIL OAK, is reported in the volume entitled "Penns Woods" by Edward E. Wildman, published by Cristopher Sower Co., Philadelphia, 1933, to be a white oak 15' 2" in circumference, situated along the old Newport and Gap turnpike, now Delaware highway route 41. The tradition relating to the tree is that General Washington and General Lafayette held council under its branches just before the battle of the Brandywine.

PENCADER PRESBYTERIAN CHURCH WHITE OAK OR WELSH TRACT OAK; a landmark tree since 1723; measures 14' 9". (Same authority as for preceding.) Blown down in storm "Connie" August 13, 1955.

UNUSUAL TREES

KENT WHIPPING POST WALNUT; an old black walnut tree standing in front if the Board of Agriculture building in Dover which prior to the razing of the old Kent County Jail and the relocation of the Agriculture building, shaded the jail whipping post. It measured 10' 2" in circumference breast high in 1938.

THE ELMS ON THE DOVER GREEN, the oldest of which were planted in 1849 comprise about half the total number of trees occupying the inner oval of the Green owned by the City of Dover. (Authority: Public Archives Commission)

THE NEW CASTLE ELMS, situated in New Castle on the old Court House grounds and nearby, are apparently of an age approximating those on the Dover Green.

DOVER'S GINKGO, situated in the back yard of the property on the northwest corner of the Dover Green, owned by Col. C. B. Thurmmel. This is a female of the species and measured 11' 7" in circumference breast high in 1938.

DOVER'S DOGWOOD, situated on a City owned plot of ground at the junction of Division Street and King's Highway, has 3 stems ranging from 7" to 10" in diameter and, when in full bloom, is generally conceded the most beautiful native conspicuously flowering tree in the State. According to the late Mrs. Walter Morris of Dover, this tree was planted about 1853 by Mr. and Mrs. Nathaniel B. Smithers.

ST. ANNE'S CHURCH TREES; being those surrounding Old St. Anne's P. E. Church south of Middletown founded in 1705, the most notable of which is a white oak reported to be 14' 4" in circumference.

CEDAR OF LEBANON, in Brandywine Cemetery, Wilmington; believed to have been planted about 1850 by the late Edward Tatnall, whose botanical gift to posterity constitutes one of his greatest monuments. Other large trees of this species may be found on old estates in New Castle County.

THE HOCKESSIN FRINGE TREE; measuring 9½" in diameter and believed to be the largest tree of its species in the State, is situated on a lawn in the northwestern side of Hockessin.

DOVER'S COFFEE TREES; one a large male Kentucky coffee tree situated on the property of Mrs. Winifred Morris McCosh, Dover, measuring 10' 8" C.B.H. (1938) and another, a female tree measuring the same, situated on the "Comegys Property" owned by Dr. Frank S. Hall of Dover.

DOVER'S BUR OAK, a tree situated on the Willim property immediately south of the "Comegys Property." A handsome tree, the trunk of which measured 13' 2" in 1938 but which separates into 4 stems of similar size at about 6' above ground.

UNUSUAL SHRUBS

BOX HUCKLEBERRY: an area of about 5 acres of this rare evergreen huckleberry was discovered in Sussex County several years ago by the author. In keeping with a policy of protecting it, the exact location is not revealed.

EVONYMUS: one measuring about 3" in diameter and of tree form situated in Angola Neck, east of Angola, Sussex County.

TREES AND MANKIND

In the course of his struggle for existence man learned that the desirable qualities of certain plants could be improved and made to better serve his needs if they were given the proper care and cultivation. Such discoveries were the beginning of the plant life sciences and arts which today are broadly grouped under agriculture and horticulture. As these interrelated sciences and arts grew they developed numerous specialized branches and became modified in scope, so that while in strict interpretation agriculture is the act of cultivating a field or land, we generally consider it as the art and science of tilling sizeable areas of land for the purpose of growing grains, vegetables, raw textile materials, forage and the raising of animals. On the other hand a strict interpretation of horticulture would be garden culture, but which today is customarily regarded as the art and science of cultivating plants for their fruits and for ornamentation. Actually there is no sharp line of demarcation between agriculture and horticulture except that which obtains by custom. Sharper lines are drawn between the specialized branches such as forestry, animal husbandry, floriculture, pomology, landscape and vegetable gardening, but each is related to the other and is connected with most of the other biological and physical sciences and arts. This close relation is evident in the definition of many of the sciences: Botany—the science of plants; dendrology —the science of trees and shrubs; floriculture—the science of flower culture; pomology—the science of cultivating fruit and fruit trees; silviculture—the science of forest culture; arboriculture—the science of tree culture.

For the most part this publication deals with the names, classification, identifying characteristics and habits of trees native to the State. It, therefore, becomes primarily a dendrological subject. Figuratively speaking, the reader is given a more or less formal but detailed introduction to each of these trees, but for his convenience these "letters of introduction" have been classified and compiled into a single volume. While most of the codes of human relations the world over provide a form of personal introduction, it does not follow that such an introduction is either necessary to the development of an intimate friendship or that such will develop as a result thereof. The same is true of the friendship man has for trees for, he has from the earliest times sought their shelter and protection and has used such of their fruits, wood, bark, and other gifts as may have been appropriate for his needs. His feelings have of course varied with the times, with the place and with the tree in much the same manner that present day man differs from men of other ages in his mode of living, and his beliefs. Now we are wont to think of our present age as the ultimate of all ages and the one in which the greatest contributions to the comfort and welfare of mankind are being made. But if we are to accept the findings of archeologists and historians who tell us that in the last 2,000 years of historic time man has not found a single species of food plant comparable in value to a single staple food plant cultivated and domesticated by prehistoric man,* we have cause to wonder and meditate.

The appreciation ancient man had for trees often assumed the form of worship and either was deified or bore close association to a deity. As an illustration we quote from P. 360 of *The Outline of History* by H. G. Wells, published by The Macmillan Company, N. Y. City. "Extraordinary attention has been given to the tree under which Gautama **[Buddha] had this sense of mental clarity. It was a tree of the fig genus [Probably *Ficus benghalensis* or Banyan Tree] and from the first was treated with peculiar veneration. It was called the Bo Tree. It has long since perished, but close at hand lives another great tree which may be its descendant, and in Ceylon there grows to this day

* Myers, *Ancient History* after DeCandolle. *Origin of Cultivated Plants.*
** Brackets enclose additions by the writer.

a tree, the oldest historical tree in the world, which we know certainly to have been planted as a cutting from the Bo Tree in the year 245 B.C. From that time to this it has been carefully tended and watered; its great branches are supported by pillars [probably natural aerial root trunks] and the earth has been terraced up about it so that it has been able to put out fresh roots continually. It helps us to realize the shortness of all human history to see so many generations spanned by the endurance of a single tree."

Unfortunately Mr. Wells does not mention the size of this tree but his comparison of its life with human history is a most impressive tribute. Here again we find ancient man showing the way to innumerable generations and delivering into the hands of present day man a living thriving tree, over which he shall exercise sacred trusteeship for a time and pass on to his successors as did his ancestors.

During much of this association man has shown more concern for those trees which furnish him with food, shade, clothing, and ornamentation than he has for those which supplied him with wood for his home, protected and conserved his water supply, tempered the winds and provided food and shelter for birds, animals and other forms of life. We refer specifically to the forest which, being more than trees grouped together over a large area, is actually a complex but natural community of living and lifeless (organic and inorganic) things in which trees predominate.

Forestry, which is the art and science of growing repeated crops of timber and of so handling forests that they yield their greatest benefits to humanity and to the owner, had its beginning as arboriculture many centuries ago in Europe where the shortage of forest resources forced adoption of its principles.

It is common misconception that the early American colonists found a vast untouched virgin forest in the New World when in fact many of the Indian tribes were agriculturists and had cleared small areas of land of its forest growth for tillage centuries before the coming of white men. They, of course, used wood for all the purposes that their crude tools would permit fashioning; and forest fires, whether set by lightning or intentionally or carelessly set by the Indians, devastated some areas. But while the Indian was at heart a conservationist the white man was both a lavish user and wanton waster in the sight of an apparently inexhaustible supply of natural resources.

American Colonial history records many attempts to regulate timber cutting and bring about other forest conservation measures, but the public, being instilled in the belief of inexhaustibility of the forest, paid little heed to them. Of particular interest to Delawareans in this connection is the stipulation William Penn is said to have made in his grants to those who took title from him "that for every five acres cleared one is to be reserved for forest growth."

Fortunately, there were among the early settlers and among generations that followed, those who were endowed with the vision and wisdom to recognize the fallacy of inexhaustibility but their protesting voices were scarcely audible above the lusty roar of a growing nation. Gradually, however, the roar died down enough that their pleading could be heard and recognized as containing evident truths.

Probably the first national action having any forestry significance is found in acts of Congress passed between 1799 and 1831. While these acts for the most part provided for the reservation of lands bearing live oak and cedar timber suitable for use of the Navy, the act of 1827 was general enough to permit the planting and culture of these species. Such a program was carried on for several years on Santa Rosa Island near Pensacola, and appears to be the first national forest culture attempt. However the first official national recognition of forestry came in 1876 with the establishment of the Division of Forestry in the United States Department of Agriculture which has since become the Forest Service in the same Department of the Federal government. In 1872, four years prior to the establishment of the Division of Forestry, the first Arbor Day was proclaimed by Governor J. Sterling Morton of Nebraska, and has since gradually become a day of observance in nearly all states of the Nation. Its observance has unquestionably been a great stimulus to tree appreciation and, in consequence, to forest appreciation. In fact, the existence of a Forestry Department in Delaware may to some extent be attributed to tree appreciation, for although an official attempt was made in 1909 to establish such a division of the State government it was not until 1927 that a forestry agency was established, largely as a result of legislative action on the findings of the Forest Conservation Commission created by an act of the 1925 General Assembly. The law instructed the Commission "to make investigation concerning the preservation and conservation of Delaware Forests, especially as to the preservation and conservation of Holly Trees."

So today as in all ages we find trees influencing the acts of man according to the appeal they make to him indidvidually and collectively. To some, trees and forests are things of beauty; to others they mean protection, comfort and utility, but to those who know them better they are benefactors for all their convenient and necessary gifts, are friends and companions, counsellors and teachers, a balm to tired nerves, a tonic to soul and body, and an inspiration to spiritual and social well-being. There is no explaining these human feelings; they simply exist.

REFERENCE BOOKS

For those who wish to make a more thorough study of the characteristics, habits, range and usefulness of trees and their place in the general scheme of nature, there are available in our public libraries numerous books and periodicals on the subject. There are also many Federal and state publications of both general and technical nature which may be purchased at a nominal cost or obtained free upon application to the proper agency. Many of the latter, books of the State Forestry Department and the author's personal collection as follows were used as references in this publication:

Manual of Trees of North America. Charles Sprague Sargent. Houghton Mifflin Co. 1926.

The Standard Cyclopedia of Horticulture. Liberty Hyde Bailey. Macmillan Co. 1937.

Handbook of the Trees of North America. Romeyn B. Hough. 1907.

Tree Habits, How to Know the Hardwoods. Joseph S. Illick. American Nature Association. 1924.

Gray's New Manual of Botany. (Revised.) Benjamin L. Robinson and Merritt L. Fernald. American Book Co. 1908.

Identification of the Economic Woods of the United States. Samuel J. Record. John Wiley & Sons, Inc. 1914.

Catalogue of the Phaenogamous and Filicoid Plants of New Castle County, Delaware, Edward Tatnall. John T. Heald, 1860. (Copy loaned to the author by Mr. H. R. Baker of Dover.

Flora of Delaware and the Eastern Shore, Robert R. Tatnall, Soc. of Nat. History of Del., 1946.

Check List of Native and Naturalized Trees. Agr. Handbook No. 41, U.S.D.A. Forest Service, Elbert L. Little, Jr., 1953.

GLOSSARY OF BOTANICAL WORDS

Abortive Defective; barren; not developed.

Abrupt Changing suddenly; not tapering gradually.

Accessory In the nature of an appendage.

Achene A small dry, hard, 1 celled and 1 seeded fruit which does not open by valves.

Alternate Placed at different heights on the stem; not opposite or whorled.

Afforestation The act of establishing a forest on land which never had or has been devoid of forest growth for a long time.

Ament An arrangement of unisexual flowers around a central stalk each subtended by a bract; a catkin.

Anther The portion of a stamen which bears the pollen, usually atop the filament.

Apophysis The exposed portion of the scale of an unopened cone.

Appressed Closely and flatly pressed against.

Arborescent Of tree form; tree like.

Armed Provided with defensive equipment as spines, thorns, stiff hairs.

Awl-shaped Narrow and sharp pointed; like an awl.

Axil The angle formed by the upper part of an organ with the branch or stem of which it is a part, as a leaf with its twig or a vein of a leaf with its midrib.

Axile Situated or lying in the axis or axil.

Axillary Of or in the axil.

Axis The central line of an organ; a main stem.

Basal sheath The tough filmy covering surrounding the base of pine needle clusters.

Berry A pulpy, few or many seeded fruit; not having a stone.

Bloom A grayish powdery or wax-like substance which easily rubs off.

Boss A conical projection; a dome-shaped bump.

Bract The small modified leaf subtending a flower.

Branch A secondary axis or division of a trunk.

Branchlet The ultimate division of a branch; a twig.

Bud The undeveloped, dormant, or beginning state of leaves, new shoots or flowers, usually covered but not necessarily with scales.

Caducous Falling early; earlier than deciduous.

Callus A hard point or prominence; a roll of new tissue.

Calyx The outer part or circle of floral envelopes.

Cambium The formative tissue lying between wood and bark.

Capsule A pod or dry fruit of more than one carpel which splits open at maturity.

Carpel A single pistil or one of the elements of a compound pistil.

Catkin A scaly bracted flower spike; an ament; common to willows and poplars.

Ciliate Fringed with hairs; bearing hairs at the margin.

Claw The long narrow base of a petal or sepal.

Complete flower All parts present, i.e. receptacle, sepal, pistil, stamens, petal.

Compound Of two or more similar parts in one organ, as in a leaf.

Compressed Flattened; out of round.

Cone A dense and usually elongated collection of flowers or fruits borne beneath or between scales, the whole with an axis forming a fruit-like body or unit.

Coniferous Cone bearing.

Convolute Rolled together or up lengthwise.

Corolla Inner circle of floral envelopes; if separate they are petals; if not separate they are teeth, lobes or divisions.

Corymb A form of flower cluster which is flat-topped, the sequence of flowering being from the margin inward and the stems or pedicels subdivided.

Cyme A form of flower cluster usually flattened but sometimes oval above, the sequence of flowering being from the center outward and the stems or pedicels alternate from a central axis.

Deciduous Falling; falling at the end of the season; not persisting.

Deltoid Triangular; delta-like.

Dentate Toothed, the teeth sharp and spreading outward.

Diffuse porous With pore of similar size evenly scattered.

Dioecious With staminate (male) and pistillate (female) flowers on different plants; unisexual.

Downy Densely covered with weak short soft hairs.

Drupe A fleshy one seeded fruit with seed enclosed in a hard shell; a stone fruit as a peach, plum, etc.

Durable Applied to wood as descriptive of unusual resistance to decay when in contact with soil or other locations favoring decay.

Entire Said of leaves, etc. when the margin is not notched or toothed; whole.

Evergreen Remaining green throughout the year, usually applied to foliage.

Exfoliating Cleaving off in thin layers, as of the outer leaves of bark.

Exotic Of foreign origin or nativity.

Fascicle A close cluster.

Fertile Said of flowers (or branches) producing seed or fruit; applies to pollen bearing stamens; capable of reproduction.

Fertilization Impregnation of the ovule.

Fibro-vascular Composed of woody fibers and ducts.

Filament The portion of a stamen (stalk) supporting the anther.

Flora The plant population of a given area or region; a listing of such.

Fluted Corrugated, grooved, channeled; round ridged without fissures.

Foliaceous Leaf like.

Forestry The science of handling woodland for the production of the greatest good.

Fruit The seed bearing organ.

Furrowed With longitudinal grooves, channels, fissures or cracks.

Glabrous Smooth; not rough or hairy.

Gland Properly a secreting organ; a prominence or appendage resembling such.

Glandular Having glands or gland like.

Glaucous Furnished or covered with a bloom or thin whitish substance which will rub off.

Habit The form, mode, style or appearance of growth.

Habitat The site, soil, climate and moisture preferred by a plant for optimum development.

Head A dense cluster of flowers, usually of spherical outline; applied to the outline form of the crown of a tree or plant.

Heart-shaped Cordate; shaped as a heart is usually drawn in caricatures of valentines.

Heartwood The mature and dead wood of an exogenous stem; usually central therein and darker in color.

Herbaceous Not woody; soft; dying down each year.

Hirsute With coarse stiff hairs.

Hoary With dense grayish or white hairs.

Horny Like horn in texture.

Hybrid A plant resulting from unlike but generally closely related parents.

Imbricated Overlapping like shingles.

Imperfect flower One lacking actively functioning organs of one sex, i.e. either stamens or pistil.

Incomplete flower One which lacks one or more of the component parts of a complete flower such as the calyx (sepals), the corolla (petals), the stamens or the pistil.

Indehiscent Not regularly opening as a seed pod or anther.

Indigenous Native to.

Intolerant Not enduring shade; requiring ample sunlight.

Involucre A whorl of bracts or small leaves attached beneath a flower or flower cluster.

Keeled With a central ridge like the bottom of a boat.

Key A dry winged indehiscent fruit; a samara.

Lanceolate Shaped like a lance or spear; widening above the base and tapering to the apex.

Leaflet A blade of a compound leaf.

Lenticels Small corky growths which serve as breathing pores and generally occur on young tree bark.

Linear Long and narrow with sides parallel or nearly so.

Lobe Any part of an organ which represents a division to about the middle.

Lunate Like a new moon; crescent shaped.

Medullary rays Narrow lighter colored or rarely colorless bands of fibre radiating from the medulla or pith of a woody stem and continuous or intermittent to the bark.

Membranaceous Like a membrane; thin and pliable.

Midrib The central vein or rib of a leaf or leaflet.

Monoecious With functioning stamens and pistils in different flowers on the same plant or tree; unisexual flowers.

Naked bud Bud without scales.

Naturalized Said of plants which are of foreign origin but are reproducing by self distributed seed or other self propagating medium.

Nectar The generally sweet secretion in flowers.

Nerve A vein; usually applies to radiating veins.

Nut A one celled and one seeded bony shelled indehiscent fruit.

Nutlet A small nut.

Ob. Prefix meaning inverted or turned about.

Oblanceolate Inversely lanceolate: broader toward the apex:

Oblong Longer than broad with sides nearly or quite parallel.

Obovate Inverse of ovate; broadest toward the apex.

Obovoid Usually applied to solids signifying an ovoid body attached at the smaller end.

Obtuse Bluntly pointed; broad pointed.

Orbicular Said of a circular plane or outline thereof.

Ovate An egg-shaped plane with the broad end as the base.

Ovoid Usually applied to solids which are ovate or oval in outline.

Ovule The part of the flower which,

after fertilization, becomes the seed.

Palmate Lobed or divided like the fingers of the human hand.

Panicle A compound or branching raceme; an inflorescence consisting of a central stem with branches which are further divided into stems of equal length supporting the flowers.

Parasite A plant or animal which fastens itself upon another living thing and by penetrating the tissue of the host derives some or all of its nutriment thereform; fungi, bacteria, etc.

Parted Cleft, cut or divided not quite to the base.

Pedicel The stem of a flower in a compound inflorescence.

Perfect flower One which has actively functioning organs of both sexes, i.e. stamens and pistil.

Persistent Said of organs remaining long attached, as leaves over winter, bracts until fall, or calyx on fruits.

Petiole The stalk of a leaf.

Petiolule The stalk of a leaflet.

Pistil The female organ of a flower consisting of stigma, style and ovary.

Pistillate flower An imperfect one in which the only functioning sex organ is the female one, despite the fact that it may have rudimentary or non-functioning organs resembling functioning male ones.

Pith The central cellular column of a stem.

Pollen The microscopic spores containing the male element which are produced by the anthers.

Pollination The act or method of transferring pollen from stamen to pistil.

Polygamous Said of plants which bear both perfect and unisexual flowers on the same individual.

Pome A fleshy fruit having a core such as an apple, pear, quince, etc.

Prickle A small sharp weak spine.

Pubescent Covered with soft short hairs; downy.

Pubescence The down or hairs which make an organ pubescent.

Raceme An inflorescence consisting of a central rachis or stalk which is simply divided into a number of about equal length flower bearing stalks, as in wild black cherry; sometimes applied to fruit clusters of similar arrangement.

Rachis Axis bearing leaflets or flowers.

Recurved Bent or curved backward or downward.

Reforestation The act or process of putting forest growth on land which was once in such growth.

Resin duct Tubular structure in the wood and leaves of conifers serv-ing the purpose of conducting resinous sap.

Ring-porous Generally applied to wood structure indicating grouping of large pores in the spring wood and much smaller and fewer ones in the summer wood of the annual growth ring.

Rufous Yellowish red.

Samara A simple, dry, winged fruit which does not break open to release the seed; a key, as in the maples, ashes and yellow poplar.

Sapwood The live sap bearing layer of wood lying between the bark and heartwood of trees.

Saprophyte A plant which lives on dead organic matter.

Scurfy Covered with small bran-like scales.

Seed The ripened ovule.

Seedling A plant grown from seed without interruption or transplanting.

Sepal The divisions of a calyx.

Serrate Having teeth; toothed; usually refers to sharp forward pointing teeth.

Sessile Attached without a stalk.

Sheath A tubular envelope or covering, as surrounds the clusters of the leaves of pines.

Shrub A woody plant which remains small and produces several inclined shoots or trunks from the base; a woody plant which does not attain a central axis and a height of 10 or more feet.

Simple Of one piece; not compound.

Sinus The recess between the lobes, usually applied to leaf descriptions.

Spike An inflorescence consisting of a central stem with sessile or nearly sessile flowers.

Spine A strong, sharp pointed, woody outgrowth.

Spinose Like a spine.

Spinous Full of or covered with sharp pointed thorns.

Spore An asexual reproductive cell capable of growing into a new plant.

Stamens The pollen bearing male organs of a flower.

Staminate Said of flowers which bear functioning male organs only.

Sterile Barren; unproductive; said of a flower without a pistil.

Stigma The top end of the pistil which receives the pollen.

Stipule A leaf-like appendage at the base of a leaf stalk.

Stomata (Plural of stoma) Orifices of the epidermis of a leaf communicating with the air cavities; the breathing pores of a leaf.

Strobile A cone.

Style The portion of a pistil between the stigma and ovary.

Superposed Said of buds when situated one above the other.

Suture A line marking the place of opening as in a hickory nut husk or carpel of willow, poplar, etc.

Tangential Applied to pores of wood radiating in lines from the annual ring.

Tomentose Densely pubescent with matted woolly hairs.

Tomentum The dense mat of hairs of tomentose organs.

Umbel A form of inflorescence in which the pedicels or flower stalk arise from a central point.

Umbo A projection; a boss; applied to cone scales means that portion exposed during the previous year.

Valve One of the portions into which a capsule splits.

Vein A branch of the woody framework of a leaf.

Veinlet Branch of a vein.

Villose

or

Villous Hairy with long soft hairs.

Whorl Arrangement of 3 or more organs about a stem or axis at or near the same level.

INDEX

In this index SMALL CAPITALS are used for Latin names of families. Text face is used for common names and accepted scientific names of species. *Italic face* is used for synonymous scientific names of species and for page numbers where the reference is of secondary importance.